1997

UNIFORM MECHANICAL CODE™

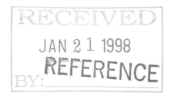

First Printing

Publication Date: February 1997

ISSN 0896-9671

ISBN 884590-77-2 (soft cover edition)
ISBN 884590-78-0 (loose leaf edition)

COPYRIGHT © 1994, 1995, 1996, 1997

by

International Conference of Building Officials
5360 WORKMAN MILL ROAD
WHITTIER, CALIFORNIA 90601-2298
(800) 284-4406 • (562) 699-0541

PRINTED IN THE U.S.A.

Preface

The *Uniform Mechanical Code* (UMC) is designed to provide complete requirements for the installation and maintenance of heating, ventilating, cooling and refrigeration systems.

The *Uniform Mechanical Code* was first published in 1967. Revised editions of this code have been published since that time at three-year intervals. New editions incorporate changes approved since the last edition. This 1997 edition reflects the results of 30 years' experience since the first edition.

The *Uniform Mechanical Code* is published as a special document designed to be compatible with the *Uniform Building Code.* See the publications list following this preface for the complete family of Uniform Codes and related publications.

Code Changes. The ICBO code development process has been suspended by the ICBO Board of Directors and, because of this action, further changes to the *Uniform Mechanical Code* will not be processed. For more information, write to the International Conference of Building Officials at the address on the copyright page. An analysis of changes between editions is published in the *Analysis of Revisions to the Uniform Codes.*

Marginal Markings. Solid vertical lines in the margins within the body of the code indicate a change from the requirements of the 1994 edition except where an entire chapter was revised, a new chapter was added or a change was minor. Where an entire chapter was revised or a new chapter was added, a notation appears at the beginning of that chapter. The letter **F** repeating in line vertically in the margin indicates that the provision is maintained under the code change procedures of the International Fire Code Institute. Deletion indicators (♦) are provided in the margin where a paragraph or item listing has been deleted if the deletion resulted in a change of requirements.

Metrication. The *Uniform Mechanical Code* was metricated in the 1994 edition. The Système International (SI) conversions follow the inch-pound (IP) units in parenthesis. Where industry has made SI conversions available, the conversions conform to current industry standards.

Formulas are also provided with SI equivalents. SI equivalent formulas immediately follow the IP formulas and are denoted by "For **SI:**" preceding the equivalent. Some formulas are dimensionless and, thus, are not provided with an SI equivalent. Multiplying conversion factors have been provided for formulas where SI forms of the formula were unavailable. Tables are provided with multiplying conversion factors in subheadings for each tabulated unit of measurement. SI tables of the Uniform Codes are available from the Conference.

CODES AND RELATED PUBLICATIONS

The International Conference of Building Officials (ICBO) publishes a family of codes, each correlated with the *Uniform Building Code*™ to provide jurisdictions with a complete set of building-related regulations for adoption. Some of these codes are published in affiliation with other organizations such as the International Fire Code Institute (IFCI) and the International Code Council (ICC). Reference materials and related codes also are available to improve knowledge of code enforcement and administration of building inspection programs. Publications and products are continually being added, so inquiries should be directed to Conference headquarters for a listing of available products. Many codes and references are also available on CD-ROM or floppy disk. These are denoted by (*). The following publications and products are available from ICBO:

CODES

*Uniform Building Code, Volumes 1, 2 and 3. The most widely adopted model building code in the United States, the performance-based *Uniform Building Code* is a proven document, meeting the needs of government units charged with the enforcement of building regulations. Volume 1 contains administrative, fire- and life-safety and field inspection provisions; Volume 2 contains structural engineering design provisions; and Volume 3 contains material, testing and installation standards.

*Uniform Mechanical Code™. Provides a complete set of requirements for the design, construction, installation and maintenance of heating, ventilating, cooling and refrigeration systems; incinerators and other heat-producing appliances.

International Plumbing Code™. Provides consistent and technically advanced requirements that can be used across the country to provide comprehensive regulations of modern plumbing systems. Setting minimum regulations for plumbing facilities in terms of performance objectives, the IPC provides for the acceptance of new and innovative products, materials and systems.

International Private Sewage Disposal Code™. Provides flexibility in the development of safety and sanitary individual sewage disposal systems and includes detailed provisions for all aspects of design, installation and inspection of private sewage disposal systems.

International Mechanical Code™. Establishes minimum regulations for mechanical systems using prescriptive and performance-related provisions. It is founded on broad-based principles that make possible the use of new materials and new mechanical designs.

Uniform Zoning Code™. This code is dedicated to intelligent community development and to the benefit of the public welfare by providing a means of promoting uniformity in zoning laws and enforcement.

*Uniform Fire Code™, Volumes 1 and 2. The premier model fire code in the United States, the *Uniform Fire Code* sets forth provisions necessary for fire prevention and fire protection. Published by the International Fire Code Institute, the *Uniform Fire Code* is endorsed by the Western Fire Chiefs Association, the International Association of Fire Chiefs and ICBO. Volume 1 contains code provisions compatible with the *Uniform Building Code,* and Volume 2 contains standards referenced from the code provisions.

*Urban-Wildland Interface Code™. Promulgated by IFCI, this code regulates both land use and the built environment in designated urban-wildland interface areas. This newly developed code is the only model code that bases construction requirements on the fire-hazard severity exposed to the structure. Developed under a grant from the Federal Emergency Management Agency, this code is the direct result of hazard mitigation meetings held after devastating wildfires.

Uniform Housing Code™. Provides complete requirements affecting conservation and rehabilitation of housing. Its regulations are compatible with the *Uniform Building Code.*

Uniform Code for the Abatement of Dangerous Buildings™. A code compatible with the *Uniform Building Code* and the *Uniform Housing Code* which provides equitable remedies consistent with other laws for the repair, vacation or demolition of dangerous buildings.

Uniform Sign Code™. Dedicated to the development of better sign regulation, its requirements pertain to all signs and sign construction attached to buildings.

Uniform Administrative Code™. This code covers administrative areas in connection with adoption of the *Uniform Building Code,* *Uniform Mechanical Code* and related codes. It contains provisions which relate to site preparation, construction, alteration, moving, repair and use and occupancies of buildings or structures and building service equipment, including plumbing, electrical and mechanical regulations. The code is compatible with the administrative provisions of all codes published by the Conference.

Uniform Building Security Code™. This code establishes minimum standards to make dwelling units resistant to unlawful entry. It regulates swinging doors, sliding doors, windows and hardware in connection with dwelling units of apartment houses or one- and two-family dwellings. The code gives consideration to the concerns of police, fire and building officials in establishing requirements for resistance to burglary which are compatible with fire and life safety.

Uniform Code for Building Conservation™. A building conservation guideline presented in code format which will provide a community with the means to preserve its existing buildings while achieving appropriate levels of safety. It is formatted in the same manner as the *Uniform Building Code,* is compatible with other Uniform Codes, and may be adopted as a code or used as a guideline.

Dwelling Construction under the Uniform Building Code™. Designed primarily for use in home building and apprentice training, this book contains requirements applicable to the construction of one- and two-story dwellings based on the requirements of the *Uniform Building Code.* Available in English or Spanish.

Dwelling Construction under the Uniform Mechanical Code™. This publication is for the convenience of the homeowner or contractor interested in installing mechanical equipment in a one- or two-family dwelling in conformance with the *Uniform Mechanical Code.*

Supplements to UBC and related codes. Published in the years between editions, the Supplements contain all approved changes, plus an analysis of those changes.

Uniform Building Code—1927 Edition. A special 60th anniversary printing of the first published *Uniform Building Code.*

One and Two Family Dwelling Code. Promulgated by ICC, this code eliminates conflicts and duplications among the model codes to achieve national uniformity. Covers mechanical and plumbing requirements as well as construction and occupancy.

Application and Commentary on the One and Two Family Dwelling Code. An interpretative commentary on the *One and Two Family Dwelling Code* intended to enhance uniformity of interpretation and application of the code nationwide. Developed by the three model code organizations, this document includes numerous illustrations of code requirements and the rationale for individual provisions.

Model Energy Code. This code includes minimum requirements for effective use of energy in the design of new buildings and structures and additions to existing buildings. It is based on American Society of Heating, Refrigeration and Air-conditioning Engineers Standard 90A-1980 and was originally developed jointly by ICBO, BOCA, SBCCI and the National Conference of States on Building Codes and Standards under a contract funded by the United States Department of Energy. The code is now maintained by ICC and is adopted by reference in the *Uniform Building Code.*

National Electrical Code®. The electrical code used throughout the United States. Published by the National Fire Protection Association, it is an indispensable aid to every electrician, contractor, architect, builder, inspector and anyone who must specify or certify electrical installations.

TECHNICAL REFERENCES AND EDUCATIONAL MATERIALS

Analysis of Revisions to the Uniform Codes™. An analysis of changes between the previous and new editions of the Uniform Codes is provided. Changes between code editions are noted either at the beginning of chapters or in the margins of the code text.

*Handbook to the Uniform Building Code. The handbook is a completely detailed and illustrated commentary on the *Uniform Building Code,* tracing historical background and rationale of the codes through the current edition. Also included are numerous drawings and figures clarifying the application and intent of the code provisions. Also available in electronic format.

*Handbook to the Uniform Mechanical Code. An indispensable tool for understanding the provisions of the current UMC, the handbook traces the historical background and rationale behind the UMC provisions, includes 160 figures which clarify the intent and application of the code, and provides a chapter-by-chapter analysis of the UMC.

*Uniform Building Code Application Manual. This manual discusses sections of the *Uniform Building Code* with a question-and-answer format, providing a comprehensive analysis of the intent of the code sections. Most sections include illustrative examples. The manual is in loose-leaf format so that code applications published in *Building Standards* magazine may be inserted. Also available in electronic format.

*Uniform Mechanical Code Application Manual. As a companion document to the *Uniform Mechanical Code,* this manual provides a comprehensive analysis of the intent of a number of code sections in an easy-to-use question-and-answer format. The manual is available in a loose-leaf format and includes illustrative examples for many code sections.

*Uniform Fire Code Applications Manual. This newly developed manual provides questions and answers regarding UFC provisions. A comprehensive analysis of the intent of numerous code sections, the manual is in a loose-leaf format for easy insertion of code applications published in IFCI's *Fire Code Journal.*

Quick-Reference Guide to the Occupancy Requirements of the 1997 UBC. Code requirements are compiled in this publication by occupancy groups for quick access. These tabulations assemble requirements for each occupancy classification in the code. Provisions, such as fire-resistive ratings for occupancy separations in Table 3-B, exterior wall and opening protection requirements in Table 5-A-1, and fire-resistive ratings for types of construction in Table 6-A, are tabulated for quick reference and comparison.

Plan Review Manual. A practical text that will assist and guide both the field inspector and plan reviewer in applying the code requirements. This manual covers the nonstructural and basic structural aspects of plan review.

Field Inspection Manual. An important fundamental text for courses of study at the community college and trade or technical school level. It is an effective text for those studying building construction or architecture and includes sample forms and checklists for use in the field.

Building Department Administration. An excellent guide for improvement of skills in departmental management and in the enforcement and application of the Building Code and other regulations administered by a building inspection department. This textbook will also be a valuable aid to instructors, students and those in related professional fields.

Building Department Guide to Disaster Mitigation. This new, expanded guide is designed to assist building departments in developing or updating disaster mitigation plans. Subjects covered include guidelines for damage mitigation, disaster-response management, immediate response, mutual aid and inspections, working with the media, repair and recovery policies, and public information bulletins. This publication is a must for those involved in preparing for and responding to disaster.

Building Official Management Manual. This manual addresses the unique nature of code administration and the managerial duties of the building official. A supplementary insert addresses the budgetary and financial aspects of a building department. It is also an ideal resource for those preparing for the management module of the CABO Building Official Certification Examination.

Legal Aspects of Code Administration. A manual developed by the three model code organizations to inform the building official on the legal aspects of the profession. The text is written in a logical sequence with explanation of legal terminology. It is designed to serve as a refresher for those preparing to take the legal module of the CABO Building Official Certification Examination.

Illustrated Guide to Conventional Construction Provisions of the UBC. This comprehensive guide and commentary provides detailed explanations of the conventional construction provisions in the UBC, including descriptive discussions and illustrated drawings to convey the prescriptive provisions related to wood-frame construction.

Introduction to the Uniform Building Code. A workbook that provides an overview of the basics of the UBC.

Uniform Building Code Update Workbook. This manual addresses many of the changes to the administrative, fire- and life-safety, and inspection provisions appearing in the UBC.

UMC Workbook. Designed for independent study or use with instructor-led programs based on the *Uniform Mechanical Code,* this comprehensive study guide consists of 16 learning sessions, with the first two sessions reviewing the purpose, scope, definitions and administrative provisions and the remaining 14 sessions progressively exploring the requirements for installing, inspecting and maintaining heating, ventilating, cooling and refrigeration systems.

UBC Field Inspection Workbook. A comprehensive workbook for studying the provisions of the UBC. Divided into 12 sessions, this workbook focuses on the UBC combustible construction requirements for the inspection of wood-framed construction.

Concrete Manual. A publication for individuals seeking an understanding of the fundamentals of concrete field technology and inspection practices. Of particular interest to concrete construction inspectors, it will also benefit employees of concrete producers, contractors, testing and inspection laboratories and material suppliers.

Reinforced Concrete Masonry Construction Inspector's Handbook. A comprehensive information source written especially for masonry inspection covering terminology, technology, materials, quality control, inspection and standards. Published jointly by ICBO and the Masonry Institute of America.

You Can Build It! Sponsored by ICBO in cooperation with CABO, this booklet contains information and advice to aid "do-it-yourselfers" with building projects. Provides guidance in necessary procedures such as permit requirements, codes, plans, cost estimation, etc.

Guidelines for Manufactured Housing Installations. A guideline in code form implementing the *Uniform Building Code* and its companion code documents to regulate the permanent installation of a manufactured home on a privately owned, nonrental site. A commentary is included to explain specific provisions, and codes applying to each component part are defined.

Accessibility Reference Guide. This guide is a valuable resource for architects, interior designers, plan reviewers and others who design and enforce accessibility provisions. Features include accessibility requirements, along with detailed commentary and graphics to clarify the provisions; cross-references to other applicable sections of the UBC and the Americans with Disabilities Act Accessibility Guidelines; a checklist of UBC provisions on access and usability requirements; and many other useful references.

Educational and Technical Reference Materials. The Conference has been a leader in the development of texts and course material to assist in the educational process. These materials include vital information necessary for the building official and subordinates in carrying out their responsibilities and have proven to be excellent references in connection with community college curricula and higher-level courses in the field of building construction technology and inspection and in the administration of building departments. Included are plan review checklists for structural, nonstructural, mechanical and fire-safety provisions and a full line of videotapes and automated products.

TABLE OF CONTENTS

SAMPLE ORDINANCE FOR ADOPTION OF THE
UNIFORM MECHANICAL CODE

ORDINANCE NO. _____

An ordinance of the __(jurisdiction)__ adopting the 1997 edition of the *Uniform Mechanical Code,* regulating and controlling the design, construction, quality of materials, erection, installation, alteration, repair, location, relocation, replacement, addition to, use or maintenance of heating, ventilating, cooling, refrigeration systems, incinerators, or other miscellaneous heat-producing appliances in the __(jurisdiction)__; providing for the issuance of permits and collection of fees therefore; repealing Ordinance No. _____ of the __(jurisdiction)__ and all other ordinances and parts of the ordinances in conflict therewith.

The __(governing body)__ of the __(jurisdiction)__ does ordain as follows:

Section 1. That certain documents, three (3) copies of which are on file in the office of the __(jurisdiction's keeper of records)__ and the __(jurisdiction)__, being marked and designated as *Uniform Mechanical Code,* including Appendix Chapter A (1997 edition) of the 1997 *Uniform Mechanical Code* published by the International Conference of Building Officials, be and is hereby adopted as the code of the __(jurisdiction)__ for regulating the design, construction, quality of materials, erection, installation, alteration, repair, location, relocation, replacement, addition to, use or maintenance of heating, ventilating, cooling, refrigeration systems, incinerators or other miscellaneous heat-producing appliances in the __(jurisdiction)__ providing for the issuance of permits and collection of fees therefore; and each and all of the regulations, provisions, conditions and terms of such *Uniform Mechanical Code,* 1997 edition, published by the International Conference of Building Officials, on file in the office of the __(jurisdiction)__ are hereby referred to, adopted and made a part hereof as if fully set out in this ordinance.

Section 2. (Incorporate penalties for violations. See Section 111.)

Section 3. That Ordinance No. _____ of __(jurisdiction)__ entitled *(fill in here the complete title of the present mechanical ordinance or ordinances in effect at the present time so that they will be repealed by definite mention)* and all other ordinances or parts of ordinances in conflict herewith are hereby repealed.

Section 4. That if any section, subsection, sentence, clause or phrase of this ordinance is, for any reason, held to be unconstitutional, such decision shall not affect the validity of the remaining portions of this ordinance. The __(governing body)__ hereby declares that it would have passed this ordinance, and each section, subsection, clause or phrase thereof, irrespective of the fact that any one or more sections, subsections, sentences, clauses and phrases be declared unconstitutional.

Section 5. That the __(jurisdiction's keeper of records)__ is hereby ordered and directed to cause this ordinance to be published. *(An additional provision may be required to direct the number of times the ordinance is to be published and to specify that it is to be in a newspaper in general circulation. Posting may also be required.)*

Section 6. That this ordinance and the rules, regulations, provisions, requirements, orders and matters established and adopted hereby shall take effect and be in full force and effect __(time period)__ from and after the date of its final passage and adoption.

Chapter 1

ADMINISTRATION

Part I—General

SECTION 101 — TITLE

These regulations shall be known as the *Uniform Mechanical Code,* may be cited as such, and will be referred to herein as "this code."

SECTION 102 — PURPOSE

The purpose of this code is to provide minimum standards to safeguard life or limb, health, property and public welfare by regulating and controlling the design, construction, installation, quality of materials, location, operation, and maintenance or use of heating, ventilating, cooling, refrigeration systems, incinerators and other miscellaneous heat-producing appliances within this jurisdiction.

The purpose of this code is not to create or otherwise establish or designate any particular class or group of persons who will or should be especially protected or benefited by the terms of this code.

SECTION 103 — SCOPE

103.1 Applicability. The provisions of this code shall apply to the erection, installation, alteration, repair, relocation, replacement, addition to, use or maintenance of any heating, ventilating, cooling, refrigeration systems, incinerators or other miscellaneous heat-producing appliances within this jurisdiction. The design and testing of equipment regulated by this code shall be subject to the approval of the building official. Mechanical equipment and systems in detached one- and two-family dwellings shall comply with the requirements of Part IV of the *One and Two Family Dwelling Code* referenced by Appendix Chapter 3, Division III of the Building Code when such appendix chapter is specifically adopted.

103.2 Alterations. Additions, alterations, repairs and replacement of equipment or systems shall comply with the provisions for new equipment and systems except as otherwise provided in Section 104 of this code.

103.3 Most Restrictive. Where, in any specific case, different sections of this code specify different materials, methods of construction or other requirements, the most restrictive shall govern. Where there is a conflict between a general requirement and a specific requirement, the specific requirement shall be applicable.

103.4 Appendix A. The Uniform Mechanical Code standards, Uniform Fire Code standards and Uniform Building Code standards contained in Appendix A shall be considered as part of this code.

103.5 Appendix B. Appendix B, Chapter 15, contains recommended practices which shall not apply unless specifically adopted.

103.6 Appendix C. Appendix C contains gas-venting tables and is intended to serve only as a guide.

103.7 Appendix D. Appendix D contains the unit conversion tables applied in metrication of this code. The gage conversion table contains information on the approximate minimum thickness for manufacturer's standard gage and galvanized sheet gage numbers that are used in this code.

SECTION 104 — APPLICATION TO EXISTING MECHANICAL SYSTEMS

104.1 Additions, Alterations or Repairs. Additions, alterations or repairs may be made to any mechanical system without requiring the existing mechanical system to comply with all the requirements of this code, provided the addition, alteration or repair conforms to that required for a new mechanical system. Additions, alterations or repairs shall not cause an existing system to become unsafe or create unhealthy or overloaded conditions.

Minor additions, alterations and repairs to existing mechanical systems may be installed in accordance with the law in effect at the time the original installation was made, when approved by the building official. Defective material or parts shall be replaced or repaired in such a manner as to preserve an approval or a listing.

104.2 Existing Installations. Mechanical systems lawfully in existence at the time of the adoption of this code may have their use, maintenance or repair continued if the use, maintenance or repair is in accordance with the original design and location and no hazard to life, health or property has been created by such mechanical system.

104.3 Changes in Building Occupancy. Mechanical systems which are a part of any building or structure undergoing a change in use or occupancy, as defined in the Building Code, shall comply with all requirements of this code which may be applicable to the new use or occupancy.

104.4 Maintenance. All mechanical systems, materials and appurtenances, both existing and new, and all parts thereof shall be maintained in proper operating condition in accordance with the original design and in a safe and hazard-free condition. All devices or safeguards which are required by this code shall be maintained in conformance with the code edition under which installed. The owner or the owner's designated agent shall be responsible for maintenance of mechanical systems and equipment. To determine compliance with this section, the building official may cause a mechanical system or equipment to be reinspected.

104.5 Moved Buildings. Mechanical systems or equipment which are a part of buildings or structures moved into or within this jurisdiction shall comply with the provisions of this code for new installations.

SECTION 105 — ALTERNATE MATERIALS AND METHODS OF CONSTRUCTION

105.1 Alternates Require Approval. The provisions of this code are not intended to prevent the use of a material or method of construction not specifically prescribed by this code provided any such alternate has been approved and the use authorized by the building official.

105.2 Equivalency of Alternates. The building official may authorize an alternate, provided the building official finds the proposed design is satisfactory for the intended use and complies with the provisions of this code and that the material, method or work offered is, for the purpose intended, at least equivalent to that prescribed by this code in suitability, strength, effectiveness, fire resistance, durability and safety.

105.3 Evidence Required. The building official shall require sufficient evidence or proof be submitted to substantiate any claims made regarding the use of alternates. The details of any action granting approval of an alternate shall be recorded and shall be entered in the files of the code enforcement agency.

SECTION 106 — MODIFICATIONS

Whenever there are practical difficulties involved in carrying out the provisions of this code, the building official may grant modifications for individual cases. The building official shall first find that a special individual reason makes the strict letter of this code impractical and the modification is in conformity with the intent and purpose of this code and that such modification does not lessen health, life-safety and firesafety requirements. The details of actions granting modifications shall be recorded and entered in the files of the code enforcement agency.

SECTION 107 — TESTS

Whenever there is insufficient evidence of compliance with the provisions of this code, or evidence that a material or method does not conform to the requirements of this code, or in order to substantiate claims for alternate materials or methods, the building official may require tests as evidence of compliance to be made at no expense to the jurisdiction.

Test methods shall be as specified in this code or by other recognized test standards. In the absence of recognized and accepted test methods, the building official shall specify the testing procedures.

Tests shall be performed by an approved agency. Reports of tests shall be retained by the building official for the period required for retention of public records.

Part II—Organization and Enforcement

SECTION 108 — POWERS AND DUTIES OF BUILDING OFFICIAL

108.1 General. The building official is hereby authorized and directed to enforce all the provisions of this code. For such purposes the building official shall have the powers of a law enforcement officer.

The building official shall have the power to render interpretations of this code and to adopt and enforce rules and regulations supplemental to this code as may be deemed necessary in order to clarify the application of the provisions of this code. Such interpretations, rules and regulations shall be in conformity with the intent and purpose of this code.

108.2 Deputies. In accordance with the prescribed procedures and with the approval of the appointing authority, the building official may appoint such number of technical officers and inspectors and other employees as shall be authorized from time to time. The building official may deputize such inspectors or employees as may be necessary to carry out the functions of the code enforcement agency.

108.3 Right of Entry. When it is necessary to make an inspection to enforce the provisions of this code, or when the building official has reasonable cause to believe that there exists in a building or upon a premises a condition which is contrary to or in viola-

tion of this code which makes the building or premises unsafe, dangerous or hazardous, the building official may enter the building or premises at reasonable times to inspect or to perform the duties imposed by this code, provided that if such building or premises be occupied that credentials be presented to the occupant and entry requested. If such building or premises be unoccupied, the building official shall first make a reasonable effort to locate the owner or other person having charge or control of the building or premises and request entry. If entry is refused, the building official shall have recourse to the remedies provided by law to secure entry.

108.4 Stop Orders. When any work is being done contrary to the provisions of this code, the building official may order the work stopped by notice in writing served on any persons engaged in the doing or causing such work to be done, and such persons shall forthwith stop work until authorized by the building official to proceed with the work.

108.5 Authority to Disconnect Utilities in Emergencies. The building official or the building official's authorized representative shall have the authority to disconnect fuel-gas utility service, or energy supplies to a building, structure, premises or equipment regulated by this code in case of emergency when necessary to eliminate an immediate hazard to life or property. The building official shall, whenever possible, notify the serving utility, the owner and occupant of the building, structure or premises of the decision to disconnect prior to taking such action, and shall notify such serving utility, owner and occupant of the building, structure or premises in writing of such disconnection immediately thereafter.

108.6 Authority to Condemn Equipment. When the building official ascertains that equipment, or a portion thereof, regulated by this code has become hazardous to life, health or property, the building official shall order in writing that the equipment either be removed or restored to a safe or sanitary condition, as appropriate. The written notice shall contain a fixed time limit for compliance with such order. Persons shall not use or maintain defective equipment after receiving a notice.

When equipment or an installation is to be disconnected, written notice of the disconnection and causes therefor shall be given within 24 hours to the serving utility, the owner and occupant of the building, structure or premises. When equipment is maintained in violation of this code, and in violation of a notice issued pursuant to the provisions of this section, the building official shall institute an appropriate action to prevent, restrain, correct or abate the violation.

108.7 Connection after Order to Disconnect. Persons shall not make connections from an energy, fuel or power supply nor supply energy or fuel to any equipment regulated by this code which has been disconnected or ordered to be disconnected by the building official, or the use of which has been ordered to be discontinued by the building official, until the building official authorizes the reconnection and use of such equipment.

108.8 Liability. The building official charged with the enforcement of this code acting in good faith and without malice in the discharge of the duties required by this code or other pertinent law or ordinance shall not thereby be rendered personally liable for damages that may accrue to persons or property as a result of an act or by reason of an act or omission in the discharge of such duties. A suit brought against the building official or employee because of such act or omission performed by the building official or employee in the enforcement of any provision of such codes or other pertinent laws or ordinances implemented through the enforcement of this code or enforced by the code enforcement agency shall be defended by this jurisdiction until final termination of such proceedings, and any judgment resulting therefrom shall be assumed by this jurisdiction.

This code shall not be construed to relieve from or lessen the responsibility of any person owning, operating or controlling any equipment regulated herein for damages to persons or property caused by defects, nor shall the code enforcement agency or its parent jurisdiction be held as assuming any such liability by reason of the inspections authorized by this code or any permits or certificates issued under this code.

108.9 Cooperation of Other Officials and Officers. The building official may request, and shall receive, the assistance and cooperation of other officials of this jurisdiction so far as is required in the discharge of the duties required by this code or other pertinent law or ordinance.

SECTION 109 — UNSAFE EQUIPMENT

109.1 Hazardous Conditions. Equipment regulated by this code, which is unsafe or which constitutes a fire or health hazard or is otherwise dangerous to human life is, for the purpose of this section, unsafe. Use of equipment regulated by this code constituting a hazard to safety, health or public welfare by reason of inadequate maintenance, dilapidation, obsolescence, fire hazard, disaster, damage or abandonment is, for the purpose of this section, an unsafe use. Unsafe equipment is hereby declared to be a public nuisance and shall be abated by repair, rehabilitation, demolition or removal in accordance with the procedures set forth in the *Uniform Code for the Abatement of Dangerous Buildings* or such alternate procedure as may be adopted by this jurisdiction. As an alternative, the building official or other employee or official of this jurisdiction as designated by the governing body may institute other appropriate action to prevent, restrain, correct or abate the violation.

SECTION 110 — BOARD OF APPEALS

110.1 General. In order to hear and decide appeals of orders, decisions or determinations made by the building official relative to the application and interpretations of this code, there shall be and is hereby created a board of appeals consisting of members who are qualified by experience and training to pass upon matters pertaining to mechanical design, construction and maintenance and the public health aspects of mechanical systems and who are not employees of the jurisdiction. The building official shall be an ex officio member and shall act as secretary to said board but shall have no vote upon any matter before the board. The board of appeals shall be appointed by the governing body and shall hold office at its pleasure. The board shall adopt rules of procedure for conducting its business and shall render all decisions and findings in writing to the appellant with a duplicate copy to the building official.

110.2 Limitations of Authority. The board of appeals shall have no authority relative to interpretation of the administrative provisions of this code nor shall the board be empowered to waive requirements of this code.

SECTION 111 — VIOLATIONS

111.1 General. It shall be unlawful for a person, firm or corporation to erect, construct, enlarge, alter, repair, move, improve, remove, convert or demolish, equip, use or maintain mechanical systems or equipment or cause or permit the same to be done in violation of this code.

Part III—Permits and Inspections

SECTION 112 — PERMITS

112.1 Permits Required. Except as permitted in Section 112.2, a mechanical system regulated by this code shall not be installed, altered, repaired, replaced or remodeled unless a separate mechanical permit for each separate building or structure has first been obtained from the building official.

112.2 Exempt Work. A mechanical permit shall not be required for the following:

1. A portable heating appliance, portable ventilating equipment, portable cooling unit or portable evaporative cooler.

2. A closed system of steam, hot or chilled water piping within heating or cooling equipment regulated by this code.

3. Replacement of any component part or assembly of an appliance which does not alter its original approval and complies with other applicable requirements of this code.

4. Refrigerating equipment which is part of the equipment for which a permit has been issued pursuant to the requirements of this code.

5. A unit refrigerating system.

112.3 Exemption from the permit requirements of this code shall not be deemed to grant authorization for work to be done in violation of the provisions of this code or other laws or ordinances of this jurisdiction.

SECTION 113 — APPLICATION FOR PERMIT

113.1 Application. To obtain a permit, the applicant shall first file an application therefor in writing on a form furnished by the code enforcement agency for that purpose. Every such application shall:

1. Identify and describe the work to be covered by the permit for which application is made.

2. Describe the land on which the proposed work is to be done by legal description, street address or similar description that will readily identify and definitely locate the proposed building or work.

3. Indicate the use or occupancy for which the proposed work is intended.

4. Be accompanied by plans, diagrams, computations and specifications and other data as required in Section 113.2.

5. Be signed by the applicant or an authorized agent of the applicant.

6. Give such other data and information as may be required by the building official.

113.2 Plans and Specifications. Plans, engineering calculations, diagrams and other data shall be submitted in one or more sets with each application for a permit. When such plans are not prepared by an architect or engineer, the building official may require any applicant submitting such plans or other data to demonstrate that state law does not require that the plans be prepared by an architect or engineer. The building official may require plans, computations and specifications to be prepared and designed by an engineer or architect licensed by the state to practice as such even if not required by state law.

EXCEPTION: The building official may waive the submission of plans, calculations or other data if it is found that the nature of the work applied for is such that reviewing of plans is not necessary to obtain compliance with this code.

113.3 Information on Plans and Specifications. Plans and specifications shall be drawn to scale upon substantial paper or cloth and shall be of sufficient clarity to indicate the location, nature and extent of the work proposed and show in detail that it will conform to the provisions of this code and relevant laws, ordinances, rules and regulations.

113.3.1 Penetrations detailed. Plans for buildings more than two stories in height of other than Group R, Division 3 and Group U Occupancies shall indicate how required structural and fire-resistive integrity will be maintained where a penetration will be made for electrical, mechanical, plumbing and communication conduits, pipes and similar systems.

113.3.2 Direct-fired gas makeup and industrial air heaters. The installer shall submit plans showing the proposed installation, indicating the location of the heater and such accessories as may be required to ensure the proper and safe performance of its function.

SECTION 114 — PERMIT ISSUANCE

114.1 Issuance. The application, plans, specifications, computations and other data filed by an applicant for permit shall be reviewed by the building official. Such plans may be reviewed by other departments of this jurisdiction to verify compliance with applicable laws under their jurisdiction. If the building official finds that the work described in an application for a permit and the plans, specifications and other data filed therewith conform to the requirements of the code and other pertinent laws and ordinances and that the fees specified in Section 304 have been paid, the building official shall issue a permit therefor to the applicant.

114.1.1 Approval stamp. When issuing a permit where plans are required, the building official shall endorse in writing or stamp the plans and specifications APPROVED. Such approved plans and specifications shall not be changed, modified or altered without authorization from the building official, and all work regulated by this code shall be done in accordance with the approved plans.

114.1.2 Partial permits. The building official may issue a permit for the construction of a part of a mechanical system before the entire plans and specifications for the whole system have been submitted or approved, provided adequate information and detailed statements have been filed complying with all pertinent requirements of this code. The holder of a partial permit may proceed without assurance that the permit for the entire building, structure or mechanical system will be granted.

114.2 Retention of Plans. One set of approved plans, specifications and computations shall be retained by the building official until final approval of the work covered therein. One set of approved plans and specifications shall be returned to the applicant, and said set shall be kept on the site of the building or work at all times during which the work authorized thereby is in progress.

114.3 Valid Permit.

114.3.1 Validity of permit. The issuance of a permit or approval of plans, specifications and computations shall not be construed to be a permit for, or an approval of, any violation of any of the provisions of this code or of other ordinances of the jurisdiction. Permits presuming to give authority to violate or cancel the provisions of this code or of other ordinances of the jurisdiction shall not be valid.

114.3.2 Erroneous permits not a bar to compliance. The issuance of a permit based on plans, specifications, computations and other data shall not prevent the building official from thereafter requiring the correction of errors in said plans, specifications,

computations and other data or from preventing building operations being carried on thereunder when in violation of this code or of other ordinances of this jurisdiction.

114.4 Permit Expiration.

114.4.1 Expiration. Every permit issued by the building official under the provisions of this code shall expire by limitation and become null and void if the work authorized by such permit is not commenced within 180 days from the date of such permit, or if the work authorized by such permit is suspended or abandoned at any time after the work is commenced for a period of 180 days. Before such work can be recommenced, a new permit shall be first obtained to do so, and the fee therefor shall be one half the amount required for a new permit for such work, provided no changes have been made or will be made in the original plans and specifications for such work and provided further that such suspension or abandonment has not exceeded one year. No permit shall be extended more than once. In order to renew action on a permit after expiration, the permittee shall pay a new full permit fee.

114.4.2 Extension of unexpired permits. A permittee holding an unexpired permit may apply for an extension of the time within which work may be commenced under that permit when the permittee is unable to commence work within the time required by this section for good and satisfactory reasons. The building official may extend the time for action by the permittee for a period not exceeding 180 days upon written request by the permittee showing that circumstances beyond the control of the permittee have prevented action from being taken.

114.5 Suspension or Revocation. The building official may, in writing, suspend or revoke a permit issued under the provisions of this code whenever the permit is issued in error or on the basis of incorrect information supplied or in violation of other ordinances or regulations of the jurisdiction.

SECTION 115 — FEES

115.1 General. Fees shall be assessed in accordance with the provisions of this section or shall be as set forth in the fee schedule adopted by this jurisdiction.

115.2 Permit Fees. The fee for each permit shall be as set forth in Table 1-A.

115.3 Plan Review Fees. When a plan or other data are required to be submitted by Section 113.2, a plan review fee shall be paid at the time of submitting plans and specifications for review. The plan review fees for mechanical work shall be equal to 25 percent of the total permit fee as set forth in Table 1-A.

115.3.1 Separate fees for plan review. The plan review fees specified in this section are separate fees from the permit fees specified in Section 115.1 and are in addition to the permit fees.

115.3.2 Incomplete or changed plans. When plans are incomplete or changed so as to require additional plan review, an additional plan review fee shall be charged at the rate shown in Table 1-A.

115.4 Expiration of Plan Review. Applications for which no permit is issued within 180 days following the date of application shall expire by limitation, and plans and other data submitted for review may thereafter be returned to the applicant or destroyed by the building official. The building official may extend the time for action by the applicant for a period not exceeding 180 days upon request by the applicant showing that circumstances beyond the control of the applicant have prevented action from being taken. An application shall not be extended more than once. In order to renew action on an application after expiration, the applicant shall resubmit plans and pay a new plan review fee.

115.5 Investigation Fees: Work without a Permit. When work for which a permit is required by this code has been commenced without first obtaining a permit, a special investigation shall be made before a permit may be issued for such work.

An investigation fee, in addition to the permit fee, shall be collected whether or not a permit is then or subsequently issued. The investigation fee shall be equal to the amount of the permit fee that would be required by this code if a permit were to be issued. The payment of an investigation fee shall not exempt a person from compliance with all other provisions of this code nor from a penalty prescribed by law.

115.6 Fee Refunds. The building official may authorize the refunding of a fee paid hereunder which was erroneously paid or collected.

115.6.1 Building permit fee refund. The building official may authorize refunding of not more than 80 percent of the permit fee paid when no work has been done under a permit issued in accordance with this code.

115.6.2 Plan review fee refund. The building official may authorize refunding of not more than 80 percent of the plan review fee paid when an application for a permit for which a plan review fee has been paid is withdrawn or canceled before any plan review effort has been expended.

115.6.3 Refund application. The building official shall not authorize refunding of a fee paid except upon written application filed by the original permittee not later than 180 days after the date of fee payment.

SECTION 116 — INSPECTIONS

116.1 General. Mechanical systems for which a permit is required by this code shall be subject to inspection by the building official and such mechanical systems shall remain accessible and exposed for inspection purposes until approved by the building official.

It shall be the duty of the permit applicant to cause the mechanical systems to remain accessible and exposed for inspection purposes. Neither the building official nor the jurisdiction shall be liable for expense entailed in the removal or replacement of any material required to permit inspection. When the installation of a mechanical system is complete, an additional and final inspection shall be made. Mechanical systems regulated by this code shall not be connected to the energy fuel-supply lines until authorized by the building official.

Approval as a result of an inspection shall not be construed to be an approval of a violation of the provisions of this code or of other ordinances of the jurisdiction. Inspections presuming to give authority to violate or cancel the provisions of this code or of other ordinances of the jurisdiction shall not be valid.

116.2 Operation of Mechanical Equipment. The requirements of this section shall not be considered to prohibit the operation of mechanical systems installed to replace existing equipment or fixtures serving an occupied portion of the building in the event a request for inspection of such equipment or fixture has been filed with the building official not more than 48 hours after such replacement work is completed, and before any portion of such mechanical system is concealed by any permanent portion of the building.

116.3 Testing of Equipment and Systems. Refrigeration equipment regulated by this code shall be tested and approved as required by Section 1122 of this code.

Steam and hot-water boilers and piping systems shall be tested and approved as required by Sections 1027, 1202.1.6 and 1208 of this code.

When applicable (see Section 103.5), fuel-gas piping systems shall be tested and approved as required by Section 1305 of this code.

116.4 Inspection Requests. It shall be the duty of the person doing the work authorized by a permit to notify the building official that such work is ready for inspection. The building official may require that every request for inspection be filed at least one working day before such inspection is desired. Such request may be in writing or by telephone at the option of the building official.

It shall be the duty of the person requesting inspections required by this code to provide access to and means for inspection of the work.

116.5 Other Inspections. In addition to the called inspections required by this code, the building official may make or require other inspections of mechanical work to ascertain compliance with the provisions of this code and other laws which are enforced by the code enforcement agency.

116.6 Reinspections. A reinspection fee may be assessed for each inspection or reinspection when such portion of work for which inspection is requested is not complete or when required corrections have not been made.

116.6.1 Reinspection fee. This provision is not to be interpreted as requiring reinspection fees the first time a job is rejected for failure to comply with the requirements of this code, but as controlling the practice of calling for inspections before the job is ready for inspection or reinspection.

116.6.2 Assessment of reinspection fees. Reinspection fees may be assessed, when the approved plans are not readily available to the inspector, for failure to provide access on the date for which inspection is requested or for deviating from plans requiring the approval of the building official.

116.6.3 How obtained. To obtain reinspection, the applicant shall file an application therefor in writing upon a form furnished for that purpose and pay the reinspection fee in accordance with Table 1-A or as set forth in the fee schedule adopted by the jurisdiction.

When reinspection fees have been assessed, no additional inspection of the work will be performed until the required fees have been paid.

SECTION 117 — CONNECTION APPROVAL

117.1 Energy Connections. Persons shall not make connections from a source of energy or fuel to a mechanical system or equipment regulated by this code and for which a permit is required until approved by the building official.

117.2 Temporary Connections. The building official may authorize temporary connection of the mechanical equipment to the source of energy or fuel for the purpose of testing the equipment, or for use under a temporary certificate of occupancy.

TABLE 1-A

1997 UNIFORM MECHANICAL CODE

TABLE 1-A—MECHANICAL PERMIT FEES

Permit Issuance and Heaters

1. For the issuance of each mechanical permit $23.50
2. For issuing each supplemental permit for which the original permit has not expired, been canceled or finaled 7.25

Unit Fee Schedule

(Note: The following do not include permit-issuing fee.)

1. **Furnaces**

    For the installation or relocation of each forced-air or gravity-type furnace or burner, including ducts and vents attached to such appliance, up to and including 100,000 Btu/h (29.3 kW) 14.80

    For the installation or relocation of each forced-air or gravity-type furnace or burner, including ducts and vents attached to such appliance over 100,000 Btu/h (29.3 kW) 18.20

    For the installation or relocation of each floor furnace, including vent 14.80

    For the installation or relocation of each suspended heater, recessed wall heater or floor-mounted unit heater 14.80

2. **Appliance Vents**

    For the installation, relocation or replacement of each appliance vent installed and not included in an appliance permit 7.25

3. **Repairs or Additions**

    For the repair of, alteration of, or addition to each heating appliance, refrigeration unit, cooling unit, absorption unit, or each heating, cooling, absorption or evaporative cooling system, including installation of controls regulated by the Mechanical Code 13.70

4. **Boilers, Compressors and Absorption Systems**

    For the installation or relocation of each boiler or compressor to and including 3 horsepower (10.6 kW), or each absorption system to and including 100,000 Btu/h (29.3 kW) 14.70

    For the installation or relocation of each boiler or compressor over three horsepower (10.6 kW) to and including 15 horsepower (52.7 kW), or each absorption system over 100,000 Btu/h (29.3 kW) to and including 500,000 Btu/h (146.6 kW) 27.15

    For the installation or relocation of each boiler or compressor over 15 horsepower (52.7 kW) to and including 30 horsepower (105.5 kW), or each absorption system over 500,000 Btu/h (146.6 kW) to and including 1,000,000 Btu/h (293.1 kW) 37.25

    For the installation or relocation of each boiler or compressor over 30 horsepower (105.5 kW) to and including 50 horsepower (176 kW), or each absorption system over 1,000,000 Btu/h (293.1 kW) to and including 1,750,000 Btu/h (512.9 kW) 55.45

    For the installation or relocation of each boiler or compressor over 50 horsepower (176 kW), or each absorption system over 1,750,000 Btu/h (512.9 kW) 92.65

5. **Air Handlers**

    For each air-handling unit to and including 10,000 cubic feet per minute (cfm) (4719 L/s), including ducts attached thereto 10.65

    Note: This fee does not apply to an air-handling unit which is a portion of a factory-assembled appliance, cooling unit, evaporative cooler or absorption unit for which a permit is required elsewhere in the Mechanical Code.

    For each air-handling unit over 10,000 cfm (4719 L/s) 18.10

6. **Evaporative Coolers**

    For each evaporative cooler other than portable type 10.65

7. **Ventilation and Exhaust**

    For each ventilation fan connected to a single duct 7.25

    For each ventilation system which is not a portion of any heating or air-conditioning system authorized by a permit 10.65

    For the installation of each hood which is served by mechanical exhaust, including the ducts for such hood 10.65

8. **Incinerators**

    For the installation or relocation of each domestic-type incinerator 18.20

    For the installation or relocation of each commercial or industrial-type incinerator 14.50

9. **Miscellaneous**

    For each appliance or piece of equipment regulated by the Mechanical Code but not classed in other appliance categories, or for which no other fee is listed in the table 10.65

Other Inspections and Fees:

1. Inspections outside of normal business hours, per hour (minimum charge—two hours) $49.50*
2. Reinspection fees assessed under provisions of Section 116.6, per inspection $49.50*
3. Inspections for which no fee is specifically indicated, per hour (minimum charge—one-half hour) $49.50*
4. Additional plan review required by changes, additions or revisions to plans or to plans for which an initial review has been completed (minimum charge—one-half hour) $49.50*

*Or the total hourly cost to the jurisdiction, whichever is the greatest. This cost shall include supervision, overhead, equipment, hourly wages and fringe benefits of the employees involved.

Chapter 2
DEFINITIONS

SECTION 201 — GENERAL

201.1 Abbreviations, Words, Terms and Phrases Defined. For the purpose of this code, certain abbreviations, terms, phrases, words and their derivatives shall be construed as specified in this chapter. Words used in the singular include the plural and the plural the singular. Words used in the masculine gender include the feminine, and the feminine the masculine.

201.2 Standards of Quality.

201.2.1 General. The standards listed below labeled a "UBC Standard" or a "UMC Standard" are also listed in Chapter 16, Part II, and are a part of this code. Other standards listed below are recognized standards. (See Sections 1601, 1602 and 1603.)

201.2.2 Noncombustible material. UBC Standard 2-1, Noncombustible material—Tests.

201.2.3 Flame-spread index. UBC Standard 8-1, Test Method for Surface-burning Characteristics of Building Materials.

201.2.4 Galvanized sheet metals. UMC Standard 2-2, Galvanized Sheet Metals (for duct construction).

201.2.5 Flash Point by the Pensky-Martens closed tester. UMC Standard 2-3, Flash Point by the Pensky-Martens Closed Tester.

201.2.6 Permissible exposure limit. 28 C.F.R. 1910.1000.

SECTION 202 — ACCEPTED MEANINGS

Except as defined in this chapter or elsewhere in this code, the interpretation of words used in this code shall be in accordance with the meanings defined in the Building Code and *Webster's Third New International Dictionary of the English Language, Unabridged,* copyright 1986.

SECTION 203 — A

ABSORPTION UNIT is an absorption refrigeration system which has been factory assembled and tested prior to its installation.

ACCESSIBLE is having access to but which first may require the removal of an access panel, door or similar obstruction covering the item described.

ACCESSIBLE, READILY, means capable of being reached safely and quickly for operation, repair or inspection without requiring those to whom ready access is requisite to climb over or remove obstacles, or to resort to the use of portable access equipment.

AIR, COMBUSTION. See "combustion air," Section 205.

AIR, CONDITIONED, is air which has been treated to achieve a desired level of temperature, humidity or cleanliness.

AIR, EXHAUST, is air being removed from any space or piece of equipment and conveyed directly to the atmosphere by means of openings or ducts.

AIR, MAKEUP, is air which is provided to replace air being exhausted.

AIR, OUTSIDE, is air from outside the building intentionally conveyed by openings or ducts to rooms or to conditioning equipment.

AIR, RETURN, is air being recirculated or transferred within a building.

AIR, SUPPLY, is air being provided to a space or piece of equipment from the outside or inside a building by means of ducts or openings.

AIR, TRANSFER, is air being provided from a room to another room. See "air, return."

AIR, VENTILATION, is air being supplied to or removed from a room or space to which an occupant of the room or space is exposed.

AIR-HANDLING UNIT is a blower or fan used for the purpose of distributing supply air to a room, space or area.

AIR-MOVING SYSTEM is a system designed to provide heating, cooling or ventilation in which one or more air-handling units are used to supply air to a common space or to draw air from a common plenum or space.

APPLIANCE is a device which utilizes fuel or other forms of energy to produce light, heat, power, refrigeration or air conditioning. This definition also shall include a vented decorative appliance.

APPLIANCE FUEL CONNECTOR is an assembly of listed semirigid or flexible tubing and fittings to carry fuel between a fuel piping outlet and a fuel-burning appliance.

APPROVED, as to materials, equipment and method of construction, refers to approval by the building official as the result of investigation and tests by the building official, or by reason of accepted principles or tests by national authorities, technical or scientific organizations.

APPROVED AGENCY is an established and recognized agency regularly engaged in conducting tests or furnishing inspection services, when such agency has been approved by the building official.

ASSEMBLY BUILDING is a building or a portion of a building used for the gathering together of 50 or more persons for such purposes as deliberation, education, instruction, worship, entertainment, amusement, drinking or dining or awaiting transportation.

AUTOMATIC BOILER. When applied to any class of boiler defined below, such boiler shall be equipped with certain controls and limit devices as specified in Section 1014 and Table 10-C.

AZEOTROPE is a refrigerant blend comprising multiple components of different volatilities that, when used in refrigeration cycles, do not change volumetric composition or saturation temperature as they evaporate or condense at constant pressure.

SECTION 204 — B

BOILER is a closed vessel used for heating water or liquid, or for generating steam or vapor by direct application of heat from combustible fuels or electricity.

BOILER, HIGH PRESSURE, is a boiler furnishing steam at pressures in excess of 15 pounds per square inch (103 kPa) or hot water at temperatures in excess of 250°F (121°C) or at pressures in excess of 160 pounds per square inch (1100 kPa).

BOILER ROOM is any room containing a steam or hot-water boiler.

BREECHING is a metal connector for medium- and high-heat appliances.

BRINE is a liquid used for the transmission of heat without a change in its state, having no flash point or a flash point above 150°F (65.5°C), as determined by the requirements of UMC Standard 2-3.

Btu/h is the listed maximum capacity of an appliance, absorption unit or burner expressed in British thermal units input per hour, unless otherwise noted.

BUILDING CODE is the *Uniform Building Code* promulgated by the International Conference of Building Officials, as adopted by this jurisdiction.

BUILDING OFFICIAL is the officer charged with the administration and enforcement of this code, or a regularly authorized deputy.

BURNER, AUTOMATIC BOILER, is a burner for an automatic boiler used to convey fuel into the combustion chamber in proximity to its combustion air supply so as to permit a stable controlled heat release compatible with the burner design and which is equipped with an ignition system to reliably ignite the entire heat-release surface of the burner assembly.

SECTION 205 — C

CAS NUMBER is the Chemical Abstract System registry number.

CATEGORY, VENTED GAS APPLIANCE, is vented gas utilization equipment classified for venting purposes into four categories as follows:

Category I: An appliance that operates with a nonpositive vent pressure and with a flue loss not less than 17 percent.

Category II: An appliance that operates with a nonpositive vent pressure and with a flue loss less than 17 percent.

Category III: An appliance that operates with a positive vent pressure and with a flue loss not less than 17 percent.

Category IV: An appliance that operates with a positive vent pressure and with a flue loss less than 17 percent.

CENTRAL HEATING PLANT or HEATING PLANT is environmental heating equipment installed in a manner to supply heat by means of ducts or pipes to areas other than the room or space in which the equipment is located.

CHIMNEY is a vertical shaft enclosing one or more flues for conveying flue gases to the outside atmosphere.

Factory-built Chimney is a listed chimney.

Masonry Chimney is a chimney of solid masonry units, bricks, stones, listed masonry units or reinforced concrete, lined with suitable flue liners.

Metal Chimney is a chimney constructed of metal with a minimum thickness not less than 0.127-inch (No. 10 manufacturer's standard gage) (3.2 mm) steel sheet.

CHIMNEY CLASSIFICATIONS:

Chimney, High-heat Appliance-type, is a factory-built, masonry or metal chimney suitable for removing the products of combustion from fuel-burning high-heat appliances producing combustion gases exceeding 2,000°F (1093°C) measured at the appliance flue outlet.

Chimney, Low-heat Appliance-type, is a factory-built, masonry or metal chimney suitable for removing the products of combustion from fuel-burning low-heat appliances producing combustion gases not exceeding 1,000°F (538°C) under normal operating conditions but capable of producing combustion gases of 1,400°F (759°C) during intermittent forced firing for periods up to one hour. All temperatures are measured at the appliance flue outlet.

Chimney, Medium-heat Appliance-type, is a factory-built, masonry or metal chimney suitable for removing the products of combustion from fuel-burning medium-heat appliances producing combustion gases not exceeding 2,000°F (1093°C) measured at the appliance flue outlet.

Chimney, Residential Appliance-type, is a factory-built or masonry chimney suitable for removing products of combustion from residential-type appliances producing combustion gases not exceeding 1,000°F (538°C), measured at the appliance flue outlet. Factory-built Type H.T. chimneys have high-temperature thermal shock resistance.

CHIMNEY CONNECTOR is the pipe which connects a fuel-burning appliance to a chimney.

CLOSED COMBUSTION SOLID-FUEL-BURNING APPLIANCE is a heat-producing appliance that employs a combustion chamber that has no openings other than the flue collar, fuel charging door and adjustable openings provided to control the amount of combustion air that enters the combustion chamber.

COMBUSTION AIR is the total amount of air provided to the space which contains fuel-burning equipment; it includes air for fuel combustion, for draft hood dilution and for ventilation of the equipment enclosure.

COMPANION OR BLOCK VALVES. See "valves, companion or block." See Section 224.

COMPARTMENT is a small enclosed room or space intended for the installation of equipment which is both a confined space and a room not large in comparison to the size of the equipment, formerly and commonly referred to as an equipment closet.

COMPRESSOR, POSITIVE DISPLACEMENT, is a compressor in which increase in pressure is attained by changing the internal volume of the compression chamber.

COMPRESSOR, REFRIGERANT, is a machine, with or without accessories, for compressing a refrigerant vapor.

CONCEALED GAS PIPING is gas piping that, when in place in a finished building, would require removal of permanent construction to gain access to the piping.

CONDENSER is that part of the system designed to liquefy refrigerant vapor by removal of heat.

CONDENSING APPLIANCE is an appliance which condenses part of the water vapor generated by the burning of hydrogen in fuels.

CONDENSING UNIT is a mechanical refrigeration system, consisting of one or more power-driven compressors, condensers, liquid receivers, if provided, and the regularly furnished accessories which have been factory assembled and tested prior to its installation.

CONDITIONED SPACE is an area, room or space normally occupied and being heated or cooled by any equipment for human habitation.

CONFINED SPACE is a room or space having a volume less than 50 cubic feet per 1,000 Btu/h (4.83 L/W) of the aggregate input rating of all fuel-burning appliances installed in that space.

CONTINUOUS PILOT is a pilot that burns without turndown throughout the entire period that the boiler is in service, whether or not the main burner is firing.

COOLING is air cooling to provide room or space temperatures of 68°F (20°C) or above.

COOLING SYSTEM is all of that equipment, including associated refrigeration, intended or installed for the purpose of cooling air by mechanical means and discharging such air into any room or space. This definition shall not include an evaporative cooler.

COOLING UNIT is a self-contained refrigeration system which has been factory assembled and tested, installed with or without conditioned air ducts and without connecting any refrigerant-containing parts. This definition shall not include a portable cooling unit or an absorption unit.

SECTION 206 — D

DAMPERS shall be defined as follows:

Ceiling Damper is an automatic-closing assembly complying with UL Standard 555C.

Fire Damper is an automatic-closing metal assembly of one or more louvers, blades, slats or vanes complying with recognized standards.

Leakage Rated Damper. See "smoke damper."

Smoke Damper is a damper arranged to seal off airflow automatically through a part of an air-duct system so as to restrict the passage of smoke.

Volume Damper is a device which, when installed, will restrict, retard or direct the flow of air in a duct, or the products of combustion in heat-producing equipment, its vent connector, vent or chimney therefrom.

DECORATIVE APPLIANCES, VENTED, are appliances whose only function lies in the aesthetic effect of the flames.

DECORATIVE APPLIANCES FOR INSTALLATION IN SOLID-FUEL-BURNING FIREPLACES are self-contained, freestanding, fuel-gas-burning appliances designed for installation only in a vented solid-fuel-burning fireplace and whose primary function lies in the aesthetic effect of the flame.

DIRECT GAS-FIRED MAKEUP AIR HEATER is a heater in which all the products of combustion generated by the gas-burning device are released into the outside airstream being heated.

DIRECT-VENT APPLIANCES are appliances which are constructed and installed so that all air for combustion is derived from the outside atmosphere and all flue gases are discharged to the outside atmosphere.

DISTRICT HEATING PLANT is a power boiler plant designed to distribute hot water or steam to users located off the premises.

DRAFT HOOD is a device built into an appliance or made a part of the vent connector from an appliance, which is designed to:

1. Ensure the ready escape of the flue gases in the event of no draft, backdraft or stoppage beyond the draft hood.

2. Prevent a back draft from entering the appliance.

3. Neutralize the effect of stack action of the chimney or gas vent upon the operation of the appliance.

DUCT is a tube or conduit for transmission of air. This definition shall not include:

1. A vent, a vent connector or a chimney connector.

2. A tube or conduit wherein the pressure of the air exceeds 1 pound per square inch (6.9 Pa).

3. The air passages of listed self-contained systems.

DUCT FURNACE is a warm-air furnace normally installed in an air-distribution duct to supply warm air for heating. This definition shall apply only to a warm-air heating appliance which depends for air circulation on a blower not furnished as part of the furnace.

DUCT SYSTEMS are all ducts, duct fittings, plenums and fans assembled to form a continuous passageway for the distribution of air.

DWELLING is a building or portion thereof which contains not more than two dwelling units.

DWELLING UNIT is a building or portion thereof which contains living facilities, including provisions for sleeping, eating, cooking and sanitation, as required by this code, for not more than one family.

SECTION 207 — E

ELECTRIC HEATING APPLIANCE is a device which produces heat energy to create a warm environment by the application of electric power to resistance elements, refrigerant compressors or dissimilar material junctions.

ELECTRICAL CODE is the *National Electrical Code* promulgated by the National Fire Protection Association, as adopted by this jurisdiction.

EMERGENCY ALARM SYSTEM is a system intended to provide the indication and warning of abnormal conditions and summon appropriate aid.

EMERGENCY CONTROL STATION is an approved location on the premises where signals from emergency equipment are received.

EQUIPMENT is a general term including materials, fittings, devices, appliances and apparatus used as part of or in connection with installations regulated by this code.

EVAPORATIVE COOLER is a device used for reducing the sensible heat of air for cooling by the process of evaporation of water into an airstream.

EVAPORATIVE COOLING SYSTEM is all of that equipment intended or installed for the purpose of environmental cooling by an evaporative cooler from which the conditioned air is distributed through ducts or plenums to the conditioned area.

EVAPORATOR is that part of a refrigeration system in which liquid refrigerant is vaporized to produce refrigeration.

SECTION 208 — F

FABRICATION AREA (FAB AREA) is an area within a Group H, Division 6 or 7 Occupancy in which there are processes involving hazardous production materials and may include ancillary rooms or areas such as dressing rooms and offices that are directly related to the fab area processes.

FIRE CODE is the *Uniform Fire Code* promulgated by the International Fire Code Institute, as adopted by this jurisdiction.

FIREPLACE, SOLID-FUEL-BURNING, is a listed and labeled factory-built or site-built hearth and fire chamber constructed of noncombustible material for use with solid fuels and provided with a chimney.

FIREPLACE STOVE is a chimney-connected, solid-fuel-burning stove (appliance) having part of its fire chamber open to the room.

FIRE-RESISTIVE CONSTRUCTION is construction complying with the requirements of the Building Code for the time period specified.

FLAMMABILITY CLASSES. Class 1 indicates refrigerants that do not show flame propagation in air when tested by prescribed methods at specific conditions. Classes 2 and 3 signify refrigerants with "lower flammability" and "higher flammability," respectively; the distinction depends on both the lower flammability limit (LFL) and heat of combustion.

FLOOR FURNACE is a completely self-contained furnace suspended from the floor of the space being heated, taking air for combustion from outside such space and with means for observing flames and lighting the appliance from such space.

FORCED-AIR-TYPE CENTRAL FURNACE is a central furnace equipped with a fan or blower which provides the primary means for circulation of air.

Downflow-type Central Furnace is a furnace designed with airflow essentially in a vertical path, discharging air at or near the bottom of the furnace.

Horizontal-type Central Furnace is a furnace designed for low headroom installations with airflow through the appliance in a horizontal path.

Upflow-type Central Furnace is a furnace designed with airflow essentially in a vertical path, discharging air at or near the top of the furnace.

FRACTIONATION is a change in composition of a blend by preferential evaporation of the more volatile component or condensation of the less-volatile component.

FUEL GAS is natural, manufactured, liquefied petroleum or a mixture of these.

FUSIBLE PLUG is a device arranged to relieve pressure by operation of a fusible member at a predetermined temperature.

SECTION 209 — G

GALVANIZED STEEL is a steel conforming to the requirements of UMC Standard 2-2.

GAS PIPING is an installation of pipe, valves or fittings that is used to convey fuel gas, installed on a premises or in a building, but shall not include:

1. Portions of the service piping.

2. Approved appliance fuel connectors 6 feet (1800 mm) or less in length between an existing gas outlet and a gas appliance in the same room with the outlet.

GAS PIPING SYSTEM is an arrangement of gas piping supplied by a single meter or each arrangement of gas piping serving a building, structure or premises, whether individually metered or not.

GAS-FIRED LOG LIGHTERS are manually operated gas-fired, solid-fuel ignition devices for installation in an approved fireplace.

GENERATOR is a device equipped with a means of heating used in an absorption system to drive refrigerant out of solution.

GRAVITY HEATING SYSTEM is a heating system consisting of a gravity-type warm-air furnace together with air ducts or pipes and accessory apparatus installed in connection therewith.

GRAVITY-TYPE WARM-AIR FURNACE is a warm-air furnace depending primarily on circulation of air through the furnace by gravity.

This definition also shall include any furnace approved with a booster-type fan which does not materially restrict free circulation of air through the furnace when the fan is not in operation.

SECTION 210 — H

HAZARDOUS LOCATION is an area or space where combustible dust, ignitible fibers or flammable, volatile liquids, gases, vapors or mixtures are or may be present in the air in quantities sufficient to produce explosive or ignitable mixtures.

HAZARDOUS PROCESS PIPING (HPP) is a process material piping or tubing conveying a liquid or gas that has a degree-of-hazard rating in health, flammability or reactivity of Class 3 or 4 as ranked by UFC Standard 79-3.

HEAT PUMP is a refrigeration system that extracts heat from one substance and transfers it to another portion of the same substance or to a second substance at a higher temperature for a beneficial purpose.

HEATING DEGREE DAY is a unit, based on temperature difference and time, used in estimating fuel consumption and specifying nominal annual heating load of a building. For any one day when the mean temperature is less than 65°F (18°C), there exist as many degree days as there are Fahrenheit degrees difference in temperature between mean temperature for the day and 65°F (18°C).

HEATING EQUIPMENT. Includes all warm-air furnaces, warm-air heaters, combustion products vents, heating air-distribution ducts and fans, all steam and hot-water piping together with all control devices and accessories installed as part of, or in connection with, any environmental heating system or appliance regulated by this code.

HEATING SYSTEM is a warm-air heating plant consisting of a heat exchanger enclosed in a casing, from which the heated air is distributed through ducts to various rooms and areas. A heating system includes the outside-air, return-air and supply-air system and all accessory apparatus and equipment installed in connection therewith.

HIGH SIDE is the portion of a refrigeration system subjected to approximately condenser pressure.

HIGH-DISTRIBUTION PRESSURE or **SECOND-STATE PRESSURE** (used in liquefied petroleum gas systems) is pressure exceeding 14 inches water column (3.5 kPa) but not exceeding 20 psig (137 kPa).

HOOD is an air-intake device connected to a mechanical exhaust system for collecting vapors, fumes, smoke, dust, steam, heat or odors from, at or near the equipment, place or area where generated, produced or released.

HOT-WATER-HEATING BOILER is a boiler having volume exceeding 120 gallons (454 L), or a heat input exceeding 200,000 Btu/h (58.58 kW), or an operating temperature exceeding 210°F (99°C) that provides hot water to be used externally to itself.

HPM STORAGE ROOM is a room used for the storage or dispensing of hazardous production material (HPM) and which is classified as a Group H, Division 1 or Division 2 Occupancy.

SECTION 211 — I

IDLH (immediately dangerous to life and health) is a concentration of airborne contaminants, normally expressed in parts per million (ppm) or milligrams per cubic meter (mg/m³), which represents the maximum level from which one could escape within 30 minutes without any escape-impairing symptoms or irreversible health effects. This level is established by the National Institute of Occupational Safety and Health (NIOSH).

INDUSTRIAL HEATING EQUIPMENT is an appliance or device for equipment used, or intended to be used, in an industrial, manufacturing or commercial occupancy for applying heat to any material being processed, but shall not include water heaters, boilers or portable equipment used by artisans in pursuit of a trade.

INSANITARY LOCATION is an area, a space or a room where the air is unfit or undesirable for circulation to occupied parts of a building.

INTERLOCK is a device which senses a limit or off-limit condition or improper sequence of events and shuts down the offending or related piece of equipment or prevents proceeding in an improper sequence in order to prevent a hazardous condition developing.

INTERMITTENT PILOT is a pilot which burns during light-off and while the main burner is firing, and which is shut off with the main burner.

INTERRUPTED PILOT is a pilot which burns during light-off and which is shut off during normal operation of the main burner.

SECTION 212 — J

JOINT, BRAZED, is a joint obtained by joining of metal parts with alloys which melt at temperatures higher than 800°F (427°C) but lower than the melting temperature of the parts being joined.

JOINT, COMPRESSION, is a multipiece joint with cup-shaped threaded nuts which, when tightened, compress tapered sleeves so that they form a tight joint on the periphery of the tubing they connect.

JOINT, FLANGED, is one made by bolting together a pair of flanged ends.

JOINT, FLARED, is a metal-to-metal compression joint in which a conical spread is made on the end of a tube that is compressed by a flare nut against a mating flare.

JOINT, MECHANICAL, is a general form of gas-tight joint obtained by the joining of metal parts through a positive holding mechanical construction (such as flanged joint, screwed joint, flared joint).

JOINT, WELDED, is a gas-tight joint obtained by the joining of metal parts in molten state.

SECTION 213 — K

No definitions.

SECTION 214 — L

LEL (lower explosive limit). See "LFL."

LFL (lower flammable limit or lower limit of flammability) is the minimum concentration of a combustible substance that is capable of propagating a flame through homogeneous mixture of the combustible and a gaseous oxidizer under the specified condition of test. The LFL is sometimes referred to as LEL (lower explosive limit); for the purposes of this definition, LFL and LEL are identical.

LINE CONTACT INSTALLATION is where a furnace is installed so that building joists, studs or framing is contacted by the furnace jacket upon the lines formed by the intersection of the jacket sides with the top surface.

LIQUEFIED PETROLEUM GAS or **LPG (LP-gas)** shall mean and include a material composed predominantly of any of the following hydrocarbons or mixtures of them: propane, propylene, butanes (normal butane or isobutane) and butylenes.

When reference is made to liquefied petroleum gas in this code, it shall refer to liquefied petroleum gases in either the liquid or gaseous state.

LIQUEFIED PETROLEUM GAS FACILITIES are tanks, containers, container valves, regulating equipment, meters and appurtenances for the storage and supply of liquefied petroleum gas for a building or premises.

LISTED and **LISTING** are terms referring to equipment or materials included in a list published by an approved testing laboratory, inspection agency or other organization concerned with product evaluation that maintains periodic inspection of current productions of listed equipment or materials and which listing states that the material or equipment complies with approved nationally recognized codes, standards or tests and has been tested or evaluated and found suitable for use in a specific manner.

LOW SIDE is the portion of a refrigeration system subjected to approximate evaporator pressure.

LOW-PRESSURE HOT-WATER-HEATING BOILER is a boiler furnishing hot water at pressures not exceeding 160 pounds per square inch (1100 kPa) and at temperatures not exceeding 250°F (121°C).

LOW-PRESSURE STEAM-HEATING BOILER is a boiler furnishing steam at pressures not exceeding 15 pounds per square inch (103 kPa).

SECTION 215 — M

MACHINERY is the refrigeration equipment forming a part of the refrigeration system, including, but not limited to, a compressor, a condenser, a liquid receiver, an evaporator and connecting piping.

MANUFACTURER is the company or organization which evidences its responsibility by affixing its name, trademark or trade name to equipment or devices.

MANUFACTURER'S INSTALLATION INSTRUCTIONS are printed instructions included with equipment or devices for the purpose of information regarding safe and proper installation whether or not as part of the conditions of listing.

MEDIUM PRESSURE is pressure exceeding 14 inches water column (3.5 kPa) but not exceeding 5 psig (34 kPa).

MINIATURE BOILER is a power boiler having an internal shell diameter of 16 inches (406 mm) or less, a gross volume of 5 cubic feet (142 L) or less, a heating surface of 20 square feet (1.86 m^2) or less (not applicable to electric boilers) and not exceeding 100 psi (685 kPa).

SECTION 216 — N

NONCOMBUSTIBLE, as applied to building construction material, means a material which, in the form in which it is used, is either one of the following:

1. Material of which no part will ignite and burn when subjected to fire. Any material conforming to UBC Standard 2-1 shall be considered noncombustible within the meaning of this section.

2. Material having a structural base of noncombustible material as defined in Item 1 above, with a surfacing material not exceeding $^1/_8$ inch (3.2 mm) thick which has a flame-spread index not higher than 50.

"Noncombustible" does not apply to surface finish materials. Material required to be noncombustible for reduced clearances to flues, heating appliances or other sources of high temperature shall refer to material conforming to Item 1. No material shall be classed as noncombustible which is subject to increase in combustibility or flame-spread index beyond the limits herein established, through the effects of age, moisture or other atmospheric condition.

Flame-spread index as used herein refers to results obtained according to tests conducted as specified in UBC Standard 8-1.

NONHAZARDOUS PROCESS PIPING (NPP) is production material piping or tubing conveying the liquid or gas which is not classified as hazardous production material piping.

SECTION 217 — O

OCCUPANCY is the purpose for which a building or part thereof is used or intended to be used.

OCCUPANCY CLASSIFICATION. For the purpose of this code, certain occupancies are defined as follows:

Group A Occupancies:

Group A Occupancies include the use of a building or structure, or a portion thereof, for the gathering together of 50 or more persons for purposes such as civic, social or religious functions, recreation, education or instruction, food or drink consumption, or awaiting transportation. A room or space used for assembly purposes by less than 50 persons and accessory to another occupancy shall be included as a part of that major occupancy. Assembly occupancies shall include the following:

Division 1. A building or portion of a building having an assembly room with an occupant load of 1,000 or more and a legitimate stage.

Division 2. A building or portion of a building having an assembly room with an occupant load of less than 1,000 and a legitimate stage.

Division 2.1. A building or portion of a building having an assembly room with an occupant load of 300 or more without a legitimate stage, including such buildings used for educational purposes and not classed as a Group B or E Occupancy.

Division 3. A building or portion of a building having an assembly room with an occupant load of less than 300 without a legitimate stage, including such buildings used for educational purposes and not classed as a Group B or E Occupancy.

Division 4. Stadiums, reviewing stands and amusement park structures not included within other Group A Occupancies. Specific and general requirements for grandstands, bleachers and reviewing stands are to be found in Chapter 10 of the Building Code.

> **EXCEPTION:** Amusement buildings or portions thereof which are without walls or a roof and constructed to prevent the accumulation of smoke in assembly areas.

Group B Occupancies:

Group B Occupancies shall include buildings, structures, or portions thereof, for office, professional or service-type transactions, which are not classified as Group H Occupancies. Such occupancies include occupancies for the storage of records and accounts, and eating and drinking establishments with an occupant load of less than 50.

Group E Occupancies:

Division 1. Any building used for educational purposes through the 12th grade by 50 or more persons for more than 12 hours per week or four hours in any one day.

Division 2. Any building used for educational purposes through the 12th grade by less than 50 persons for more than 12 hours per week or four hours in any one day.

Division 3. Any building or portion thereof used for day-care purposes for more than six persons.

Group F Occupancies:

Group F Occupancies shall include the use of a building or structure, or a portion thereof, for assembling, disassembling, fabricating, finishing, manufacturing, packaging, repair or processing operations that are not classified as Group H Occupancies.

Division 1. Moderate-hazard factory and industrial occupancies shall include factory and industrial uses which are not classified as Group F, Division 2 Occupancies.

Division 2. Low-hazard factory and industrial occupancies shall include facilities producing noncombustible or nonexplosive materials which, during finishing, packing or processing, do not involve a significant fire hazard.

Group H Occupancies:

Group H Occupancies shall include buildings or structures, or portions thereof, that involve the manufacturing, processing, generation or storage of materials that constitute a high fire, explosion or health hazard. For definitions, identification and control of hazardous materials and pesticides, and the display of nonflammable solid and nonflammable or noncombustible liquid hazardous materials in Group B, F, M or S Occupancies, see the Fire Code.

Division 1. Occupancies with a quantity of material in the building in excess of those listed in Table 3-D of the Building Code, which present a high explosion hazard.

Division 2. Occupancies where combustible dust is manufactured, used or generated in such a manner that concentrations and conditions create a fire or explosion potential; occupancies with a quantity of material in the building in excess of those listed in Table 3-D of the Building Code, which present a moderate explosion hazard or a hazard from accelerated burning.

Division 3. Occupancies where flammable solids, other than combustible dust, are manufactured, used or generated.

Division 4. Repair garages not classified as Group S, Division 3 Occupancies.

Division 5. Aircraft repair hangars and heliports not classified as Group S, Division 5 Occupancies.

Division 6. Semiconductor fabrication facilities and comparable research and development areas in which hazardous production materials (HPM) are used and the aggregate quantity of materials are in excess of those listed in Table 3-D or 3-E of the Building Code.

Division 7. Occupancies having quantities of materials in excess of those listed in Table 3-E of the Building Code that are health hazards.

Group I Occupancies:

Division 1.1. Nurseries for the full-time care of children under the age of six (each accommodating more than five children).

Hospitals, sanitariums, nursing homes with nonambulatory patients and similar buildings (each accommodating more than five patients).

Division 1.2. Health-care centers for ambulatory patients receiving outpatient medical care which may render the patient incapable of unassisted self-preservation (each tenant space accommodating more than five such patients).

Division 2. Nursing homes for ambulatory patients, homes for children six years of age or over (each accommodating more than five patients or children).

Division 3. Mental hospitals, mental sanitariums, jails, prisons, reformatories and buildings where personal liberties of inmates are similarly restrained.

Group M Occupancies:

Group M Occupancies shall include buildings, structures, or portions thereof, used for the display and sale of merchandise, and involving stocks of goods, wares or merchandise, incidental to such purposes and accessible to the public.

Group R Occupancies:

Division 1. Hotels and apartment houses.

Congregate residences (each accommodating more than 10 persons).

Division 2. Not used.

Division 3. Dwellings and lodging houses.

Congregate residences (each accommodating 10 persons or less).

Group S Occupancies:

Group S Occupancies shall include the use of a building or structure, or a portion thereof, for storage not classified as a hazardous occupancy.

Division 1. Moderate hazard storage occupancies shall include buildings or portions of buildings used for storage of combustible materials that are not classified as a Group S, Division 2 or as a Group H Occupancy.

Division 2. Low-hazard storage occupancies shall include buildings, structures, or portions thereof, used for storage of non-combustible materials such as products on wood pallets or in paper cartons with or without single-thickness divisions, or in paper wrappings and shall include ice plants, power plants and pumping plants.

Division 3. Division 3 Occupancies shall include repair garages where work is limited to exchange of parts and maintenance requiring no open flame or welding, motor vehicle fuel-dispensing stations, and parking garages not classed as Group S, Division 4 open parking garages or Group U private garages.

Division 4. Open parking garages.

Division 5. Aircraft hangars where work is limited to exchange of parts and maintenance requiring no open flame or welding and helistops.

Group U Occupancies:

Division 1. Private garages, carports, sheds and agricultural buildings.

Division 2. Fences over 6 feet (1829 mm) high, tanks and towers.

SECTION 218 — P

PACKAGE BOILER may be any class of boiler defined herein and shall be a boiler equipped and shipped complete with fuel-burning equipment, automatic controls and accessories, and mechanical draft equipment, if used.

PEL (Permissible Exposure Limit) is the maximum permitted eight-hour time-weighted average concentration of an airborne contaminant. The maximum permitted time-weighted average exposures to be utilized are those published in 29 C.F.R. 1910.1000.

PILOT is a burner smaller than the main burner, which is ignited by a spark or other independent and stable ignition source, and which provides ignition energy required to immediately light off the main burner.

PIPELINE WELDER is a person qualified in welding pipes who holds a valid certificate of competency from an approved agency based on demonstrated ability in meeting the requirements of Section IX of the ASME Boiler and Pressure Vessel Code.

PIPING is the pipe or tube mains for interconnecting the various parts of a system. Piping includes pipe, tube, flanges, bolting, gaskets, valves, fittings, the pressure-containing parts of other components such as expansion joints, strainers and devices which serve such purposes as mixing, separating, snubbing, distributing, metering or controlling flow, pipe-supporting fixtures and structural attachments.

PLENUM is an air compartment or chamber, including uninhabited crawl spaces, areas above a ceiling or below a floor, including air spaces below raised floors of computer/data processing centers, or attic spaces, to which one or more ducts are connected and which forms part of either the supply-air, return-air or exhaust-air system, other than the occupied space being conditioned.

PLUMBING CODE is the Plumbing Code as adopted by this jurisdiction.

PORTABLE COOLING UNIT is a self-contained refrigerating system, not over 3 horsepower rating, which has been factory assembled and tested, installed without supply-air ducts and without connecting any refrigerant-containing parts. This definition shall not include an absorption unit.

PORTABLE EVAPORATIVE COOLER is an evaporative cooler which discharges the conditioned air directly into the conditioned area without the use of ducts and can be readily transported from place to place without dismantling any portion thereof.

PORTABLE HEATING APPLIANCE is a heating appliance designed for environmental heating which may have a self-contained fuel supply and is not secured or attached to a building by any means other than by a factory-installed power-supply cord.

PORTABLE VENTILATING EQUIPMENT is ventilating equipment that can be readily transported from place to place without dismantling a portion thereof and which is not connected to a duct.

POSITIVE DISPLACEMENT COMPRESSOR is a compressor in which increase in pressure is attained by changing the internal volume of the compression chamber.

POWER BOILER is a boiler in which steam is generated at pressures exceeding 15 psi (103 kPa).

POWER BOILER PLANT is one or more power steam boilers or power hot-water boilers and connecting piping and vessels within the same premises.

POWER HOT-WATER BOILER (HIGH-TEMPERATURE WATER BOILER) is a boiler used for heating water or liquid to a pressure exceeding 160 psi (1103 kPa) or to a temperature exceeding 250°F (121°C).

PRESSURE, DESIGN, is the maximum working pressure for which a specific part of a refrigeration system is designed.

PRESSURE, FIELD TEST, is a test performed in the field to prove system tightness.

PRESSURE TEST is the minimum gage pressure to which a specific system component is subjected under test condition.

PRESSURE VESSEL (Unfired) is a closed container, having a nominal internal diameter exceeding 6 inches (153 mm) and a volume exceeding $1^1/_2$ cubic feet (42 L), for liquids, gases or vapors subjected to pressures exceeding 15 psi (103 kPa) or steam under any pressure.

PRESSURE VESSEL—REFRIGERANT is a refrigerant-containing receptacle which is a portion of a refrigeration system, but shall not include evaporators, headers or piping of certain limited size and capacity.

PRESSURE-IMPOSING ELEMENT is a device or portion of the equipment used for the purpose of increasing the pressure of the refrigerant vapor.

PRESSURE-LIMITING DEVICE is a pressure-responsive mechanism designed to automatically stop the operation of the pressure-imposing element at a predetermined pressure.

PRESSURE-RELIEF DEVICE is a pressure-actuated valve or rupture member or fusible plug designed to automatically relieve excessive pressure.

PROCESS PIPING is piping or tubing which conveys liquid or gas and which is used directly in research, laboratory or production processes and which is not regulated under the mechanical or plumbing code.

PURGE is an acceptable method of scavenging the combustion chamber, boiler passes and breeching to remove all combustible gases.

SECTION 219 — Q

QUICK-DISCONNECT DEVICE is a hand-operated device which provides a means for connecting and disconnecting an appliance or an appliance connector to a gas supply. The device is equipped with an automatic means to shut off the gas supply when the device is disconnected.

SECTION 220 — R

RADIANT HEATER is a heater designed to transfer heat primarily by direct radiation.

RECEIVER, LIQUID, is a vessel permanently connected to a refrigeration system by inlet and outlet pipes for storage of liquid refrigerant.

RECLAIMED REFRIGERANTS are refrigerants reprocessed to the same specifications as for new refrigerants by means that may include distillation. Such refrigerants have been chemically analyzed to verify that the specifications have been met. Reclaiming usually implies the use of processes or procedures that are available only at a reprocessing or manufacturing facility.

RECOVERED REFRIGERANTS are refrigerants removed from a system in any condition without necessarily testing or processing them.

RECYCLED REFRIGERANTS are refrigerants for which contaminants have been reduced by oil separation, noncondensable gases removal, and single or multiple passes through devices that reduce moisture, acidity and particulate matter, such as replaceable core filter driers. These procedures usually are performed at the field job site or in a local service shop.

REFRIGERANT SAFETY CLASSIFICATIONS are groupings that indicate the toxicity and flammability classes in accordance with Section 1102. The classification group is made up of a letter (A or B), which indicates the toxicity class, followed by a number (1, 2 or 3), which indicates the flammability class. Refrigerant blends are similarly classified, based on the composition at their worst cases of fractionation, as separately determined for toxicity and flammability. In some cases, the worst case of fractionation is the original formulation.

REFRIGERATED ROOM or SPACE is a room or space in which an evaporator or brine coil is located for the purpose of reducing or controlling the temperature within the room or space to below 68°F (20°C).

REFRIGERATION CAPACITY RATING expressed as 1 horsepower, 1 ton or 12,000 Btu/h (3.52 kW) shall all mean the same quantity.

REFRIGERATION MACHINERY ROOM is a space that is designed to safely house compressors and pressure vessels.

REFRIGERATION SYSTEM, ABSORPTION, is a heat-operated, closed refrigeration cycle in which a secondary fluid, the absorbent, absorbs a primary fluid, the refrigerant, that has been vaporized in the evaporator.

REFRIGERATION SYSTEM, MECHANICAL, is a combination of interconnected refrigerant-containing parts constituting one closed refrigerant circuit in which a refrigerant is circulated for the purpose of extracting heat and in which a compressor is used for compressing the refrigerant vapor.

REFRIGERATION SYSTEM, SELF-CONTAINED, is a complete factory-assembled and tested system that is shipped in one or more sections and has no refrigerant-containing parts that are joined in the field by other than companion or block valves.

RESIDENTIAL BUILDING is a building or portion thereof designed or used for human habitation.

RISER HEAT PIPE is a duct which extends at an angle of more than 45 degrees from the horizontal. This definition shall not include any boot connection.

ROOM HEATER is a freestanding, nonrecessed, environmental heating appliance installed in the space being heated and not connected to ducts.

ROOM LARGE IN COMPARISON WITH SIZE OF EQUIPMENT is one having a volume of at least 12 times the total volume of a furnace or air-conditioning appliance and at least 16 times the total volume of a boiler. Total volume of the appliance is determined from exterior dimensions and includes fan compartments and burner vestibules when used. When the actual ceiling height of a room is greater than 8 feet (2438 mm), the volume of the room is figured on the basis of a ceiling height of 8 feet (2438 mm).

RUPTURE MEMBER is a pressure-relief device that operates by the rupture of a diaphragm within the device on a rise to a predetermined pressure.

SECTION 221 — S

SEAM, WELDED. See "joint, welded."

SELF-CONTAINED means having all essential working parts except energy and control connections so contained in a case or framework that they do not depend on appliances or fastenings outside of the machine.

SERVICE CORRIDOR is a fully enclosed passage used for transporting hazardous production materials and purposes other than required exiting.

SERVICE PIPING is the piping and equipment between the street gas main and the gas piping system inlet which is installed by and is under the control and maintenance of the serving gas supplier.

SHAFT is an interior space enclosed by walls or construction extending through one or more stories or basements which connects openings in successive floors or floors and roof, to accommodate elevators, dumbwaiters, mechanical equipment or similar devices to transmit light or ventilation air.

SHAFT ENCLOSURE is the walls or construction forming the boundaries of a shaft.

SMOKE DETECTOR is an approved device that senses visible or invisible particles of combustion.

SOLDERED JOINT is a joint obtained by the joining of metal parts with metallic mixtures or alloys which melt at a temperature below 800°F (427°C) and above 400°F (204°C).

STEAM-HEATING BOILER is a boiler operated at pressures not exceeding 15 psi (103 kPa) for steam.

STOP VALVE is a device to shut off the flow of refrigerant.

STRENGTH, ULTIMATE, is the highest stress level which the component can tolerate without rupture.

SECTION 222 — T

TOXICITY CLASSES. Classes A and B signify refrigerants with "lower toxicity" and "higher toxicity," respectively, based on prescribed measures of chronic (long-term, repeated exposures) toxicity.

SECTION 223 — U

UBC STANDARDS are those standards published in Volume 3 of the *Uniform Building Code* promulgated by the International Conference of Building Officials, as adopted by this jurisdiction.

UNCONFINED SPACE is a room or space having a volume equal to at least 50 cubic feet per 1,000 Btu/h (4.831 L/W) of the aggregate input rating of all fuel-burning appliances installed in that space. Rooms communicating directly with the space in which the appliances are installed, through openings not furnished with doors, are considered a part of the unconfined space.

UNIT HEATER is a heating appliance designed for nonresidential space heating and equipped with an integral means for circulation of air.

UNUSUALLY TIGHT CONSTRUCTION is construction where:

1. Walls and ceilings exposed to the outside atmosphere have a continuous water vapor retarder with a rating of 1 perm or less with any openings gasketed or sealed, and

2. Weatherstripping on openable windows and doors, and

3. Caulking or sealants are applied to areas such as joints around window and door frames, between sole plates and floors, between wall-ceiling joints, between wall panels and at penetrations for plumbing, electrical and gas lines and at other openings.

USE (MATERIAL) is the placing in action or making available for service by opening or connecting any container utilized for confinement of material whether a solid, liquid or gas.

SECTION 224 — V

VALVE, PRESSURE RELIEF, is a pressure-actuated valve held closed by a spring or other means and designed to automatically relieve pressure in excess of its setting; also called a safety valve.

VALVE, STOP, is a device in a piping system to shut off the flow of the fluid.

VALVE, THREE-WAY-TYPE STOP, is a manually operated valve with one inlet which alternately can stop flow to either of two outlets.

VALVES, COMPANION OR BLOCK, are pairs of mating stop valves valving off sections of refrigeration systems and arranged so that these sections may be joined before opening these valves or separated after closing them.

VENT is a listed factory-made vent pipe and vent fittings for conveying flue gases to the outside atmosphere.

Type B Gas Vent is a factory-made gas vent listed by a nationally recognized testing agency for venting listed or approved appliances equipped to burn only gas.

Type BW Gas Vent is a factory-made gas vent listed by a nationally recognized testing agency for venting listed or approved gas-fired vented wall furnaces.

Type L is a venting system consisting of listed vent piping and fittings for use with oil-burning appliances listed for use with Type L or with listed gas appliances.

VENT CONNECTOR, GAS, is that portion of a gas-venting system which connects a listed gas appliance to a gas vent and is installed within the space or area in which the appliance is located.

VENTED DECORATIVE APPLIANCE is a vented appliance whose only function lies in the esthetic effect of the flames.

VENTED WALL FURNACE is a vented environmental heating appliance designed for incorporation in, or permanent attachment to, a wall, floor, ceiling or partition and arranged to furnish heated air by gravity or by a fan. This definition shall not include floor furnaces, unit heaters and room heaters.

VENTILATING CEILING is a suspended ceiling containing many small apertures through which air, at low pressure, is forced downward from an overhead plenum dimensioned by the concealed space between suspended ceiling and the floor or roof above.

VENTILATION SYSTEM is all of that equipment intended or installed for the purpose of supplying air to, or removing air from, any room or space by mechanical means.

VENTING COLLAR is the outlet opening of an appliance provided for connection of the vent system.

VENTING SYSTEM is the vent or chimney and its connectors assembled to form a continuous open passageway from an appliance to the outside atmosphere for the purpose of removing products of combustion. This definition also shall include a venting assembly which is an integral part of an appliance.

VENTING SYSTEM—GRAVITY-TYPE is a system which depends entirely on the heat from the fuel being used to provide the energy required to vent an appliance.

VENTING SYSTEM—POWER-TYPE is a system which depends on a mechanical device to provide a positive draft within the venting system.

VOLUME, INTERNAL GROSS, is the volume as determined from internal dimensions of the container with no allowance for the volume of the internal parts.

SECTION 225 — W

WALL HEATER. See definition of "vented wall furnace."

WARM-AIR FURNACE is an environmental heating appliance designed or arranged to discharge heated air through any duct or ducts.

This definition shall not include a unit heater.

WATER HEATER or **HOT-WATER-HEATING BOILER** is an appliance designed primarily to supply hot water and is equipped with automatic controls limiting water temperature to a maximum of 210°F (99°C).

SECTION 226 — X

No definitions.

SECTION 227 — Y

No definitions.

SECTION 228 — Z

ZEOTROPE is a blend comprising multiple components of different volatilities that, when used in refrigeration cycles, change volumetric composition and saturation temperatures as they evaporate or condense at constant pressure.

Chapter 3
GENERAL REQUIREMENTS

NOTE: This chapter has been revised in its entirety.

SECTION 301 — SCOPE

301.1 General. Mechanical equipment providing space heating, ventilating, air conditioning or refrigeration and water heaters shall comply with the general requirements of this chapter and the specific requirements elsewhere in this code. Mechanical equipment providing other services to or within buildings, except for plumbing, is also covered by these requirements.

301.2 Standards of Quality. The standards listed below labeled a "UMC Standard" or a "UBC Standard" are also listed in Chapter 16, Part II, and are a part of this code. The other standards listed below are recognized standards. (See Sections 1601, 1602 and 1603.)

301.2.1 *National Electrical Code.* ANSI/NFPA 70 *National Electrical Code.*

301.2.2 Flame spread index. UBC Standard 8-1, Test Method for Surface-burning Characteristics of Building Materials.

SECTION 302 — APPROVAL OF EQUIPMENT

302.1 Listed Equipment. Equipment shall be approved prior to installation. Listed equipment may be approved by the building official upon determination that it is safe for use and complies with applicable nationally recognized standards as evidenced by the listing and label of an approved agency. Part III of Chapter 16, Recognized Standards, provides guidance as to available nationally recognized standards. Installers shall furnish satisfactory evidence that the appliance is constructed in conformity with the requirements of this code. A permanently attached label of an approved agency may be accepted as such evidence. Installers shall leave the manufacturer's installation and operating instructions attached to the equipment.

302.2 Unlisted Equipment. Unlisted equipment shall be approved prior to installation. Unlisted equipment may be approved by the building official upon determination that it is safe for use. Compliance with appropriate recognized standards as determined by the building official may be used in granting such approval. Part III of Chapter 16, Recognized Standards, provides guidance as to some recognized standards. Installers shall furnish satisfactory evidence that the appliance is constructed in conformity with the requirements of this code. A permanently attached label of an approved agency may be accepted as such evidence. Installers shall leave the manufacturer's installation and operating instructions attached to the equipment.

302.3 Tests. Nothing contained herein shall be construed to limit the building official's authority to require reasonable tests or other satisfactory evidence in making a determination of safe and appropriate use in granting approval of mechanical equipment.

SECTION 303 — INSTALLATION

303.1 General. Equipment shall be installed as required by the terms of its approval. The conditions of listing and the manufacturer's installation instructions shall be the minimum requirements for installation. The specific requirements of this code and

other relevant codes and regulations of this jurisdiction shall be additional requirements for approved installations.

303.1.1 Prohibited installations. No unvented or direct fired fuel-burning equipment shall be installed or used to provide comfort heating within any occupancy group other than Group F, S or U.

303.1.2 Floor furnaces. Vented floor furnaces shall not be installed in a slab on grade or where it extends down into other than a raised, underfloor crawl space.

303.1.3 Elevation of ignition source. Equipment which has a flame, generates a spark or uses a glowing ignition source open to the space in which it is installed shall be elevated such that the source of ignition is at least 18 inches (457 mm) above the floor in Group S, Division 3, 4 or 5 and Group U, Division 1 Occupancies. When appliances installed within a Group U, Division 1 Occupancy are enclosed in a separate, approved compartment having access only from outside of the garage, such equipment may be installed at floor level, providing the required combustion air is taken from and discharged to the exterior of the garage. Such equipment shall not be installed in Group H Occupancies or control areas where open use, handling or dispensing of combustible, flammable or explosive materials occurs.

303.2 Conflicts. Where conflicts between this code and the conditions of listing or the manufacturer's installation instructions occur, the more restrictive provisions shall be followed as determined by the building official.

SECTION 304 — LOCATION

304.1 General. Equipment shall be located as required by this section, specific requirements elsewhere in this code and the conditions of the equipment's approval.

304.2 Indoor Locations. Equipment inside buildings shall be located in compliance with the special hazards provisions of the Building Code. Fuel-burning equipment other than boilers not listed for closet or alcove installation shall be installed in rooms or spaces having a volume at least 12 times the total volume of the fuel-burning equipment. Boilers not listed for closet or alcove installation shall be installed in rooms having a volume at least 16 times the total volume of the boilers. The room volume shall be computed using the gross floor area and the actual ceiling height up to a maximum computational height of 8 feet (2438 mm). Such rooms or spaces shall be considered large in comparison with the size of the equipment.

> **EXCEPTION:** Approved equipment, listed and labeled for installation in rooms or spaces not large in comparison with the size of the equipment, such as those listed for installation in compartments or alcoves.

304.3 Outdoor Locations. Equipment installed outside buildings shall be listed and labeled for outdoor installation or shall be installed within an approved weatherproof enclosure.

304.4 Pit Locations. Equipment installed in pits or excavations shall not come in direct contact with the surrounding soil. The sides of the pit or excavation shall be held back a minimum of 12 inches (305 mm) from the equipment. When the depth exceeds 12 inches (305 mm) below adjoining grade, the walls of the pit or excavation shall be lined with concrete or masonry extending a minimum of 4 inches (102 mm) above adjoining grade having sufficient lateral-bearing capacity to resist collapse. The equipment shall be protected from flooding in an approved manner.

> **EXCEPTIONS:** 1. Equipment designed for direct burial.
>
> 2. When approved, pits deeper than 12 inches (305 mm), but less than 36 inches (915 mm), may use stable earth with a slope no greater than 2 units vertical in 1 unit horizontal (200% slope).

304.5 Prohibited Locations. Equipment shall not be located in a hazardous location unless listed and approved for the specific installation. Fuel-burning equipment, electric resistance heating devices or electrostatic air cleaners shall not be installed in a surgical procedure or medical treatment room. Fuel-burning equipment shall not be installed in a closet, bathroom or a room readily usable as a bedroom, or in a room, compartment or alcove opening directly into any of these.

> **EXCEPTIONS:** 1. Direct vent equipment and electric heat furnaces.
>
> 2. Access to furnaces located in an attic or underfloor crawl space may be through a closet.
>
> 3. A vented appliance located in an unconfined space in accordance with the combustion air requirements of Chapter 7.
>
> 4. A fireplace may be approved for installation in a bathroom or bedroom if equipped with an approved method of obtaining combustion air from outside.
>
> 5. A warm-air furnace in an enclosed space with combustion air obtained from outside the building in conformance with Chapter 7 and having a tightfitting gasketed door with a closer may have access through a bathroom or bedroom.

Equipment burning liquefied petroleum gas (LPG) or liquid fuel shall not be located in a pit, an underfloor space, below grade or similar location where vapors or fuel might unsafely collect unless an approved method for the safe collection, removal and containment or disposal of the vapors or fuel is provided.

In areas subject to flooding, equipment which would be damaged or create hazardous conditions if subjected to inundation shall not be installed at or below grade unless suitably protected by elevation or other approved means.

304.6 Clearances to Combustible Construction. Listed, heat-producing equipment shall be installed in such a manner as to maintain the required clearances to combustible construction specified in the listing. Unlisted, heat-producing equipment shall be installed in such a manner as to maintain the clearances to combustible construction specified in Table 3-A. Clearances to combustible construction for unlisted equipment in Table 3-A may be reduced from the required clearances by using the methods of protection specified in Table 3-B. Clearances from combustibles shall include but not be limited to such considerations as door swing, drawer pull, overhead projections or shelving and window swing, shutters, coverings and drapes. Devices such as door stops or limits, closers, drapery ties or guards, and the like shall not be used to provide the required clearances.

304.7 Clearances for Maintenance and Replacement. Clearances around equipment to elements of permanent construction, including other installed equipment, shall be sufficient to allow inspection, service, repair or replacement without removing such elements of permanent construction or disabling the function of a required fire assembly. Clearances to construction for furnaces and boilers in rooms or spaces not large in comparison with the size of the equipment shall not be reduced by any method from the clearances required by the terms of listing and the manufacturer's installation instructions. Warm-air furnaces within compartments or alcoves shall have a minimum working space clearance of 3 inches (76 mm) along the sides, back and top with a total width of the enclosing space being at least 12 inches (305 mm) wider

than the furnace. Furnaces having a firebox open to the atmosphere shall have at least 6 inches (152 mm) working space along the front combustion chamber side.

> **EXCEPTION:** Replacement warm-air furnaces or air-conditioning cooling coils may be installed in an existing compartment or alcove with lesser width and depth when approved by the building official and provided that such width and depth are in compliance with conditions of listing. Combustion-air openings at the rear or side of the compartment shall comply with the requirements of Chapter 7 of this code.

304.8 Clearances from Grade. Equipment installed at grade level shall be supported on a level concrete slab or other approved material extending a minimum of 3 inches (76 mm) above adjoining grade or it shall be suspended a minimum of 6 inches (152 mm) above adjoining grade.

304.9 Protection from Damage. Equipment shall not be installed in a location where it is subject to mechanical damage unless protected by approved, substantial barriers.

SECTION 305 — TYPE OF FUEL AND FUEL CONNECTIONS

305.1 General. Fuel-burning equipment shall be designed for use with the type of fuel to which it will be connected and the altitude at which it is installed. Appliances shall not be converted from the fuel specified on the rating plate for use with a different fuel without securing reapproval from the building official and as recommended by the manufacturer of either the original equipment or the conversion equipment. The serving gas supplier may convert appliances in accordance with procedures approved by the building official without securing reapproval of the equipment if properly relabeled. Equipment shall not be installed or altered in violation of the provisions of this code nor shall the fuel input rate be increased beyond or decreased below the approved rating for the altitude at which the equipment is installed.

305.2 Fuel Shutoff Valves. An approved fuel shutoff valve shall be installed in the fuel supply piping serving each piece of fuel-burning equipment at an accessible location ahead of the union or appliance connector. The shutoff valve shall be located such that it is within 3 feet (914 mm) of the piece of equipment, in the same room or enclosure, and within sight of the equipment, and shall not interfere with maintenance or removal of any equipment.

> **EXCEPTIONS:** 1. Shutoff valves may be accessibly located inside or under an appliance when such appliance can be removed without removal of the shutoff valve.
>
> 2. Shutoff valves may be accessibly located inside wall heaters and wall furnaces listed for recessed installation where necessary maintenance can be performed without removal of the shutoff valve.

305.3 Connections. Each piece of equipment shall be connected to its fuel supply piping by a union type connection; an approved appliance connector; or an approved, listed quick-disconnect device. Appliance connectors shall be listed for the fuel used and shall not exceed 3 feet (914 mm) in length.

> **EXCEPTION:** Connectors for domestic range and domestic clothes dryer shall not exceed 6 feet (1830 mm) in length.

Appliance connectors shall not be concealed within or extend through a wall, partition, floor or ceiling. Appliance connectors shall not extend through the equipment housing or casing. Appliance connectors shall be of adequate size to provide the total demand of the connected equipment in accordance with Table 3-D-1 or 3-D-2, as applicable. Appliance connectors installed outdoors shall be listed for outdoor installation. Appliance connectors shall not be in contact with soil and use of aluminum alloy connectors shall be limited to interior locations and shall not be in contact with masonry, plaster or insulation nor shall they be subject to repeated corrosive wettings.

305.4 Prohibited Connections. Equipment shall not be connected to a fuel supply by means of a hose.

> **EXCEPTIONS:** 1. Movable laboratory or shop equipment using approved fuel hose material not exceeding 6 feet (1830 mm) in length.
>
> 2. Outdoor portable appliances using an approved outdoor fuel hose material not exceeding 15 feet (4572 mm) in length connected to an approved outdoor shutoff valve and piping.

Equipment shall not be connected to fuel piping by quick-disconnect devices, swivel joint mechanisms or devices that rely on the use of gaskets, ferrules or similar compression sealing methods unless such fittings are listed for the intended use and approved for the specific installation.

SECTION 306 — ELECTRICAL CONNECTIONS

306.1 General. Electrical connections to equipment regulated by this code shall be in accordance with the Electrical Code.

306.2 Means of Disconnect. An approved, independent means of disconnect for the electrical supply to each piece of equipment shall be provided in sight of the equipment served when the supply voltage exceeds 50 volts.

306.3 Service Receptacle. A 120-volt service receptacle shall be located within 25 feet (7620 mm) of, and on the same level as, the equipment for maintenance. The service receptacle shall not be connected on the load side of the required means of disconnect.

306.4 Illumination. Permanent switch controlled lighting shall be installed for maintenance of equipment required by this code to be accessible or readily accessible. Such lighting shall provide sufficient illumination to safely approach the equipment and perform the tasks for which access is provided. Control of the lighting shall be provided at the access entrance.

> **EXCEPTIONS:** 1. When fixed lighting of the building will provide the required illumination, separate illumination is not required.
>
> 2. Equipment located on the roof or exterior wall of a building need not be provided with permanent lighting.

SECTION 307 — ACCESS AND SERVICE SPACE

307.1 General. Equipment requiring routine inspection or maintenance shall be provided with sufficient access to allow inspection, maintenance and replacement without removing permanent construction or other equipment or disabling the function of required fire-resistant construction.

307.2 Equipment in Rooms. Rooms containing equipment requiring access shall be provided with a door and an unobstructed passageway measuring not less than 36 inches (914 mm) wide and 80 inches (2032 mm) high.

> **EXCEPTION:** Residential-type appliances installed in a compartment, alcove, basement or similar space may be accessed by an opening or door and an unobstructed passageway measuring not less than 24 inches (610 mm) wide and large enough to permit removal of the largest appliance in the space, provided that a service space of not less than 30 inches (762 mm) deep and the height of the appliance, but not less than 30 inches (762 mm) is present at the front or service side of the appliance with the door open.

307.3 Equipment in Attics. Attics containing equipment requiring access shall be provided with the following:

1. An access opening large enough to remove the largest piece of equipment, but not less than 30 inches by 22 inches (762 mm by 559 mm);

2. An unobstructed passageway which:

2.1 Is large enough to remove the largest piece of equipment but not less than 30 inches (762 mm) high and 30 inches (762 mm) wide,

2.2 Is no more than 20 feet (6096 mm) in length when measured along the center line of the passageway from the access opening to the equipment, and

2.3 Has continuous solid flooring not less that 24 inches (610 mm) wide throughout its length; and

3. A level service space at least 30 inches (762 mm) deep and 30 inches (762 mm) wide located at the front or service side of the equipment.

> **EXCEPTION:** The passageway and level service space may be omitted if the equipment can be serviced and removed through the access opening.

307.4 Equipment under Floors. Underfloor spaces containing equipment requiring access shall be provided with the following:

1. An access opening large enough to remove the largest piece of equipment, but not less than 30 inches by 22 inches (762 mm by 559 mm);

2. An unobstructed passageway which:

2.1 Is large enough to remove the largest piece of equipment but not less than 30 inches (762 mm) high and 30 inches (762 mm) wide, and

2.2 Is no more than 20 feet (6096 mm) in length when measured along the center line of the passageway from the access opening to the equipment;

3. A level service space at least 30 inches (762 mm) deep and 30 inches (762 mm) wide located at the front or service side of the equipment; and

4. Where the depth of the passageway or the service space exceeds 12 inches (305 mm) below the adjoining grade, the walls of the passageway shall be lined with concrete or masonry extending 4 inches (102 mm) above the adjoining grade and have sufficient lateral-bearing capacity to resist collapse.

> **EXCEPTION:** The passageway may be omitted if the level service space is present with the access open and the equipment can be serviced and removed through the access opening.

307.5 Equipment on Roofs or Elevated Structures. Roofs or elevated structures containing equipment requiring access shall be provided with the following:

1. An approved means of permanent access, the extent of which shall be from grade or floor level to the equipment and its level service space. Such access shall not require climbing over obstructions greater than 30 inches (762 mm) high or walking on roofs having a slope greater than 4 units vertical in 12 units horizontal (33% slope).

> **EXCEPTIONS:** 1. Equipment may be accessed by a portable ladder on the single-story portion of a Group R Occupancy or a Group U, Division 1 garage or carport.
>
> 2. Equipment may be accessed by portable ladder on the single-story portion of an existing building that does not exceed 16 feet (4880 mm) in height.

2. A level service platform at least 30 inches (762 mm) deep and 30 inches (762 mm) wide located at the front or service side of the equipment. The sides of the service platform shall be provided with a substantial railing not less than 42 inches (1067 mm) high and constructed so as to prevent the passage of a 21-inch-diameter (533 mm) sphere where a side of the platform is within 10 feet (3048 mm) of a drop greater than 30 inches (762 mm).

Ladders and catwalks providing the required access shall be as required by the relevant safety regulations but shall not be less than the following:

1. Ladders shall:

1.1 Not be less than 14 inches (356 mm) wide,

1.2 Have a rung spacing not more than 14 inches (356 mm) on center,

1.3 Have a toe space at least 6 inches (152 mm) deep,

1.4 Provide intermediate landings not more than 18 feet (5486 mm) apart, and

1.5 Have side railings which extend at least 30 inches (762 mm) above the scuttle opening or coping to the step off.

2. Catwalks shall:

2.1 Not be less than 24 inches (610 mm) wide and

2.2 Have railings as required for service platforms.

Permanent ladders and catwalks shall be fixed to the structure as required by the Building Code. Stairways providing the required access shall comply with the Building Code.

307.6 Equipment in Overhead Spaces. Overhead spaces containing equipment requiring access shall be arranged to permit the required access and the surface below the equipment shall permit the safe use of a portable ladder or staging sufficient to accomplish the purposes for which the access was required or permanent access shall be provided as required by other provisions of this section.

SECTION 308 — EQUIPMENT SUPPORTS AND RESTRAINTS

308.1 General. Equipment shall be supported by substantial bases or hangers capable of supporting the loads to which they will be subjected as determined by the Building Code. Stationary equipment shall be fixed in position by substantial means which will prevent its incidental displacement. Such restraint shall accommodate both vertical and lateral loads including, where applicable, wind, snow and seismic as required by the Building Code.

308.2 Vibration Isolation. When vibration isolation of equipment is employed, an approved means of supplemental restraint shall be used to accomplish the support and restraint required by this section.

308.3 Prohibited Conditions. Piping, electrical conduit, ductwork, vents and the like shall not be used to provide support or restraint of equipment.

Where other portions of this code or provisions of the Building Code require noncombustible construction or supports, noncombustible materials shall also be used to meet the requirements of this section.

SECTION 309 — DISCHARGE OF BYPRODUCTS

309.1 General. Byproducts generated in the normal operation of equipment shall be collected and disposed in an approved manner.

309.2 Fuel-burning Equipment. Gaseous combustion byproducts of fuel-burning equipment shall be vented to the outside as required by the applicable provisions of Chapter 5, 8 or 9 of this code. Liquid combustion byproducts of condensing appliances shall be collected and discharged to an approved plumbing fixture or disposal area in accordance with the manufacturer's approved instructions. Approved corrosion-resistant condensate piping

shall not be smaller than the drain pan connection on the approved equipment and shall maintain a minimum horizontal slope in the direction of discharge of not less than $^1/_8$ unit vertical in 12 units horizontal (1%).

309.3 Chilled Water and Evaporator Coils. Condensate, defrost and overflow discharges from cooling coils shall be collected and discharged to an approved plumbing fixture or disposal area. Approved corrosion-resistant discharge piping shall not be smaller than the drain pan connection on the approved equipment and shall maintain a minimum horizontal slope in the direction of discharge of not less than $^1/_8$ unit vertical in 12 units horizontal (1%). When serving shop or field-fabricated drain pans or more than one piece of equipment, such drains shall be sized as required by Chapter 11 of this code.

309.4 Evaporative Coolers and Cooling Towers. Overflow, blowdown and service drains from evaporative coolers or air washers and cooling towers shall be collected and discharged to an approved plumbing fixture capable of receiving the flow rate of either the equipment make-up system or the blowdown discharge, whichever is greater.

SECTION 310 — IDENTIFICATION

310.1 General. Fuel-burning and electrically operated equipment shall, as a minimum, have affixed a permanent and legible, factory-applied nameplate on which shall appear:

1. Name or trademark of the manufacturer.

2. Model and serial numbers.

3. Symbol of the listing agency certifying compliance with recognized standards.

4. Required clearances from combustibles, when applicable.

5. Type of fuel, when applicable.

6. Fuel input rating in Btu/h (W), when applicable.

7. Volts, amps and, for multiphase equipment, the number of phases.

8. Heat output in Btu/h (kW), when applicable.

9. Fusing requirements, when applicable.

10. Instructions for safe start-up, operation and shut-off.

310.2 Refrigeration Equipment. Equipment in refrigeration systems shall be further identified as required by Chapter 11 of this code.

310.3 Area Served. Equipment serving different areas of a building other than where it is installed shall be marked in an approved manner to permanently and uniquely identify the piece of equipment and the area served.

310.4 Direction of Flow. Equipment which relies on a particular direction of fluid flow in order to operate properly or safely shall be permanently marked in an approved manner to indicate the correct direction of flow.

SECTION 311 — CONTROLS

311.1 General. Equipment shall be provided with safety controls to limit or stop its operation when unsafe conditions occur from out of limits operation or failure of a sequence or component.

311.2 Temperature. Heating appliances connected to ducts shall have automatically resetting temperature limiting controls which will prevent the discharge temperature from exceeding 200°F (93°C) under normal conditions and manually resetting temperature limiting controls which will prevent the discharge temperature from exceeding 250°F (121°C).

311.3 Burners. Fuel-burning equipment shall be equipped with an approved automatic means which will shut off the fuel supply to the equipment in the event of ignition or flame failure.

> **EXCEPTION:** The listed shutoff devices shall not be required on range or cooking tops, log lighters, lights or other open-burner manually operated appliances, or listed appliances not requiring such devices and specific industrial appliances as approved by the building official.

SECTION 312 — PERSONNEL PROTECTION

312.1 Moving Parts. Exposed moving parts such as, but not limited to, flywheels, fans, pulleys, belts, shaft couplings and the like shall be provided with a suitable and substantial metal guard to prevent inadvertent contact. Such guards shall be removable for required maintenance.

312.2 Extreme Temperatures. Equipment which is intended to operate at temperatures above or below that at which injury by contact is likely to occur shall be so designed as to permit safe use or be insulated or isolated so as to prevent inadvertent contact.

312.3 Electrical Hazards. Equipment which presents a shock hazard shall be enclosed or installed as required by the Electric Code to guard against such hazards. Equipment capable of generating dangerous levels of electromagnetic fields shall be suitably shielded, grounded and isolated.

TABLE 3-A—STANDARD INSTALLATION CLEARANCES, IN INCHES, FOR UNLISTED HEAT-PRODUCING APPLIANCES
See Section 304.

RESIDENTIAL-TYPE APPLIANCES	Fuel	APPLIANCE				
		Above Top of Casing or Appliance	From Top and Sides of Warm-air Bonnet or Plenum	From Front[1]	From Back	From Sides
		× 25.4 for mm				
Boilers and water heaters Steam boilers—15 psi (103.4 Pa) Water boilers—250°F. (121°C) Water heaters—200°F. (93°C) All water walled or jacketed	Automatic oil or comb. gas-oil	6		24	6	6
	Automatic gas	6		18	6	6
	Solid	6		48	6	6
Furnaces—central; or heaters—electric central Warm-air furnaces Gravity, upflow, downflow, horizontal and duct Warm-air—250°F (121°C) max.	Automatic oil or comb. gas-oil	6	6	24	6	6
	Automatic gas	6	6	18	6	6
Furnaces—floor For mounting in combustible floors	Solid	18[2]	18[2]	48	18	18
	Electric	6	6	18	6	6
	Automatic oil or comb. gas-oil	36		12	12	12
	Automatic gas	36		12	12	12
Heat exchanger Steam—15 psi max. (103.4 Pa max.) Hot water—250°F (121°C) max.		1	1	1	1	1
Room heaters[3] Circulating type	Oil or solid	36		24	12	12
	Gas	36		24	12	12
Radiant or other type	Oil or solid	36		36	36	36
	Gas	36		36	18	18
	Gas with double metal or ceramic back	36		36	12	18
Fireplace stove	Solid	48[4]		54	48[4]	48[4]
Radiators Steam or hot water[5]		36		6	6	6

Ranges—cooking stoves		Above Top of Casing or Appliance		From Front[1]	Firing Side	Opp. Side
	Oil	30[6]			24	18
				9		
	Gas	30[6]			6	6
				6		
	Solid clay-lined firepot	30[6]			24	18
				24		
	Solid unlined firepot	30[6]			36	18
				36		
	Electric	30[6]			6	6
				6		
Incinerators Domestic types		36[7]		48	36	36

(Continued)

TABLE 3-A

1997 UNIFORM MECHANICAL CODE

TABLE 3-A—STANDARD INSTALLATION CLEARANCES, IN INCHES, FOR UNLISTED HEAT-PRODUCING APPLIANCES—(Continued)
See Section 304.

COMMERCIAL INDUSTRIAL-TYPE LOW-HEAT APPLIANCES ANY AND ALL PHYSICAL SIZES EXCEPT AS NOTED	Fuel	APPLIANCE				
		Above Top of Casing or Appliance[8]	From Top and Sides of Warm-air Bonnet or Plenum	From Front[1]	From Back[8]	From Sides[8]
		× 25.4 for mm				
Boilers and water heaters 100 cu. ft. (2.83 m³) or less Any psi steam	All fuels	18		48	18	18
50 psi (342 Pa) or less Any size	All fuels	18		48	18	18
Unit heaters Floor mounted or suspended—any size	Steam or hot water	1			1	1
Suspended—100 cu. ft. (2.83 m³) or less	Oil or comb. gas-oil	6		24	18	18
Suspended—100 cu. ft. (2.83 m³) or less	Gas	6		18	18	18
Suspended—Over 100 cu. ft. (2.83 m³)	All fuels	18		48	18	18
Floor mounted—any size	All fuels	18		48	18	18
Ranges—restaurant-type Floor mounted	All fuels	48		48	18	18
Other low-heat industrial appliances Floor mounted or suspended	All fuels	18	18	48	18	18

COMMERCIAL INDUSTRIAL-TYPE MEDIUM-HEAT APPLIANCES	Fuel	APPLIANCE				
		Above Top of Casing or Appliance[9]	From Top and Sides of Warm-air Bonnet or Plenum	From Front[1]	From Back[9]	From Sides[9]
		× 25.4 for mm				
Boilers and water heaters Over 50 psi (345 Pa) Over 100 cu. ft. (2.83 m³)	All fuels	48		96	36	36
Other medium-heat industrial appliances All sizes	All fuels	48	36	96	36	36
Incinerators All sizes		48		96	36	36
INDUSTRIAL-TYPE HIGH-HEAT APPLIANCES High-heat industrial appliances All sizes	All fuels	180		360	120	120

[1]The minimum dimension shall be that necessary for servicing the appliance, including access for cleaning and normal care, tube removal, etc.

[2]The dimension may be 6 inches (152 mm) for an automatically stoker-fired forced-warm-air furnace equipped with 250°F (121°C) limit control and with barometric draft control operated by draft intensity and permanently set to limit draft to a maximum intensity of 0.13-inch water gage (32 Pa).

[3]Approved appliances shall be installed on noncombustible floors and may be installed on protected combustible floors. Heating appliances approved for installation on protected combustible flooring shall be so constructed that flame and hot gases do not come in contact with the appliance base. Protection for combustible floors shall consist of 4-inch (102 mm) hollow masonry covered with sheet metal at least 0.021 inch (0.5 mm) thick (No. 24 manufacturer's standard gage). Masonry shall be permanently fastened in place in an approved manner with the ends unsealed and joints matched so as to provide free circulation of air through the masonry. Floor protection shall extend 12 inches (305 mm) at the sides and rear of the appliance, except that at least 18 inches (457 mm) shall be required on the appliance-opening side or sides measured horizontally from the edges of the opening.

[4]The 48-inch (1219 mm) clearance may be reduced to 36 inches (914 mm) when protection equivalent to that provided by Items 1 through 8 of Table 3-A is applied to the combustible construction.

[5]Steampipes and hot-water-heating pipes shall be installed with a clearance of at least 1 inch (25 mm) to all combustible construction or material, except that at the points where pipes carrying steam at not over 15 pounds gage pressure (103 kPa) or hot water emerge from a floor, wall or ceiling, the clearance at the opening through the finish floorboards or wall-ceiling boards may be reduced to not less than 1/2 inch (13 mm). Each such opening shall be covered with a plate of noncombustible material.

Such pipes passing through stack shelving shall be covered with not less than 1 inch (25 mm) of approved insulation.

Wood boxes or casings enclosing uninsulated steam or hot-water-heating pipes or wooden covers to recesses in walls in which uninsulated pipes are placed shall be lined with metal or insulating millboard.

Where the temperature of the boiler piping does not exceed 160°F (71°C), the provisions of this table do not apply.

Coverings or insulation used on steam or hot-water pipes shall be of material suitable for the operating temperature of the system. The insulation or jackets shall be of noncombustible materials, or the insulation or jackets and lap-seal adhesives shall be tested as a composite product. Such composite product shall have a flame-spread rating of not more than 25 and a smoke-developed rating not to exceed 50 when tested in accordance with UBC Standard 8-1.

[6]To combustible material or metal cabinets. If the underside of such combustible material or metal cabinet is protected with insulating millboard at least 1/4 inch (6 mm) thick covered with sheet metal of not less than 0.013 inch (0.3 mm) (No. 28 gage), the distance may be reduced to 24 inches (610 mm).

[7]Clearance above charging door must be at least 48 inches (1219 mm).

[8]If the appliance is encased in brick, the 18-inch (457 mm) clearance above and at sides and rear may be reduced to 12 inches (305 mm).

[9]If the appliance is encased in brick, the clearance above may be reduced to 36 inches (914 mm) and at sides and rear may be reduced to 18 inches (457 mm).

TABLE 3-B—CLEARANCES, IN INCHES, WITH SPECIFIED FORMS OF PROTECTION[1,2]

TYPE OF PROTECTION — Applied to the Combustible Material Unless Otherwise Specified and Covering All Surfaces within the Distance Specified as the Required Clearance with No Protection (Thicknesses are Minimum) × 25.4 for mm	36 Inches Above	Sides and Rear	Chimney or Vent Connector	18 Inches Above	Sides and Rear	Chimney or Vent Connector	12 Inches Above	Sides and Rear	Chimney or Vent Connector	6 Inches Above	Sides and Rear	Chimney or Vent Connector
1. 1/4" in insulating millboard spaced out 1"[3]	30	18	30	15	9	12	9	6	6	3	2	3
2. 0.013" (No. 28 manufacturer's standard gage) steel sheet on 1/4" insulating millboard	24	18	24	12	9	12	9	6	4	3	2	2
3. 0.013" (No. 28 manufacturer's standard gage) steel sheet spaced out 1"[3]	18	12	18	9	6	9	6	4	4	2	2	2
4. 0.013" (No. 28 manufacturer's standard gage) steel sheet on 1/8" insulating millboard spaced out 1"[3]	18	12	18	9	6	9	6	4	4	2	2	2
5. 1 1/2" insulating cement covering on heating appliance	18	12	36	9	6	18	6	4	9	2	1	6
6. 1/4" insulating millboard on 1" mineral fiber batts reinforced with wire mesh or equivalent	18	12	18	6	6	6	4	4	4	2	2	2
7. 0.027" (No. 22 manufacturer's standard gage) steel sheet on 1" mineral fiber batts reinforced with wire or equivalent	18	12	12	4	3	3	2	2	2	2	2	2
8. 1/4" insulating millboard	36	36	36	18	18	18	12	12	9	4	4	4

[1]For appliances complying with Sections 304.2 and 304.3.
[2]Except for the protection described in Item 5, all clearances shall be measured from the outer surface of the appliance to the combustible material, disregarding any intervening protection applied to the combustible material.
[3]Spacers shall be of noncombustible material.

NOTE: Insulating millboard is a factory-made product formed of noncombustible materials, normally fibers, and having a thermal conductivity of 1 Btu-inch per square foot per degree Fahrenheit [1.73W/(m·K)] or less.

TABLE 3-C—CHIMNEY CONNECTOR AND VENT CONNECTOR CLEARANCES FROM COMBUSTIBLE MATERIALS

DESCRIPTION OF APPLIANCE	MINIMUM CLEARANCE (inches)[1] × 25.4 for mm
Residential-type Appliances	
Single-wall Metal Pipe Connectors[2]	
Gas appliances without draft hoods	18
Electric, gas and oil incinerators	18
Oil and solid-fuel appliances	18
Unlisted gas appliances with draft hoods	9
Boilers and furnaces equipped with listed gas burners and with draft hoods	9[3]
Oil appliances listed as suitable for use with Type L venting systems (but only when connected to chimneys)	9
Listed gas appliances with draft hood	6
Type L Venting System Piping Connectors	
Gas appliances without draft hoods	9
Electric, gas and oil incinerators	9
Oil and solid-fuel appliances	9
Unlisted gas appliances with draft hoods	6
Boilers and furnaces equipped with listed gas burners and with draft hoods	6
Oil appliances listed as suitable for use with Type L venting systems	4
Listed gas appliances with draft hoods	5
Type B Gas Vent Piping Connectors	
Listed gas appliances with draft hoods	5
Commercial-industrial-type Appliances	
Low-heat Appliances	
Single-wall Metal Pipe Connectors[2]	
Gas, oil and solid-fuel boilers, furnaces and water heaters	18
Ranges, restaurant-type	18
Oil unit heaters	18
Unlisted gas unit heaters	18
Listed gas unit heaters with draft hoods	6
Other low-heat industrial appliances	18
Medium-heat Appliances	
Single-wall Metal Pipe Connectors[2]	
All gas, oil and solid-fuel appliances	36

[1]These clearances apply except if the listing of an appliance specifies different clearance, in which case the listed clearance takes precedence.
[2]The clearances from connectors to combustible materials may be reduced if the combustible material is protected in accordance with Table 3-B.
[3]The dimension may be 6 inches (152 mm), provided the maximum flue temperatures entering the draft hood do not exceed 550°F (288°C).
[4]If listed Type L venting system piping is used, the clearance may be in accordance with the venting system listing.
[5]If listed Type B or L venting system piping is used, the clearance may be in accordance with the venting system listing.

TABLE 3-D-1
FIGURE 3-1

1997 UNIFORM MECHANICAL CODE

TABLE 3-D-1—CAPACITIES OF LISTED METAL APPLIANCE CONNECTORS[1]
For use with gas pressures 8-inch (2 kPa) or more water column.

SEMIRIGID CONNECTOR O.D.[2] (inch)	FLEXIBLE CONNECTOR NOMINAL I.D.[3] (inch)	MAXIMUM CAPACITIES IN THOUSANDS Btu/h [Based on pressure drop of 0.4-inch water column (1 kPa)] NAT. GAS[4] OF 1,100 Btu/cu. ft. (41 MJ/m³)							
		1'	1¹/₂'	2'	2¹/₂'	3'	4'	5'	6'
		× 304.8 for mm							
		All Gas Appliances					Ranges and Clothes Dryers		
× 25.4 for mm		× 293.07 for W							
³/₈	¹/₄	40	33	29	27	25			
¹/₂	³/₈	93	76	66	62	58			
⁵/₈	¹/₂	189	155	134	125	116	101	90	80
—	³/₄	404	330	287	266	244			
—	1	803	661	573	534	500			

[1]Gas connectors are certified by the testing agency as complete assemblies including the fittings and valves. Capacities shown are based on the use of fittings and valves supplied with the connector.
[2]Semirigid connector listings are based on outside diameter.
[3]Flexible connector listings are based on nominal diameter.
[4]For liquefied petroleum gas, use 1.6 times the natural gas capacities shown.

TABLE 3-D-2—CAPACITIES OF LISTED METAL APPLIANCE CONNECTORS[1]
For use with gas pressures less than 8-inch (2 kPa) water column.

SEMIRIGID CONNECTOR O.D.[2] (inch)	FLEXIBLE CONNECTOR NOMINAL I.D.[3] (inch)	CAPACITIES FOR VARIOUS LENGTHS IN THOUSANDS Btu/h [Based on pressure drop of 0.2-inch water column (500 Pa)] NAT. GAS[4] OF 1,100 Btu/cu. ft. (41 MJ/m³)							
		1'	1¹/₂'	2'	2¹/₂'	3'	4'	5'	6'
		× 304.8 for mm							
		All Gas Appliances					Ranges and Clothes Dryers		
× 25.4 for mm		× 293.07 for W							
³/₈	¹/₄	28	23	20	19	17			
¹/₂	³/₈	66	54	47	44	41			
⁵/₈	¹/₂	134	110	95	88	82	72	63	57
—	³/₄	285	233	202	188	174			
—	1	561	467	405	378	353			

[1]Gas connectors are certified by the testing agency as complete assemblies including the fittings and valves. Capacities shown are based on the use of fittings and valves supplied with the connector.
[2]Semirigid connector listings are based on outside diameter.
[3]Flexible connector listings are based on nominal diameter.
[4]For liquefied petroleum gas, use 1.6 times the natural gas capacities shown.

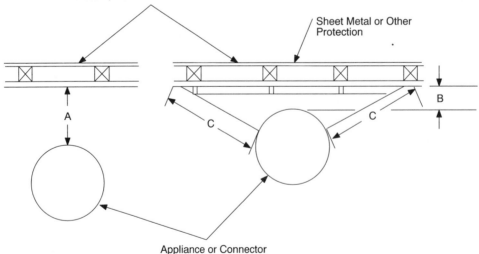

A—Dimension shall not be less than the required clearance with no protection set forth in Tables 3-A and 3-C and in the sections applying to various types of appliances.

B—Dimension shall not be less than the reduced clearance set forth in Table 3-B.

C—Dimension shall not be less than the clearance required for dimension A.

**FIGURE 3-1—EXTENT OF PROTECTION REQUIRED TO REDUCE
CLEARANCES FROM APPLIANCE, CHIMNEY OR VENT CONNECTORS**

Chapter 4
VENTILATION AIR SUPPLY

NOTE: This chapter has been revised in its entirety.

SECTION 401 — SCOPE

401.1 General. Mechanical equipment providing supply air to buildings or portions thereof shall comply with this chapter and other requirements elsewhere in this code.

401.2 Standards of Quality. The standard listed below labeled a "UMC Standard" is listed in Chapter 16, Part II, and is a part of this code.

401.2.1 Test Performance of Air Filter Units. UMC Standard 4-1, Test Performance of Air Filter Units, is UL 900.

SECTION 402 — SUPPLY AIR

402.1 General. Ventilation air supply to a room or space shall be obtained from an approved outside air source or a return air source, or both, and conveyed to the room or space served by ducts complying with Chapter 6 of this code unless the approved equipment does not require duct connections.

402.2 Screened Openings. Inlets and outlets of ventilation air supply systems shall be equipped with screen, grills or louvers to prevent the introduction of foreign materials and to deny vermin admission to the system. Screens, grilles or louvers shall not pass an object larger than a $1/4$-inch-diameter (6.4 mm) sphere.

402.3 Filters. Air filters shall be installed in supply air systems upstream of fans, heat exchangers, coils, burners and the like. Filters shall be listed as Class I or II in compliance with UMC Standard 4-1.

> **EXCEPTIONS:** 1. Filters serving a guest room or dwelling units need not be listed.
>
> 2. Evaporation pads in an evaporative cooler.

In Group I, Divisions 1.1 and 1.2 Occupancies, ventilation air supply systems serving sensitive areas, including but not limited to operating rooms, delivery rooms, intensive care rooms, recovery rooms, nurseries, isolation rooms and laboratory media preparation rooms, shall be equipped with additional filters having a minimum efficiency of 90 percent downstream of cooling, coils, humidification equipment and the associated supply fans.

402.4 Make-up Air. Ventilation air supply shall be sufficient to provide make-up air for exhaust systems when required by this code or the Building Code. Make-up air systems shall be electrically interlocked with their associated exhaust systems.

402.5 Duct Size. Ducts in ventilation supply air systems shall be sized as required by the equipment manufacturer's approved installation instructions or approved good engineering practice.

SECTION 403 — OUTSIDE AIR

403.1 General. Ventilation air supply from outside shall be provided as required in Chapter 12 of the Building Code. Alternate provisions may be found in Appendix Chapter 12 and for Group R, Division 3 Occupancies in Appendix Chapter 3, Division 3 of the Building Code.

403.2 Location. Outside air shall be obtained from an approved location exterior to the building. Outside air shall not be obtained from the following locations:

1. Closer than 10 feet (3048 mm) from a vent serving fuel-burning equipment.

> **EXCEPTION:** Listed outdoor appliance equipped with outdoor air inlet and appliance vent.

2. Closer than 10 feet (3048 mm) from a plumbing drainage system vent or from an exhaust system outlet, unless the outlet is 3 feet (914 mm) above the outside air inlet.

3. Where it will pick up objectionable odors, fumes or flammable vapors; or when it is less than 10 feet (3048 mm) above the surface of any abutting public way or driveway; or when it is in a horizontal position in a sidewalk, street, alley or driveway.

4. A hazardous location.

5. An insanitary location.

SECTION 404 — RETURN AIR

404.1 Location. Return air shall be obtained from an approved interior location of the same building. Return air shall not be obtained from the following locations:

1. Where it will pick up objectionable odors, fumes or flammable vapors.

2. A hazardous location.

3. An unsanitary location.

4. An area having a volume less than 25 percent of the entire volume served by the supply air system, unless there is a sufficient permanent communicating opening to areas having a volume equal to the required 25 percent. Appropriately sized transfer grills or door undercuts may be used to provide the required opening.

> **EXCEPTION:** Such opening when used for a warm-air furnace in a dwelling unit may be reduced to no less than 50 percent of the required area, provided the balance of the required return air is taken from a room or hall having at least three doors leading to other rooms served by the furnace.

5. A refrigeration machinery room.

6. A room or space containing fuel-burning equipment.

> **EXCEPTIONS:** 1. Fireplaces, fireplace appliances, residential cooking appliances, direct-vent appliances, enclosed furnaces and domestic-type clothes dryers.
>
> 2. A listed vented wall furnace.
>
> 3. A blower-type system where:
>
> 3.1 The return air is taken from a room or space having a volume exceeding 1 cubic foot for each (10 Btu/h),
>
> 3.2 At least 75 percent of the supply air is discharged back into the same room or space, and
>
> 3.3 The return-air inlet shall not be located within 10 feet (3048 mm) of any appliance firebox or draft diverter in the same enclosed room or confined space.

7. A closet, bathroom, toilet room or kitchen.

8. A corridor, exit passageway or exit enclosure required by the Building Code to be of fire-resistive construction.

9. A dwelling unit, guest room or patient room other than the room in which the air originates.

SECTION 405 — DIRECT GAS-FIRED MAKE-UP AIR SYSTEMS

405.1 General. Direct gas-fired make-up air heaters shall not be installed for comfort heating in other than Group F and S Occupancies.

405.2 Installation. Installation of direct gas-fired make-up air heaters shall comply with their listing and approved manufacturer's installation instructions. A refrigerant containing evaporator coil shall not be located upstream of the burner. Burner operation shall be electrically interlocked with a source of outside air ventilation supplying at least 4 cubic feet per minute per 1,000 Btu/h (0.00644 L/s·W).

Chapter 5
EXHAUST SYSTEMS

Part I—Product-conveying and Environmental Air Systems

SECTION 501 — SCOPE OF PART I

Part I of this chapter applies to environmental air-ventilation systems that are not a part of a heating or cooling system and to product-conveying duct systems. For commercial hood and kitchen ventilation systems, see Part II of this chapter.

SECTION 502 — DEFINITIONS

For the purposes of Part I, the following definitions apply:

ENVIRONMENTAL AIR DUCT is ducting used for conveying air at temperatures not exceeding 250°F (121°C) to or from occupied areas of any occupancy through other than heating or air-conditioning systems, such as ventilation for human usage, domestic kitchen range exhaust, bathroom exhaust ducts, and domestic-type clothes dryer exhaust ducts.

FLAMMABLE VAPOR OR FUMES is the concentration of flammable constituents in air that exceeds 10 percent of its lower flammability limit (LFL).

PRODUCT-CONVEYING DUCT is ducting used for conveying solid particulates, such as refuse, dust, fumes and smoke; liquid particulate matter, such as spray residue, mists and fogs; vapors, such as vapors from flammable or corrosive liquids; noxious and toxic gases; and air at temperatures exceeding 250°F (121°C).

SECTION 503 — MOTORS AND FANS

503.1 General. Motors and fans shall be sized to provide the required air movement. Motors in areas which contain flammable vapors or dusts shall be of a type approved for such environments. A manually operated remote control installed at an approved location shall be provided to shut off fans or blowers in flammable vapor or dust systems. Electrical equipment used in operations that generate explosive or flammable vapors, fumes or dusts shall be interlocked with the ventilation system so that the equipment cannot be operated unless the ventilation fans are in operation. Motors for fans used to convey flammable vapors or dusts shall be located outside the duct or shall be protected with approved shields and dustproofing. Motors and fans shall be accessible for servicing and maintenance.

503.2 Fans. Parts of fans in contact with explosive or flammable vapors, fumes or dusts shall be of nonferrous or nonsparking materials or their casing shall be lined or constructed of such material. When the size and hardness of materials passing through a fan could produce a spark, both the fan and the casing shall be of nonsparking materials. When fans are required to be spark resistant, their bearings shall not be within the airstream, and all parts of the fan shall be grounded. Fans in systems handling materials that are likely to clog the blades, and fans in buffing or woodworking exhaust systems, shall be of the radial-blade or tube-axial type.

503.2.1 Equipment identification plate. Equipment used to exhaust explosive or flammable vapors, fumes or dusts shall bear an identification plate stating the ventilation rate for which the system was designed.

503.2.2 Corrosion-resistant fans. Fans located in systems conveying corrosives shall be of materials that are resistant to the corrosive or shall be coated with corrosion-resistant materials.

SECTION 504 — ENVIRONMENTAL AIR DUCTS

504.1 Makeup and Exhaust Air Ducts. Environmental air ducts not regulated by other provisions of this code shall comply with this section. Ducts shall be substantially airtight and shall comply with the provisions of Chapter 6. Exhaust ducts shall terminate outside the building and shall be equipped with backdraft dampers. Environmental air ducts which have an alternate function as a part of an approved smoke-control system do not require design as Class I product-conveying ducts.

504.2 Domestic Range Vents. Ducts used for domestic kitchen range ventilation shall be of metal and shall have smooth interior surfaces.

> **EXCEPTION:** Ducts for domestic kitchen downdraft grill-range ventilation installed under a concrete slab floor may be of approved Schedule 40 PVC provided:
>
> 1. The under-floor trench in which the duct is installed shall be completely backfilled with sand or gravel.
>
> 2. Not more than 1 inch (25 mm) of 6-inch-diameter (152 mm) PVC coupling may protrude above the concrete floor surface.
>
> 3. PVC pipe joints shall be solvent cemented to provide an air- and grease-tight duct.
>
> 4. The duct shall terminate above grade outside the building and shall be equipped with a backdraft damper.

504.3 Domestic Dryer Vent. Domestic clothes dryer moisture exhaust ducts shall be of metal and shall have smooth interior surfaces.

> **EXCEPTION:** Approved flexible duct connectors not more than 6 feet (1829 mm) in length may be used in connection with domestic dryer exhausts. Flexible duct connectors shall not be concealed within construction.

504.3.1 Moisture-exhaust ducts. Moisture-exhaust ducts for domestic clothes dryers shall terminate on the outside of the building and shall be equipped with a back-draft damper. Screens shall not be installed at the duct termination. Ducts for exhausting clothes dryers shall not be connected or installed with sheet metal screws or other fasteners which will obstruct the flow. Clothes-dryer moisture-exhaust ducts shall not be connected to a gas vent connector, gas vent or chimney. Clothes-dryer moisture-exhaust ducts shall not extend into or through ducts or plenums.

504.3.2 Length limitation. Unless otherwise permitted or required by the dryer manufacturer's installation instructions and approved by the building official, domestic dryer moisture exhaust ducts shall not exceed a total combined horizontal and vertical length of 14 feet (4267 mm), including two 90-degree elbows. Two feet (610 mm) shall be deducted for each 90-degree elbow in excess of two.

504.4 Commercial Dryer Exhaust Systems. Commercial dryer moisture-exhaust ducts shall be installed in accordance with their listing.

504.5 Gypsum Wallboard Ducts. Bathroom and laundry room exhaust ducts may be of gypsum wallboard subject to the limitations of Section 601.1.3.

504.6 Exhaust Outlets. Outlets for exhausts that exceed 600°F (315°C) shall comply with Table 8-D.

The termination point for environmental air duct exhausts discharging to the atmosphere shall not be less than 3 feet (914 mm) from a property line or from openings into a building.

SECTION 505 — PRODUCT-CONVEYING SYSTEMS

505.1 General. A mechanical ventilation or exhaust system shall be installed to control, capture and remove emissions generated from product use or handling when required by the Building Code or Fire Code and when such emissions result in a hazard to life or property. The design of the system shall be such that the emissions are confined to the area in which they are generated by air currents, hoods or enclosures and shall be exhausted by a duct system to a safe location or treated by removing contaminants. Ducts conveying explosives or flammable vapors, fumes or dusts shall extend directly to the exterior of the building without entering other spaces. Exhaust ducts shall not extend into or through ducts and plenums.

> **EXCEPTION:** Ducts conveying vapor or fumes having flammable constituents less than 25 percent of their lower flammability limit may pass through other spaces.

505.2 Incompatible Materials. Separate and distinct systems shall be provided for incompatible materials.

505.3 Recirculation. Contaminated air shall not be recirculated to occupied areas unless contaminants have been removed. Air contaminated with explosive or flammable vapors, fumes or dusts; flammable or toxic gases, or radioactive material shall not be recirculated.

505.4 Minimum Velocities and Circulation. The velocity and circulation of air in work areas shall be such that contaminants are captured by an airstream at the area where the emissions are generated and conveyed into a product-conveying duct system. Mixtures within work areas where contaminants are generated shall be diluted below 25 percent of their lower explosive limit or lower flammability limit with air which does not contain other contaminants. The velocity of air within the duct shall not be less than set forth in Table 5-A.

505.5 Design. Systems for removal of vapors, gases and smoke shall be designed by the constant velocity or equal friction methods. Systems conveying particulate matter shall be designed employing the constant velocity method. Systems conveying explosive or radioactive materials shall be prebalanced through duct sizing. Other systems may be designed with balancing devices such as dampers. Dampers provided to balance air flow shall be provided with securely fixed minimum-position blocking devices to prevent restricting flow below the required volume or velocity.

505.6 Makeup Air. Makeup air shall be provided to replenish air exhausted by the ventilation system. Makeup-air intakes shall be located so as to avoid recirculation of contaminated air within enclosures.

505.7 Hoods and Enclosures. Hoods and enclosures shall be used when contaminants originate in a concentrated area. The design of the hood or enclosure shall be such that air currents created by the exhaust systems will capture the contaminants and transport them directly to the exhaust duct. The volume of air shall be sufficient to dilute explosive or flammable vapors, fumes or dusts as set forth in Section 505.4. Hoods of steel shall have a base metal thickness not less than 0.027 inch (0.68 mm) (22 gage) for Class 1 and Class 5 metal duct systems; 0.033 inch (0.84 mm) (20 gage) for hoods serving a Class 2 duct system; 0.044 inch (1.12 mm) (18 gage) for hoods serving a Class 3 duct system; and 0.068 inch (1.73 mm) (14 gage) for hoods serving a Class 4 duct system. Approved nonmetallic hoods and duct systems may be used for Class 5 corrosive systems when the corrosive mixture is nonflammable. Metal hoods used with Class 5 duct systems shall be protected with suitable corrosion-resistant material. Edges of hoods shall be rounded. The minimum clearance between hoods and combustible construction shall be the clearance required by the duct system.

505.8 Small Hobby Kiln Exhaust Systems. The provisions of this section apply to kilns used for firing ceramics, having a maximum interior volume of 20 cubic feet (0.57 m³), used for hobby and other noncommercial purposes.

505.8.1 Hoods. A canopy-type hood shall be installed directly above each kiln. The face opening area of the hood shall be equal to or greater than the top horizontal surface area of the kiln. The hood shall be constructed of not less than 0.024-inch (0.61 mm) (No. 24 U.S. gage) galvanized steel or equivalent and be supported at a height of between 12 inches and 30 inches (305 mm and 762 mm) above the kiln by noncombustible supports.

> **EXCEPTION:** Electric kilns installed with listed exhaust blowers may be used when marked as being suitable for the kiln and installed in accordance with manufacturer's instructions.

505.8.2 Gravity ventilation ducts. Each kiln hood shall be connected to a gravity ventilation duct extending in a vertical direction to outside the building. This duct shall be of the same construction as the hood and shall have a minimum cross-sectional area of not less than one fifteenth of the face opening area of the hood. The duct shall terminate a minimum of 12 inches (305 mm) above any portion of a building within 4 feet (1219 mm) and terminate no less than 4 feet (1219 mm) from any openable windows or other openings into the building or adjacent property line. The duct opening to the outside shall be shielded, without reduction of duct area, to prevent entrance of rain into the duct. The duct shall be supported at each section by noncombustible supports.

505.9 Exhaust Outlets. Outlets for exhausts that exceed 600°F (315°C) shall comply with Table 8-D.

The termination point for exhaust ducts discharging to the atmosphere shall not be less than the following:

1. Ducts conveying explosive or flammable vapors, fumes or dusts: 30 feet (9144 mm) from property line, 10 feet (3048 mm) from openings into the building, 6 feet (1829 mm) from exterior walls or roofs, 30 feet (9144 mm) from combustible walls or openings into a building which are in the direction of the exhaust discharge, and 10 feet (3048 mm) above adjoining grade.

2. Other product-conveying outlets: 10 feet (3048 mm) from property line, 3 feet (914 mm) from exterior wall or roof, 10 feet (3048 mm) from openings into the building, and 10 feet (3048 mm) above adjoining grade.

SECTION 506 — PRODUCT-CONVEYING DUCT SYSTEMS

506.1 Classification. Product-conveying ducts shall be classified according to their use, as follows:

Class 1. Ducts conveying nonabrasives, such as smoke, spray, mists, fogs, noncorrosive fumes and gases, light fine dusts or powders.

Class 2. Ducts conveying moderately abrasive particulate in light concentrations, such as sawdust and grain dust, buffing and polishing dust.

Class 3. Ducts conveying Class 2 materials in high concentrations and highly abrasive materials in low concentrations, such as manganese, steel chips and coke.

Class 4. Ducts conveying highly abrasive material in high concentrations.

Class 5. Ducts conveying corrosives, such as acid vapors.

Part II—Commercial Kitchens

SECTION 507 — COMMERCIAL KITCHEN HOODS AND KITCHEN VENTILATION SYSTEMS

507.1 Scope. Part II of Chapter 5 is applicable to commercial kitchen hoods and kitchen ventilation systems.

507.2 Definitions. For the purpose of Part II, the following definitions shall apply:

COMMERCIAL FOOD HEAT-PROCESSING EQUIPMENT is equipment used in a food establishment for heat-processing food or utensils and which produces grease vapors, steam, fumes, smoke or odors which are required to be removed through a local exhaust ventilation system.

COMPENSATING HOOD is a hood that has an outside air supply with air delivered below or within the hood. When makeup air is diffused directly into the exhaust within the hood cavity, it becomes a short-circuit hood.

GREASE FILTER is a device used to capture by entrapment, impingement, adhesion or similar means, grease and similar contaminants before they enter a duct system.

HOOD is an air-intake device connected to a mechanical exhaust system for collecting and removing grease, vapors, fumes, smoke, steam, heat or odors from commercial food heat-processing equipment.

Type I Hood is a kitchen hood for collecting and removing grease and smoke.

Type II Hood is a general kitchen hood for collecting and removing steam, vapor, heat or odors.

507.3 Grease Duct Materials. Grease ducts and plenums serving a Type I hood shall be constructed of at least 0.055-inch-thick (1.40 mm) (No. 16 manufacturer's standard gage) steel or stainless at least 0.044 inch (1.10 mm) in thickness.

507.3.1 Fan casing. Exhaust fan housings serving a Type I hood shall be constructed of steel.

> **EXCEPTION:** Fans listed as "power roof ventilators for restaurant cooking appliances."

507.3.2 Joints and seams of grease ducts. Joints and seams shall be made with a continuous liquid-tight weld or braze made on the external surface of the duct system. A vibration isolation connector may be used, provided it consists of noncombustible packing in a metal sleeve joint of approved design.

507.3.3 Grease duct supports. Duct bracing and supports shall be of noncombustible material securely attached to the structure and designed to carry gravity and lateral loads within the stress limitations of the Building Code. Bolts, screws, rivets and other mechanical fasteners shall not penetrate duct walls.

507.3.4 Nongrease ducts. Ducts and plenums serving Type II hoods shall be constructed of rigid metallic materials as set forth in Chapter 6. Duct bracing and supports shall comply with Chapter 6. Ducts subject to positive pressure shall be adequately sealed.

507.3.5 Corrosion protection. Ducts exposed to the outside atmosphere or subject to a corrosive environment shall be protected against corrosion. Galvanization of metal parts, protection with noncorrosive paints and waterproof insulation are considered acceptable methods of protection.

507.4 Prevention of Grease Accumulation. Duct systems serving a Type I hood shall be so constructed and installed that grease cannot become pocketed in any portion thereof, and the system shall slope not less than $^1/_4$ unit vertical in 12 units horizontal (2% slope) toward the hood or toward an approved grease reservoir. Where horizontal ducts exceed 75 feet (22 860 mm) in length the slope shall be not less than 1 unit vertical in 12 units horizontal (8.3% slope). When a centrifugal fan is used it shall be positioned so the discharge outlet is either vertical or bottom horizontal with the air so diverted that there will be no impingement on the roof, other equipment or parts of the structure. A vertical discharge fan shall be manufactured with an approved drain outlet at the bottom of the housing to permit drainage of grease to an approved collection device.

507.4.1 Grease diverter. When a centrifugal fan with bottom horizontal discharge is located outside the building, a duct or duct fitting that diverts the discharge from the grease exhaust duct system in an upward direction may be connected to the fan outlet, provided the following conditions are met:

1. The duct or duct fitting shall be constructed of metal as set forth in Tables 6-A and 6-B or UMC Standard 6-1.

2. The maximum total developed length of the duct or duct fitting measured along the center line shall not exceed three times the vertical dimension of the fan outlet.

3. The duct or duct fitting shall be provided with openings at the lowest point to permit drainage of grease to an approved collection device.

507.5 Cleanouts and Other Openings. Grease duct systems shall not have openings therein other than those required for proper operation and maintenance of the system. Any portion of such system having sections inaccessible from the duct entry or discharge shall be provided with adequate cleanout openings. Cleanout openings shall be equipped with tightfitting doors constructed of steel having a thickness not less than that required for the duct. Doors shall be equipped with a substantial method of latching, sufficient to hold the door tightly closed. Doors shall be so designed that they can be opened without the use of a tool.

507.6 Duct Enclosure. A grease duct serving a Type I hood which penetrates a ceiling, wall or floor shall be enclosed in a duct enclosure from the point of penetration. A duct may only penetrate exterior walls at locations where unprotected openings are permitted by the Building Code. Duct enclosures shall be constructed as the Building Code requires shaft enclosures to be constructed. Duct enclosures shall be of at least one-hour fire-resistive construction in all buildings and shall be of two-hour fire-resistive construction in Types I and II fire-resistive buildings. The duct enclosure shall be sealed around the duct at the point of penetration and vented to the exterior through weather-protected openings. The enclosure shall be separated from the duct by at least 3 inches and not more than 12 inches (at least 76 mm and not more than 305 mm) and shall serve a single grease exhaust duct system.

507.7 Fire-resistive Access Opening. When cleanout openings are located in ducts within a fire-resistive shaft or enclosure, access openings shall be provided in the shaft or enclosure at each cleanout point. These access openings shall be equipped with tightfitting sliding or hinged doors which are equal in fire-resistive protection to that of the shaft or enclosure.

507.8 Air Velocity. Grease duct systems serving a Type I hood shall be designed and installed in a manner to provide an air velocity within the duct system of not less than 1,500 feet per minute (7.5 m/s) and not to exceed 2,500 feet per minute (12.7 m/s).

507.9 Separation of Grease Duct System. A separate grease duct system shall be provided for each Type I hood, except that a single duct system may serve more than one hood located in the same story of the building, provided that all hoods served by the system shall be located in the same room or adjoining rooms; portions of the interconnecting ducts shall not pass through any construction which would require the opening to be fire protected as specified in the Building Code.

507.10 Clearances. Exposed grease duct systems serving a Type I hood shall have a clearance from unprotected combustible construction of at least 18 inches (457 mm). This clearance may be reduced to not less than 3 inches (76 mm), provided the combustible construction is protected with material required for one-hour fire-resistive construction.

507.11 Exhaust Outlets. Exhaust outlets for grease ducts serving Type I hoods shall extend through the roof unless otherwise approved by the building official. Such extension shall be at least 2 feet (610 mm) above the roof surface, at least 10 feet (3048 mm) from parts of the same or neighboring buildings, adjacent property line or air intake opening into any building, and shall be located at least 10 feet (3048 mm) above the adjoining grade level. Exhaust outlets for ducts serving Type II hoods over heat-processing equipment shall terminate at least 10 feet (3048 mm) from adjacent property lines or air intake openings into any building, and shall be located at least 10 feet (3048 mm) above adjoining grade level.

> **EXCEPTIONS:** 1. Exhaust outlets for grease ducts serving commercial food heat-processing equipment may terminate not less than 5 feet (1524 mm) from an adjacent building, adjacent property line or air intake opening into a building if the air from the exhaust outlet is discharged away from such locations.
>
> 2. Upon approval of the building official, the exhaust from any hood serving commercial food heat-processing equipment may terminate in a properly engineered air-recovery system for recirculation to the room in which the hood is located.

507.12 Fuel-burning Appliances. When vented fuel-burning appliances are located in the same room or space as the hood, the vent shall be arranged to prevent the hood system from interfering with normal operation of the appliance vent.

SECTION 508 — COMMERCIAL KITCHEN HOODS

508.1 Where Hoods Are Required. Hoods shall be installed at or above all commercial-type deep fat fryers, broilers, fry grills, steam-jacketed kettles, hot-top ranges, ovens, barbecues, rotisseries, dishwashing machines and similar equipment which produce comparable amounts of steam, smoke, grease or heat in a food-processing establishment. For the purpose of this section a food-processing establishment shall include any building or portion thereof used for the processing of food but shall not include a dwelling unit.

508.2 Materials and Installation. Types I and II hoods shall be constructed of galvanized steel, stainless steel, copper or other material approved by the building official for the use intended.

508.2.1 Type I hoods. Type I hoods constructed of galvanized steel shall be at least 0.030 inch (0.76 mm) (No. 22 gage) steel.

508.2.2 Type II hoods. Type II hoods shall be constructed of at least 0.024-inch (0.61 mm) (No. 24 gage) steel.

Hoods constructed of copper shall be of copper sheets weighing at least 24 ounces per square foot (7.3 kg/m^2). Hoods constructed of stainless steel shall have a minimum thickness of 0.030 inch (0.76 mm).

508.2.3 Supports. Hoods shall be secured in place by noncombustible supports.

508.2.4 Joints and seams. Joints and seams shall be substantially tight. Solder shall not be used except for sealing a joint or seam.

508.3 Cleaning and Grease Gutters. When installed, a hood shall be designed to provide for thorough cleaning of the entire hood. When grease gutters are provided, they shall drain to a collecting receptacle, fabricated, designed and installed to be accessible for cleaning.

508.4 Clearances for Type I Hood. A Type I hood shall be installed with clearance of at least 18 inches (457 mm) from combustible construction. This clearance may be reduced to 3 inches (76 mm), provided the combustible material is protected with materials as specified for one-hour fire-resistive construction on the hood side. Hoods less than 12 inches (305 mm) from the ceiling or wall shall be flashed solidly with materials of the thickness specified in Section 508.2 or materials conforming to one-hour fire-resistive construction.

508.4.1 Hoods penetrating a ceiling. Type I hoods or portions thereof penetrating a ceiling, wall or furred space shall comply with all the requirements of Section 507.6.

508.5 Grease Filters. Type I hoods shall be equipped with approved grease filters designed for the specific purpose. Grease-collecting equipment shall be accessible for cleaning. The lowest edge of a grease filter located above the cooking surface shall be at least the height set forth in Table 5-D.

508.5.1 Criteria. Filters shall be of such size, type and arrangement as will permit the required quantity of air to pass through such units at rates not exceeding those for which the filter or unit was designed or approved. Filter units shall be installed in frames or holders with handles by which they may be readily removed without the use of tools, unless designed and installed to be cleaned in place and the system is equipped for such cleaning in place. They shall be sized and made removable so they may be passed through a dishwashing machine or cleaned in a pot sink and so arranged in place or provided with drip intercepting devices as to avoid grease or other condensate from dripping into food or on food preparation surfaces.

508.5.2 Mounting position. Filters shall be installed at an angle greater than 45 degrees from the horizontal and shall be equipped with a drip tray beneath the lower edge of the filters.

508.6 Canopy Size and Location. For canopy-type commercial cooking hoods the inside edge thereof shall overhang or extend a horizontal distance of not less than 6 inches (152 mm) beyond the edge of the cooking surface on all open sides, and the vertical distance between the lip of the hood and the cooking surface shall not exceed 4 feet (1219 mm).

> **EXCEPTION:** Listed exhaust hoods are to be installed in accordance with the terms of their listing and manufacturer's installation instructions.

508.7 Capacity of Hoods. Canopy-type commercial cooking hoods shall exhaust through the hood a minimum quantity of air determined by application of the following formulas:

WHERE:

A = the horizontal surface area of the hood, in square feet (m^2).

D = distance in feet (m) between the lower lip of the hood and the cooking surface.

P = that part of the perimeter of the hood that is open, in feet (m).

Q = quantity of air, in cubic feet per minute (m^3/s).

When cooking equipment is installed back to back and is covered by a common island-type hood, the airflow required may be calculated using the formula for three sides exposed. Type II hood airflow requirements shall be in accordance with the requirements for low-temperature appliance hoods.

508.7.1 Solid fuel. Type I hoods for use over solid-fuel cooking equipment shall be provided with separate exhaust systems. Undefined cooking equipment other than solid-fuel cooking equipment may be installed under a common hood. The minimum airflow for solid-fuel cooking equipment, grease-burning charboilers, and undefined equipment shall be:

Number of Exposed Sides	Formula	
		For **SI:**
4 (island or central hood)	$Q = 300A$	$Q = 0.46\,A$
3 or less	$Q = 200A$	$Q = 0.31\,A$
Alternate formula	$Q = 100PD$	$Q = 0.16\,PD$

> **EXCEPTION:** Listed exhaust hoods are to be installed in accordance with the terms of their listing and the manufacturer's installation instructions.

508.7.2 High temperature. Type I hoods when the cooking equipment includes high-temperature appliances such as deep-fat fryers:

Number of Exposed Sides	Formula	
		For **SI:**
4 (island or central hood)	$Q = 150A$	$Q = 0.23\,A$
3 or less	$Q = 100A$	$Q = 0.16\,A$
Alternate formula	$Q = 100PD$	$Q = 0.16\,PD$

> **EXCEPTION:** Listed exhaust hoods are to be installed in accordance with the terms of their listing and the manufacturer's installation instructions.

508.7.3 Medium temperature. Type I hoods when the cooking equipment includes medium-temperature appliances such as rotisseries, grills and ranges:

Number of Exposed Sides	Formula	
		For **SI:**
4 (island or central hood)	$Q = 100A$	$Q = 0.16\,A$
3 or less	$Q = 75A$	$Q = 0.12\,A$
Alternate formula	$Q = 50PD$	$Q = 0.08\,PD$

> **EXCEPTION:** Listed exhaust hoods are to be installed in accordance with the terms of their listing and the manufacturer's installation instructions.

508.7.4 Low temperature. Type I hoods where the cooking equipment includes low-temperature appliances such as medium-to-low-temperature ranges, roasters, roasting ovens, pastry ovens and equipment approved for use under a Type II hood, such as pizza ovens:

Number of Exposed Sides	Formula	
		For **SI:**
4 (island or central hood)	$Q = 75A$	$Q = 0.12\,A$
3 or less	$Q = 50A$	$Q = 0.08\,A$
Alternate formula	$Q = 50PD$	$Q = 0.08\,PD$

> **EXCEPTION:** Listed exhaust hoods are to be installed in accordance with the terms of their listing and the manufacturer's installation instructions.

508.8 Capacity for Noncanopy Hoods. In addition to all other requirements for hoods specified in this section, the volume of air exhausting through a noncanopy-type hood to the duct system shall not be less than 300 cubic feet per minute per lineal foot [0.046 $m^3/(s \cdot m)$] of cooking equipment. Listed noncanopy grease hoods and filters shall be sized and installed in accordance with the terms of their listing and the manufacturer's installation instructions.

508.9 Exhaust Outlet. An exhaust outlet within the hood shall be so located as to optimize the capture of particulate matter. Each outlet shall serve not more than a 12-foot (3658 mm) section of hood.

> **EXCEPTION:** Listed exhaust hoods are to be installed in accordance with terms of their listing and the manufacturer's installation instructions.

508.10 Performance Test. Upon completion and before final approval of the installation of a ventilation system serving commercial food heat-processing equipment, a performance test may be required to verify the rate of airflow and proper operation as specified in this chapter. The permittee shall furnish the necessary test equipment and devices required to perform the tests.

SECTION 509 — FANS, MOTORS AND SAFETY DEVICES

509.1 General. Motors and fans shall be of sufficient capacity to provide the required air movement as specified in this chapter. Electrical equipment shall be approved for the class of use as provided in the Electrical Code. Motors and fans shall be accessible for servicing or maintenance. Motors shall not be installed within ducts or under hoods.

509.2 Where Required. Approved automatic fire-extinguishing systems shall be provided for the protection of commercial-type cooking equipment.

> **EXCEPTION:** The requirement for protection does not include steam kettles and steam tables or equipment which as used do not create grease-laden vapors.

509.3 Type of System. The system used for the protection of commercial cooking equipment shall be either a system listed for application with such equipment or an automatic fire-extinguishing system that is specifically designed for such application.

Systems shall be installed in accordance with this code, their listing and the manufacturer's installation instructions. Other systems shall be an approved design and shall be one of the following types:

1. Automatic sprinkler system.

2. Dry-chemical extinguishing system.

3. Carbon dioxide extinguishing system.

4. Wet-chemical extinguishing system.

509.4 Extent of Protection.

509.4.1 General. The automatic fire-extinguishing system used to protect ventilating hoods and ducts and cooking appliances shall be installed to include cooking surfaces, deep-fat fryers, griddles, upright broilers, charbroilers, range tops and grills. Protection shall also be provided for the enclosed plenum space within the hood above filters and exhaust ducts serving the hood.

509.4.2 Carbon dioxide systems. When carbon dioxide systems are used, there shall be a nozzle at the top of the ventilating duct. Additional nozzles that are symmetrically arranged to give uniform distribution shall be installed within vertical ducts exceeding 20 feet (6096 mm) and horizontal ducts exceeding 50 feet (15 240 mm). Dampers shall be installed at either the top or the bottom of the duct and shall be arranged to operate automatically upon activation of the fire-extinguishing system. When the damper is installed at the top of the duct, the top nozzle shall be immediately below the damper. Carbon dioxide automatic fire-extinguishing systems shall be sufficiently sized to protect all hazards venting through a common duct simultaneously.

509.5 Automatic Power, Fuel and Ventilation Shutoff.

509.5.1 General. Automatic fire-extinguishing systems shall be interconnected to the fuel or current supply for the cooking equipment. The interconnection shall be arranged to automatically shut off all cooking equipment amd electrical receptacles which are located under the hood when the system is actuated.

Shutoff valves or switches shall be of a type that requires manual operation to reset.

509.5.2 Carbon dioxide system. Commercial-type cooking equipment protected by an automatic carbon dioxide extinguishing system shall be arranged to shut off the ventilation system upon activation.

509.6 Special Provisions for Automatic Sprinkler Systems. Commercial-type cooking equipment protected by auto-matic sprinkler systems shall be supplied from a separate, readily accessible indicating-type control valve that is identified.

Sprinklers used for protection of fryers shall be listed for that application and installed in accordance with their listing.

509.7 Manual System Operation. A readily accessible manual activation device installed at an approved location shall be provided for dry-chemical, wet-chemical and carbon dioxide systems. The activation device is allowed to be mechanically or electrically operated. If electrical power is used, the system shall be connected to a standby power system and a visual means shall be provided to show that the extinguishing system is energized. Instructions for operating the fire-extinguishing system shall be posted adjacent to manual activation devices.

509.8 Fire Dampers. Fire dampers shall not be installed in a grease duct system unless listed for such use as part of a listed exhaust hood, fire-extinguishing system or an approved fan by-pass.

TABLE 5-A—MINIMUM CONVEYING VELOCITIES
(feet per minute) (m/s)

PRODUCT CONVEYED	FEET PER MINUTE
	× 0.005 for m/s
Vapors, gases, smoke, fumes	Any
Fine light dusts, such as cotton, lint and wood flour (100 mesh and under)	2,000
Dry dusts; powders, such as fine rubber molding powder, soap dust	2,500[1]
Industrial dusts	
Average dusts, such as sawdust, grinding dust, coal dust	3,500
Heavy dusts, such as metal turnings, lead dusts	4,000
Moist dusts and chips, such as lead dust with chips, sticky buffing lint, quick-lime dust	4,500

[1]The velocity for aluminum and magnesium powder shall not be less than 4,000 feet per minute (20.3 m/s).

TABLE 5-B—MINIMUM SHEET METAL THICKNESS FOR ROUND DUCTS

NEGATIVE PRESSURE	REINF. SPACING (inches)	Up to 7"	8" to 11"	12" to 15"	16" to 19"	20" to 23"	24" to 35"	36" to 47"	48" to 59"	60"
× 249 for Pa					× 25.4 for mm					
CLASS 1										
To 7"	0	.021 (24 ga.)	.021 (24 ga.)	.033 (20 ga.)	.044 (18 ga.)	.055 (16 ga.)	.068 (14 ga.)	.127 (10 ga.)		
	96	.021 (24 ga.)	.021 (24 ga.)	.021 (24 ga.)	.027 (22 ga.)	.033 (20 ga.)	.044 (18 ga.)	.055 (16 ga.)	.068 (14 ga.)	.068 (14 ga.)
	48	.021 (24 ga.)	.021 (24 ga.)	.021 (24 ga.)	.021 (24 ga.)	.021 (24 ga.)	.027 (22 ga.)	.033 (20 ga.)	.044 (18 ga.)	.055 (16 ga.)
	24	.021 (24 ga.)	.021 (24 ga.)	.021 (24 ga.)	.021 (24 ga.)	.021 (24 ga.)	.021 (24 ga.)	.027 (22 ga.)	.033 (20 ga.)	.044 (18 ga.)
8" to 11"	0	.021 (24 ga.)	.027 (22 ga.)	.044 (18 ga.)	.055 (16 ga.)	.068 (14 ga.)	.097 (12 ga.)			
	96	.021 (24 ga.)	.027 (22 ga.)	.027 (22 ga.)	.044 (18 ga.)	.044 (18 ga.)	.044 (18 ga.)	.068 (14 ga.)	.097 (12 ga.)	.097 (12 ga.)
	48	.021 (24 ga.)	.021 (24 ga.)	.021 (24 ga.)	.027 (22 ga.)	.033 (20 ga.)	.033 (20 ga.)	.055 (16 ga.)	.068 (14 ga.)	.068 (14 ga.)
	24	.021 (24 ga.)	.021 (24 ga.)	.021 (24 ga.)	.021 (24 ga.)	.027 (22 ga.)	.027 (22 ga.)	.044 (18 ga.)	.055 (16 ga.)	.055 (16 ga.)
12" to 15"	0	.021 (24 ga.)	.033 (20 ga.)	.055 (16 ga.)	.068 (14 ga.)	.097 (12 ga.)	.097 (12 ga.)			
	96	.021 (24 ga.)	.027 (22 ga.)	.044 (18 ga.)	.044 (18 ga.)	.055 (16 ga.)	.055 (16 ga.)	.097 (12 ga.)	.112 (11 ga.)	.112 (11 ga.)
	48	.021 (24 ga.)	.027 (22 ga.)	.027 (22 ga.)	.033 (20 ga.)	.044 (18 ga.)	.044 (18 ga.)	.068 (14 ga.)	.068 (14 ga.)	.097 (12 ga.)
	24	.021 (24 ga.)	.021 (24 ga.)	.021 (24 ga.)	.027 (22 ga.)	.027 (22 ga.)	.027 (22 ga.)	.055 (16 ga.)	.055 (16 ga.)	.055 (16 ga.)
16" to 20"	0	.021 (24 ga.)	.044 (18 ga.)	.068 (14 ga.)	.097 (12 ga.)	.112 (11 ga.)				
	96	.021 (24 ga.)	.033 (20 ga.)	.055 (16 ga.)	.055 (16 ga.)	.068 (14 ga.)	.068 (14 ga.)	.112 (11 ga.)	.112 (11 ga.)	.112 (11 ga.)
	48	.021 (24 ga.)	.027 (22 ga.)	.033 (20 ga.)	.044 (18 ga.)	.055 (16 ga.)	.055 (16 ga.)	.068 (14 ga.)	.097 (12 ga.)	.112 (11 ga.)
	24	.021 (24 ga.)	.021 (24 ga.)	.027 (22 ga.)	.033 (20 ga.)	.044 (18 ga.)	.044 (18 ga.)	.055 (16 ga.)	.068 (14 ga.)	.097 (12 ga.)
CLASS 2										
To 7"	0	.027 (22 ga.)	.027 (22 ga.)	.033 (20 ga.)	.044 (18 ga.)	.055 (16 ga.)	.068 (14 ga.)	.127 (10 ga.)		
	96	.027 (22 ga.)	.027 (22 ga.)	.033 (20 ga.)	.033 (20 ga.)	.044 (18 ga.)	.044 (18 ga.)	.055 (16 ga.)	.068 (14 ga.)	.068 (14 ga.)
	48	.027 (22 ga.)	.027 (22 ga.)	.033 (20 ga.)	.033 (20 ga.)	.044 (18 ga.)	.044 (18 ga.)	.055 (16 ga.)	.055 (16 ga.)	.055 (16 ga.)
	24	.027 (22 ga.)	.027 (22 ga.)	.033 (20 ga.)	.033 (20 ga.)	.044 (18 ga.)	.044 (18 ga.)	.055 (16 ga.)	.055 (16 ga.)	.055 (16 ga.)
8" to 11"	0	.027 (22 ga.)	.027 (22 ga.)	.044 (18 ga.)	.055 (16 ga.)	.068 (14 ga.)	.097 (12 ga.)			
	96	.027 (22 ga.)	.027 (22 ga.)	.033 (20 ga.)	.044 (18 ga.)	.044 (18 ga.)	.044 (18 ga.)	.068 (14 ga.)	.097 (12 ga.)	.097 (12 ga.)
	48	.027 (22 ga.)	.027 (22 ga.)	.033 (20 ga.)	.033 (20 ga.)	.044 (18 ga.)	.044 (18 ga.)	.055 (16 ga.)	.068 (14 ga.)	.068 (14 ga.)
	24	.027 (22 ga.)	.027 (22 ga.)	.033 (20 ga.)	.033 (20 ga.)	.044 (18 ga.)	.044 (18 ga.)	.055 (16 ga.)	.055 (16 ga.)	.055 (16 ga.)
12" to 15"	0	.027 (22 ga.)	.033 (20 ga.)	.055 (16 ga.)	.068 (14 ga.)	.097 (12 ga.)	.097 (12 ga.)			
	96	.027 (22 ga.)	.033 (20 ga.)	.044 (18 ga.)	.044 (18 ga.)	.055 (16 ga.)	.055 (16 ga.)	.097 (12 ga.)	.112 (11 ga.)	.112 (11 ga.)
	48	.027 (22 ga.)	.027 (22 ga.)	.033 (20 ga.)	.033 (20 ga.)	.044 (18 ga.)	.044 (18 ga.)	.068 (14 ga.)	.068 (14 ga.)	.097 (12 ga.)
	24	.027 (22 ga.)	.027 (22 ga.)	.033 (20 ga.)	.033 (20 ga.)	.044 (18 ga.)	.044 (18 ga.)	.055 (16 ga.)	.055 (16 ga.)	.055 (16 ga.)
16" to 20"	0	.027 (22 ga.)	.044 (18 ga.)	.068 (14 ga.)	.097 (12 ga.)	.112 (11 ga.)				
	96	.027 (22 ga.)	.033 (20 ga.)	.055 (16 ga.)	.055 (16 ga.)	.068 (14 ga.)	.068 (14 ga.)	.112 (11 ga.)	.112 (11 ga.)	.112 (11 ga.)
	48	.027 (22 ga.)	.033 (20 ga.)	.033 (20 ga.)	.044 (18 ga.)	.055 (16 ga.)	.055 (16 ga.)	.068 (14 ga.)	.068 (14 ga.)	.097 (12 ga.)
	24	.027 (22 ga.)	.033 (20 ga.)	.033 (20 ga.)	.033 (20 ga.)	.044 (18 ga.)	.044 (18 ga.)	.055 (16 ga.)	.055 (16 ga.)	.055 (16 ga.)
To 7"	0	.033 (20 ga.)	.033 (20 ga.)	.044 (18 ga.)	.044 (18 ga.)	.055 (16 ga.)	.068 (14 ga.)	.127 (10 ga.)		
	96	.033 (20 ga.)	.033 (20 ga.)	.044 (18 ga.)	.044 (18 ga.)	.055 (16 ga.)	.055 (16 ga.)	.068 (14 ga.)	.068 (14 ga.)	.068 (14 ga.)
	48	.033 (20 ga.)	.033 (20 ga.)	.044 (18 ga.)	.044 (18 ga.)	.055 (16 ga.)	.055 (16 ga.)	.068 (14 ga.)	.068 (14 ga.)	.068 (14 ga.)
	24	.033 (20 ga.)	.033 (20 ga.)	.044 (18 ga.)	.044 (18 ga.)	.055 (16 ga.)	.055 (16 ga.)	.068 (14 ga.)	.068 (14 ga.)	.068 (14 ga.)
8" to 11"	0	.033 (20 ga.)	.033 (20 ga.)	.044 (18 ga.)	.055 (16 ga.)	.068 (14 ga.)	.097 (12 ga.)			
	96	.033 (20 ga.)	.033 (20 ga.)	.044 (18 ga.)	.044 (18 ga.)	.055 (16 ga.)	.055 (16 ga.)	.068 (14 ga.)	.097 (12 ga.)	.097 (12 ga.)
	48	.033 (20 ga.)	.033 (20 ga.)	.044 (18 ga.)	.044 (18 ga.)	.055 (16 ga.)	.055 (16 ga.)	.068 (14 ga.)	.068 (14 ga.)	.068 (14 ga.)
	24	.033 (20 ga.)	.033 (20 ga.)	.044 (18 ga.)	.044 (18 ga.)	.055 (16 ga.)	.055 (16 ga.)	.068 (14 ga.)	.068 (14 ga.)	.068 (14 ga.)
12" to 15"	0	.033 (20 ga.)	.033 (20 ga.)	.055 (16 ga.)	.068 (14 ga.)	.097 (12 ga.)	.097 (12 ga.)			
	96	.033 (20 ga.)	.033 (20 ga.)	.044 (18 ga.)	.044 (18 ga.)	.055 (16 ga.)	.055 (16 ga.)	.097 (12 ga.)	.112 (11 ga.)	.112 (11 ga.)
	48	.033 (20 ga.)	.033 (20 ga.)	.044 (18 ga.)	.044 (18 ga.)	.055 (16 ga.)	.055 (16 ga.)	.068 (14 ga.)	.068 (14 ga.)	.068 (14 ga.)
	24	.033 (20 ga.)	.033 (20 ga.)	.044 (18 ga.)	.044 (18 ga.)	.055 (16 ga.)	.055 (16 ga.)	.068 (14 ga.)	.068 (14 ga.)	.068 (14 ga.)
16" to 20"	0	.033 (20 ga.)	.044 (18 ga.)	.068 (14 ga.)	.097 (12 ga.)	.112 (11 ga.)				
	96	.033 (20 ga.)	.033 (20 ga.)	.055 (16 ga.)	.055 (16 ga.)	.068 (14 ga.)	.068 (14 ga.)	.112 (11 ga.)	.112 (11 ga.)	.112 (11 ga.)
	48	.033 (20 ga.)	.033 (20 ga.)	.044 (18 ga.)	.044 (18 ga.)	.055 (16 ga.)	.055 (16 ga.)	.068 (14 ga.)	.068 (14 ga.)	.097 (12 ga.)
	24	.033 (20 ga.)	.033 (20 ga.)	.044 (18 ga.)	.044 (18 ga.)	.055 (16 ga.)	.055 (16 ga.)	.068 (14 ga.)	.068 (14 ga.)	.068 (14 ga.)
CLASS 4										
To 7"	0	.055 (16 ga.)	.055 (16 ga.)	.055 (16 ga.)	.055 (16 ga.)	.068 (14 ga.)	.068 (14 ga.)	.127 (10 ga.)		
	96	.055 (16 ga.)	.055 (16 ga.)	.055 (16 ga.)	.055 (16 ga.)	.068 (14 ga.)	.068 (14 ga.)	.097 (12 ga.)	.097 (12 ga.)	.097 (12 ga.)
	48	.055 (16 ga.)	.055 (16 ga.)	.055 (16 ga.)	.055 (16 ga.)	.068 (14 ga.)	.068 (14 ga.)	.097 (12 ga.)	.097 (12 ga.)	.097 (12 ga.)
	24	.055 (16 ga.)	.055 (16 ga.)	.055 (16 ga.)	.055 (16 ga.)	.068 (14 ga.)	.068 (14 ga.)	.097 (12 ga.)	.097 (12 ga.)	.097 (12 ga.)
8" to 11"	0	.055 (16 ga.)	.055 (16 ga.)	.055 (16 ga.)	.055 (16 ga.)	.068 (14 ga.)	.097 (12 ga.)			
	96	.055 (16 ga.)	.055 (16 ga.)	.055 (16 ga.)	.055 (16 ga.)	.068 (14 ga.)	.068 (14 ga.)	.097 (12 ga.)	.097 (12 ga.)	.097 (12 ga.)
	48	.055 (16 ga.)	.055 (16 ga.)	.055 (16 ga.)	.055 (16 ga.)	.068 (14 ga.)	.068 (14 ga.)	.097 (12 ga.)	.097 (12 ga.)	.097 (12 ga.)
	24	.055 (16 ga.)	.055 (16 ga.)	.055 (16 ga.)	.055 (16 ga.)	.068 (14 ga.)	.068 (14 ga.)	.097 (12 ga.)	.097 (12 ga.)	.097 (12 ga.)
12" to 15"	0	.055 (16 ga.)	.055 (16 ga.)	.055 (16 ga.)	.068 (14 ga.)	.097 (12 ga.)	.097 (12 ga.)			
	96	.055 (16 ga.)	.055 (16 ga.)	.055 (16 ga.)	.055 (16 ga.)	.068 (14 ga.)	.068 (14 ga.)	.097 (12 ga.)	.112 (11 ga.)	.112 (11 ga.)
	48	.055 (16 ga.)	.055 (16 ga.)	.055 (16 ga.)	.055 (16 ga.)	.068 (14 ga.)	.068 (14 ga.)	.097 (12 ga.)	.097 (12 ga.)	.097 (12 ga.)
	24	.055 (16 ga.)	.055 (16 ga.)	.055 (16 ga.)	.055 (16 ga.)	.068 (14 ga.)	.068 (14 ga.)	.097 (12 ga.)	.097 (12 ga.)	.097 (12 ga.)
16" to 20"	0	.055 (16 ga.)	.055 (16 ga.)	.068 (14 ga.)	.097 (12 ga.)	.112 (11 ga.)				
	96	.055 (16 ga.)	.055 (16 ga.)	.055 (16 ga.)	.055 (16 ga.)	.068 (14 ga.)	.068 (14 ga.)	.112 (11 ga.)	.112 (11 ga.)	.112 (11 ga.)
	48	.055 (16 ga.)	.055 (16 ga.)	.055 (16 ga.)	.055 (16 ga.)	.068 (14 ga.)	.068 (14 ga.)	.097 (12 ga.)	.097 (12 ga.)	.097 (12 ga.)
	24	.055 (16 ga.)	.055 (16 ga.)	.055 (16 ga.)	.055 (16 ga.)	.068 (14 ga.)	.068 (14 ga.)	.097 (12 ga.)	.097 (12 ga.)	.097 (12 ga.)

TABLE 5-C
TABLE 5-D

1997 UNIFORM MECHANICAL CODE

TABLE 5-C—MINIMUM SHEET METAL THICKNESS FOR RECTANGULAR DUCTS

NEGATIVE PRESSURE	REINF. SPACING	LONGEST SIDE OF DUCT									
		Class 1					Class 2				
		Up to 12″	13″ to 24″	25″ to 36″	37″ to 48″	49″ to 60″	Up to 12″	13″ to 24″	25″ to 36″	37″ to 48″	49″ to 60″
× 249 for Pa		× 25.4 for mm									
To 7″	48	.021 (24 ga.)	.033 (20 ga.)	.055 (16 ga.)	.068 (14 ga.)		.033 (20 ga.)	.044 (18 ga.)	.055 (16 ga.)	.068 (14 ga.)	
To 7″	24	.021 (24 ga.)	.027 (22 ga.)	.033 (20 ga.)	.033 (20 ga.)	.033 (20 ga.)	.033 (20 ga.)	.044 (18 ga.)	.055 (16 ga.)	.055 (16 ga.)	.055 (16 ga.)
To 7″	12	.021 (24 ga.)	.021 (24 ga.)	.021 (24 ga.)	.021 (24 ga.)	.021 (24 ga.)	.033 (20 ga.)	.044 (18 ga.)	.055 (16 ga.)	.055 (16 ga.)	.055 (16 ga.)
8″ to 11″	48	.027 (22 ga.)	.068 (14 ga.)	.097 (12 ga.)	.098 (12 ga.)		.033 (20 ga.)	.068 (14 ga.)	.097 (12 ga.)	.097 (12 ga.)	
8″ to 11″	24	.027 (22 ga.)	.055 (16 ga.)	.055 (16 ga.)	.068 (14 ga.)	.068 (14 ga.)	.033 (20 ga.)	.055 (16 ga.)	.055 (16 ga.)	.068 (14 ga.)	.068 (14 ga.)
8″ to 11″	12	.021 (24 ga.)	.027 (22 ga.)	.027 (22 ga.)	.027 (22 ga.)	.027 (22 ga.)	.033 (20 ga.)	.044 (18 ga.)	.055 (16 ga.)	.055 (16 ga.)	.055 (16 ga.)
12″ to 15″	48	.044 (18 ga.)	.097 (12 ga.)				.044 (18 ga.)	.044 (18 ga.)			
12″ to 15″	24	.044 (18 ga.)	.055 (16 ga.)	.097 (12 ga.)	.097 (12 ga.)	.097 (12 ga.)	.044 (18 ga.)	.044 (18 ga.)	.097 (12 ga.)	.097 (12 ga.)	.097 (12 ga.)
12″ to 15″	12	.027 (22 ga.)	.044 (18 ga.)	.044 (18 ga.)	.044 (18 ga.)	.044 (18 ga.)	.033 (20 ga.)	.044 (18 ga.)	.055 (16 ga.)	.055 (16 ga.)	.055 (16 ga.)
16″ to 20″	48	.068 (14 ga.)	.112 (11 ga.)				.068 (14 ga.)	.112 (11 ga.)			
16″ to 20″	24	.068 (14 ga.)	.068 (14 ga.)	.112 (11 ga.)	.112 (11 ga.)	.112 (11 ga.)	.068 (14 ga.)	.068 (14 ga.)	.112 (11 ga.)	.112 (11 ga.)	.112 (11 ga.)
16″ to 20″	12	.033 (20 ga.)	.068 (14 ga.)	.068 (14 ga.)	.068 (14 ga.)	.068 (14 ga.)	.033 (20 ga.)	.044 (18 ga.)	.068 (14 ga.)	.068 (14 ga.)	.068 (14 ga.)
		Class 3					Class 4				
To 7″	48	.044 (18 ga.)	.055 (16 ga.)	.068 (14 ga.)	.068 (14 ga.)		.055 (16 ga.)	.068 (14 ga.)	.097 (12 ga.)	.097 (12 ga.)	
To 7″	24	.044 (18 ga.)	.055 (16 ga.)	.068 (14 ga.)	.068 (14 ga.)	.068 (14 ga.)	.055 (16 ga.)	.068 (14 ga.)	.097 (12 ga.)	.097 (12 ga.)	.097 (12 ga.)
To 7″	12	.044 (18 ga.)	.055 (16 ga.)	.068 (14 ga.)	.068 (14 ga.)	.068 (14 ga.)	.055 (16 ga.)	.068 (14 ga.)	.097 (12 ga.)	.097 (12 ga.)	.097 (12 ga.)
8″ to 11″	48	.044 (18 ga.)	.068 (14 ga.)	.097 (12 ga.)	.097 (12 ga.)		.055 (16 ga.)	.068 (14 ga.)	.097 (12 ga.)	.097 (12 ga.)	
8″ to 11″	24	.044 (18 ga.)	.055 (16 ga.)	.068 (14 ga.)	.068 (14 ga.)	.068 (14 ga.)	.055 (16 ga.)	.068 (14 ga.)	.097 (12 ga.)	.097 (12 ga.)	.097 (12 ga.)
8″ to 11″	12	.044 (18 ga.)	.055 (16 ga.)	.068 (14 ga.)	.068 (14 ga.)	.068 (14 ga.)	.055 (16 ga.)	.068 (14 ga.)	.097 (12 ga.)	.097 (12 ga.)	.097 (12 ga.)
12″ to 15″	48	.044 (18 ga.)	.097 (12 ga.)				.055 (16 ga.)	.097 (12 ga.)			
12″ to 15″	24	.044 (18 ga.)	.055 (16 ga.)	.097 (12 ga.)	.097 (12 ga.)	.097 (12 ga.)	.055 (16 ga.)	.068 (14 ga.)	.097 (12 ga.)	.097 (12 ga.)	.097 (12 ga.)
12″ to 15″	12	.044 (18 ga.)	.055 (16 ga.)	.068 (14 ga.)	.068 (14 ga.)	.068 (14 ga.)	.055 (16 ga.)	.068 (14 ga.)	.097 (12 ga.)	.097 (12 ga.)	.098 (12 ga.)
16″ to 20″	48	.068 (14 ga.)	.112 (11 ga.)				.055 (16 ga.)	.112 (11 ga.)			
16″ to 20″	24	.068 (14 ga.)	.068 (14 ga.)	.112 (11 ga.)	.112 (11 ga.)	.112 (11 ga.)	.055 (16 ga.)	.068 (14 ga.)	.112 (11 ga.)	.112 (11 ga.)	.112 (11 ga.)
16″ to 20″	12	.044 (18 ga.)	.068 (14 ga.)	.068 (14 ga.)	.068 (14 ga.)	.068 (14 ga.)	.055 (16 ga.)	.068 (14 ga.)	.097 (12 ga.)	.097 (12 ga.)	.097 (12 ga.)

TABLE 5-D—MINIMUM DISTANCE BETWEEN THE LOWEST EDGE OF A GREASE FILTER AND THE COOKING SURFACE OR THE HEATING SURFACE

CONDITION	DUCT SYSTEM AND HOOD WITH FIRE-EXTINGUISHING SYSTEM (feet)
	× 305 for mm
No exposed flame grills, french fryers, etc.	2
Exposed-flame and burners	2
Exposed charcoal and charbroil-type fires	$3\frac{1}{2}$

Chapter 6
DUCT SYSTEMS

SECTION 601 — SCOPE

Ducts and plenums which are portions of a heating, cooling, absorption or evaporative cooling system shall comply with the requirements of this chapter.

601.1 Material. Supply air, return air and outside air for heating, cooling or evaporative cooling systems shall be conducted through duct systems constructed of metal as set forth in Tables 6-A, 6-B and 6-C; metal ducts complying with UMC Standard 6-1 with prior approval; or factory-made air ducts complying with UL181. Ducts, plenums and fittings may be constructed of asbestos cement, concrete, clay or ceramics when installed in the ground or in a concrete slab, provided the joints are tightly sealed.

601.1.1 Use of corridor as plenum. Corridors shall not be used to convey air to or from rooms if the corridor is required to be of fire-resistive construction by Section 1005 of the Building Code.

601.1.2 Use of concealed space as plenum. Concealed building spaces or independent construction within buildings may be used as ducts or plenums.

601.1.3 Gypsum products exposed in ducts. When gypsum products are exposed in ducts or plenums, the air temperature shall be restricted to a range from 50°F to 125°F (10°C to 50°C) and moisture content shall be controlled so that the material is not adversely affected. For the purpose of this section, gypsum products shall not be exposed in ducts serving as supply from evaporative coolers, and in other air-handling systems regulated by this chapter when the temperature of the gypsum product will be below the dew point temperature.

See Chapter 8 for limitations on combustion products venting systems extending into or through ducts or plenums.

See Chapter 5 for limitations on environmental air systems exhaust ducts extending into or through ducts or plenums.

601.2 Standards of Quality.

601.2.1 General. The standards listed below labeled "UMC Standards," "UBC Standards" and "UFC Standards" are also listed in Chapter 16, Part II, and are part of this code. The other standards listed below are recognized standards. (See Sections 1601, 1602 and 1603.)

601.2.1.1 Standard for metal ducts. UMC Standard 6-1, Standard for Metal Ducts.

601.2.1.2 Standard for installation of factory-made air ducts. UMC Standard 6-3, Standard for Installation of Factory-Made Air Ducts.

601.2.1.3 Flame spread index. UBC Standard 8-1, Test Method for Surface-burning Characteristics of Building Materials.

601.2.1.4 Test method for fire and smoke characteristics of electrical cable and plastic sprinkler pipe. UMC Standard 6-2, Test Method for Fire and Smoke Characteristics of Electrical Cable and Plastic Sprinkler Pipe.

601.2.1.5 Galvanized sheet metals. UMC Standard 2-2, Galvanized Sheet Metals.

601.2.1.6 Testing procedures for local, auxiliary, remote station and proprietary protective signaling systems. UFC Standard 10-2, Testing Procedures for Local, Auxiliary, Remote Station and Proprietary Protective Signaling Systems.

601.2.2 Recognized Standards.

601.2.2.1 Leakage-rated dampers for use in smoke control systems. Leakage Rated Dampers for Use in Smoke Control Systems, UL 555S, 1983.

601.2.2.2 Fire dampers. Fire Dampers, UL 555, 1990.

601.2.2.3 Ceiling dampers. Ceiling Dampers, UL 555C, 1992.

601.2.2.4 Factory-made air ducts. Factory-made Air Ducts and Connectors, UL 181, 1994.

601.2.2.5 Closure systems for rigid factory-made air ducts. Closure Systems for Use with Flexible Air Ducts and Air Connectors, UL 181B, 1995.

601.3 Contamination Prevention. Exhaust ducts under positive pressure and venting systems shall not extend into or pass through ducts or plenums. For appliance vents and chimneys, see Chapter 8.

601.4 Combustibles within Ducts or Plenums. Materials exposed within ducts or plenums shall have a flame-spread index of not more than 25 and a smoke-developed rating of not more than 50 when tested in accordance with the test for Surface Burning Characteristics of Building Materials, UBC Standard 8-1.

EXCEPTIONS: 1. Return-air and outside-air ducts, plenums or concealed spaces which serve a dwelling unit may be of combustible construction.

2. Air filters meeting the requirements of Section 403.

3. Water evaporation media in an evaporative cooler.

4. Charcoal filters when protected with an approved fire-suppression system.

5. Electrical wiring and optical fiber raceways in plenums shall comply with the Electrical Code. Flame propagation and smoke production characteristics of exposed electric cables and optical fiber raceways installed in concealed air space used as air plenums shall:

5.1 Exhibit a flame travel of 5 feet (1524 mm) or less, and

5.2 Produce smoke having an average optical density not greater than 0.15 and having a peak optical density of 0.5 or less when tested in accordance with UMC Standard 6-2.

5.3 Wiring meeting these requirements shall be listed and labeled as plenum cable as required by the Electrical Code.

5.4 Optical fiber raceways meeting these requirements shall be listed and labeled as plenum optical fiber raceways as required by the Electrical Code.

6. Nonmetallic fire sprinkler piping in plenums shall be listed and shall meet the following requirements:

6.1 Exhibit flame travel of 5 feet (1524 mm) or less, and

6.2 Produce smoke having an average optical density not greater than 0.15 and having a peak optical density of 0.5 or less when tested in accordance with UMC Standard 6-2.

601.5 Factory-made Air Ducts. Factory-made air ducts shall be approved for the use intended or shall conform to the requirements of UL 181. Each portion of a factory-made air duct system shall be identified by the manufacturer with a label or other suitable identification indicating compliance with UL 181 and its class designation. These ducts shall be listed and shall be installed in accordance with the terms of their listing, and the requirements of UL 181. Flexible air connectors are not permitted.

601.6 Joints and Seams of Ducts. Joints, seams and fittings of duct systems shall be made substantially airtight by means of tapes, mastics, gasketing or other means.

601.6.1 Residential round ducts. Crimp joints for residential round ducts shall have a contact lap of at least $1^{1}/_{2}$ inches (38 mm) and shall be mechanically fastened by means of at least three sheet-metal screws equally spaced around the joint, or an equivalent fastening method.

601.6.2 Residential rectangular ducts. Joints and seams for 0.016-inch (0.41 mm) (No. 28 gage) and 0.013-inch (0.33 mm) (No. 30 gage) residential rectangular ducts shall be as specified in Table 6-A for 0.019-inch (0.48 mm) (No. 26 gage) material.

601.6.3 Rectangular ducts. Joints and seams for rectangular duct systems shall be as specified in Table 6-A.

601.6.4 Oval ducts. Joints and seams for flat oval ducts and round ducts in other than single dwelling units shall be as specified in Table 6-B.

601.6.5 Listed ducts. Joints and seams and all reinforcements for factory-made air ducts and plenums shall meet with the conditions of prior approval in accordance with the installation instructions that shall accompany the product. Closure systems for rigid Class 1 air ducts and plenums shall conform to UL 181A, and flexible Class 1 air ducts shall conform to UL 181B.

601.7 Metal. Every duct, plenum or fitting of metal shall comply with Table 6-A or Table 6-B.

> **EXCEPTIONS:** 1. Ducts, plenums and fittings for systems serving single dwelling units may comply with Table 6-C.
> 2. Duct systems complying with UL 181.

601.8 Tinned Steel. Existing tinned steel ducts may be used when cooling coils are added to a heating system, provided the first 10 feet (3048 mm) of the duct or plenum measured from the cooling coil discharge are constructed of metal of the gage thickness set forth in Table 6-A, 6-B or 6-C of this chapter or are of approved material and construction. Tinned ducts completely enclosed in inaccessible concealed areas need not be replaced. All accessible ducts shall be insulated to comply with Table 6-D of this chapter. For the purpose of this subsection, ducts shall be considered accessible if the access space is 30 inches (762 mm) or greater in height.

601.9 Vibration Isolators. Vibration isolators installed between mechanical equipment and metal ducts (or casings) shall be made of an approved material and shall not exceed 10 inches (254 mm) in length.

SECTION 602 — QUALITY OF MATERIAL

Galvanized steel shall be of lock-forming quality with a minimum coating of 1.25 ounces per square foot ($0.38 kg/m^2$) of zinc conforming to the requirements of UMC Standard 2-2.

SECTION 603 — INSTALLATION OF DUCTS

603.1 Metal Ducts. Ducts shall be securely fastened in place at each change of direction and as set forth in Table 6-E. Vertical rectangular ducts and vertical round ducts shall be supported as set forth in Table 6-E, Part I. Riser ducts shall be held in place by means of metal straps or angles and channels to secure the riser to the structure.

Metal ducts shall be installed with at least 4 inches (102 mm) of separation from earth. Metal ducts when installed in or under concrete slab shall be encased in at least 2 inches (51 mm) of concrete.

603.1.1 Fire-resistive coatings. Ducts shall be located so as to maintain the minimum required thickness of fire-resistive materials applied to structural members to provide the required fire-resistive rating.

603.1.2 Rectangular duct supports. Supports for rectangular ducts as set forth in Table 6-E when suspended from above shall be installed on two opposite sides of each duct and shall be riveted, bolted or metal screwed to each side of the duct at not more than the intervals specified.

603.1.3 Horizontal round duct supports. Horizontal round ducts 40 inches (1016 mm) or less in diameter when suspended from above shall be supported at intervals not more than as set forth in Table 6-E with one hanger installed to comply with the requirements listed below:

1. Ducts shall be equipped with tightfitting circular bands extending around the entire perimeter of the duct at each specified support interval.

2. Circular bands shall not be less than 1 inch (25 mm) wide nor less than equivalent to the gage of the duct material it supports.

> **EXCEPTION:** Ducts 10 inches (254 mm) and less in diameter may be supported by No. 18 gage (10 mm) galvanized steel wire.

3. Each circular band shall be provided with a suitable means of connecting to the suspending support.

4. Ducts shall be braced and guyed to prevent lateral or horizontal swing.

603.2 Factory-made Air Ducts. Approved Class 0 or Class 1 factory-made air ducts may be installed in any occupancy covered by this code.

603.2.1 Used as risers. Factory-made air ducts shall not be used for vertical risers in air-duct systems serving more than two stories. Such ducts shall not penetrate construction where fire dampers are required.

603.2.2 Protection. Factory-made air ducts shall be installed with at least 4 inches (102 mm) of separation from earth, except when installed as a liner inside of concrete, tile or metal pipe; they shall be protected from physical damage.

603.2.3 Temperature. The temperature of the air to be conveyed in any of these classes of ducts shall be less than 251°F (122°C).

603.3 Protection of Ducts. Ducts installed in locations where they are exposed to mechanical damage by vehicles or from other causes shall be protected by approved barriers.

603.4 Support of Ducts. Installers shall furnish the manufacturer's field fabrication and installation instructions to building officials.

Support spacing and methods shall meet the requirements of UMC Standard 6-3.

Support materials shall be galvanized steel or meet the flame resistance and corrosion requirements of UL 181.

603.5 Outside-air and Return-air Duct Size. Outside-air and return-air ducts shall have the following minimum areas:

603.5.1 Gravity furnaces. The minimum unobstructed total area of the outside or return-air ducts or openings to a gravity-type warm-air furnace shall not be less than 7 square inches per 1,000 Btu/h ($15.4 mm^2/W$) approved output rating or as indicated by the conditions of listing of the furnace.

603.5.2 Blower-type furnaces. The minimum unobstructed total area of the outside or return-air ducts or openings to a blower-type warm-air furnace shall not be less than 2 square inches per 1,000 Btu/h ($4.4 mm^2/W$) approved output rating or bonnet capacity of the furnace.

603.5.3 Listing conditions. The total area of the outside or return-air ducts or openings need not be larger than the minimum indicated by the conditions of listing of the furnace.

603.5.4 Heat pumps. The minimum unobstructed total area of the outside or return-air ducts or openings to a heat pump shall not be less than 6 square inches per 1,000 Btu/h (13.2 mm^2/W) nominal output rating or as indicated by the conditions of listing of the heat pump.

603.6 Dampers. Volume dampers shall not be placed in the air inlet to a furnace in a manner which will reduce the required air to the furnace.

603.7 Ducts for Blower-type Warm-air Furnace. Except as provided in Section 404.1, air for every fuel-burning blower-type warm-air furnace shall be conducted into the blower housing from outside the furnace space by continuous airtight ducts.

603.8 Supply-air Duct Size.

603.8.1 Area. The minimum unobstructed total area of the supply-air ducts from a blower-type warm-air furnace shall not be less than 2 square inches per 1,000 Btu/h (4.4 mm^2/W) approved output rating of the furnace, and the minimum unobstructed total area of the supply-air ducts from a gravity-type warm-air furnace shall not be less than 7 square inches per 1,000 Btu/h (15.4 mm^2/W) approved output rating or as specified by the conditions of listing of the furnace. The total area of the supply-air ducts need not exceed the area of the furnace outlet plenum collar.

For the purpose of this section, a volume damper, grille or register installed to control airflow shall not be considered an obstruction.

603.8.2 Supply-air duct size heat pump. The minimum unobstructed total area of the supply-air ducts from a heat pump shall not be less than 6 square inches per 1,000 Btu/h (13.2 mm^2/W) nominal output rating or as indicated by the conditions of the listing of the heat pump.

603.8.3 Surgical operating room. Warm-air furnace duct openings serving a surgical operating room shall be at least 5 feet (1524 mm) above the floor.

SECTION 604 — INSULATION OF DUCTS

604.1 Amount of Insulation. Supply- and return-air ducts and plenums of a heating or cooling system shall be insulated with not less than the amount of insulation set forth in Table 6-D, except for ducts and plenums used exclusively for evaporative cooling systems.

604.2 Lining Materials. Approved materials shall be installed within ducts and plenums for insulating, sound deadening or other purposes. Materials shall have a mold-, humidity- and erosion-resistant surface that meets the requirements of UL 181. Duct liners in systems operating with air velocities exceeding 2,000 feet per minute (10.2 m/s) shall be fastened with both adhesive and mechanical fasteners, and exposed edges shall have adequate treatment to withstand the operating velocity.

604.3 External Insulation. Insulation applied to the exterior surface of ducts located in buildings shall have a flame spread index of not more than 25 and a smoke-density index not exceeding 50 when tested as a composite installation, including insulation, facing materials, tapes and adhesives as normally applied.

EXCEPTION: Insulation having a flame-spread index not exceeding 50 and a smoke-density index not greater than 100 may be installed

in dwellings or apartment houses where the duct system serves not more than one dwelling unit.

604.4 Identification. Factory-made air ducts and faced insulations intended for installation on the exterior of metal ducts shall be legibly printed with the name of the manufacturer, the thermal resistance (R) value at installed thickness, and the flame-spread index and smoke-developed index of the composite material.

SECTION 605 — DAMPERS IN DUCT SYSTEMS

605.1 Smoke Dampers. Smoke dampers complying with recognized standards in Chapter 16, Part III, shall be installed in accordance with approved manufacturer's installation instructions when required by Chapters 7 and 9 of the Building Code. Smoke dampers shall be labeled by an approved agency.

605.2 Fire Dampers. Fire dampers complying with recognized standards in Chapter 16, Part III, shall be installed in accordance with approved manufacturer's installation instructions when required by Chapter 7 of the Building Code. Fire dampers shall have been tested for closure under airflow conditions and shall be labeled for both maximum airflow permitted and direction of flow. When more than one damper is installed at a point in a single air path, the entire airflow shall be assumed to be passing through the smallest damper area. Fire dampers shall be labeled by an approved agency. Only fire dampers labeled for use in dynamic sysems shall be installed in heating, ventilation and air-conditioning systems which are intended to operate with fans "on" during a fire; see UBC Section 713.12.

Ductwork shall be connected to damper sleeves or assemblies in such a way that collapse of the ductwork will not dislodge the damper or impair its proper operation.

605.3 Ceiling Dampers. Ceiling dampers complying with recognized standards in Chapter 16, Part III, shall be installed in accordance with manufacturer's approved installation instructions in the fire-resistive ceiling element of floor-ceiling and roof-ceiling assemblies when required by Chapter 7 of the Building Code. Fire dampers not meeting the temperature limitation of ceiling dampers shall not be used as substitutes. Ceiling dampers shall be labeled by an approved agency.

605.4 Multiple Arrangements. When size requires the use of multiple dampers, the installation shall be framed in an approved manner to ensure that the dampers remain in place.

605.5 Access and Identification. Dampers shall be provided with an approved means of access, large enough to permit inspection and maintenance of the damper and its operating parts. The access shall not impair fire-resistive construction. Access shall not require the use of tools, keys or special knowledge. Access points shall be permanently identified on the exterior by a label with letters not less than $^1/_2$ inch (13 mm) in height reading: SMOKE DAMPER or FIRE DAMPER. Access doors in ducts shall be tightfitting and suitable for the required duct construction.

605.6 Freedom from Interference. Dampers shall be installed in a manner to ensure positive closing or opening as required by function. Interior liners or insulation shall be held back from portions of a damper, its sleeve or an adjoining duct which would interfere with the damper's proper operation. Exterior materials shall be installed so as to avoid interference with the operation or maintenance of external operating devices needed for proper function.

605.7 Temperature Classification of Operating Elements. Fusible links, thermal sensors, and pneumatic or electric operators shall have a temperature rating or classification as required by the Building Code.

SECTION 606 — VENTILATING CEILINGS

606.1 General. Perforated ceilings may be used for air supply within the limitations of this section. Exit corridors when required to be of fire-resistive construction by Section 1005.7 of the Building Code shall not have ventilating ceilings.

606.2 Requirements. Ventilating ceilings shall comply with the following provisions:

1. Suspended ventilating ceiling material shall have a Class I flame-spread index on both sides determined in accordance with Table 8-A of the Building Code. Suspended ventilating ceiling supports shall be of noncombustible materials.

2. Lighting fixtures recessed into the ventilating ceiling shall be of a type approved for that purpose.

SECTION 607 — UNDER-FLOOR SPACE USED AS PLENUMS

An under-floor space may be used as a supply plenum, provided:

1. The use of under-floor space shall be limited to dwelling units not more than two stories in height. Except for the floor immediately above the under-floor plenum, supply ducts shall be provided extending from the plenum to registers on other floor levels.

2. Such spaces shall be cleaned of all loose combustible scrap material and shall be tightly and substantially enclosed.

3. The enclosing material of the under-floor space, including the sidewall insulation, shall not be more flammable than 1-inch (25 mm) (nominal) wood boards (flame-spread index of 200). Installation of foam plastics is regulated by the Building Code.

4. Access shall be through an opening in the floor and shall not be less than 24 inches by 24 inches (610 mm by 610 mm).

5. A furnace supplying warm air to under-floor space shall be equipped with an automatic control which will start the air-circulating fan when the air in the furnace bonnet reaches a temperature not higher than 150°F (65°C). Such control shall be one that cannot be set higher than 150°F (65°C).

6. A furnace supplying warm air to such space shall be equipped with an approved temperature limit control that will limit outlet air temperature to 200°F (93°C).

7. A noncombustible receptacle shall be placed below each floor opening into the air chamber, and such receptacle shall conform to the following:

   7.1 The receptacle shall be securely suspended from the floor members and shall not be more than 18 inches (457 mm) below the floor opening.

   7.2 The area of the receptacle shall extend 3 inches (76 mm) beyond the opening on all sides.

   7.3 The perimeter of the receptacle shall have a vertical lip at least 1 inch (25 mm) high at the open sides if it is at the level of the bottom of the joists, or 3 inches (76 mm) high if the receptacle is suspended.

8. Floor registers shall be designed for easy removal in order to give access for cleaning the receptacles.

9. Exterior walls and interior stud partitions shall be fire blocked at the floor.

10. Each wall register shall be connected to the air chamber by a register box or boot.

11. A duct conforming with Section 601.1 shall extend from the furnace supply outlet at least 6 inches (152 mm) below combustible framing.

12. The entire ground surface of the under-floor space shall be covered with a vapor barrier having a minimum thickness of 4 mils (0.1 mm) and a flame-spread index of 200 or less.

13. Fuel-gas lines and plumbing waste cleanouts are not located within the space.

SECTION 608 — SHUTOFF FOR SMOKE CONTROL

Air-moving systems supplying air in excess of 2,000 cubic feet per minute (940 L/s) to enclosed spaces within buildings shall be equipped with an automatic shutoff. Automatic shutoff shall be accomplished by interrupting the power source of the air-moving equipment upon detection of smoke in the main supply-air duct served by such equipment. Smoke detectors shall be labeled by an approved agency for air-duct installation and shall be installed in accordance with the manufacturer's installation instructions. Such devices shall be compatible with the operating velocities, pressures, temperatures and humidities of the system. Where fire detection or alarm systems are provided for the building, the smoke detectors required by this section shall be supervised by such systems.

> **EXCEPTIONS:** 1. When the space supplied by the air-moving equipment is served by a total coverage smoke-detection system complying with UFC Standard 10-2, interconnection to such system may be used to accomplish the required shutoff.
>
> 2. Automatic shutoff is not required when all occupied rooms served by the air-handling equipment have direct exit to the exterior and the travel distance does not exceed 100 feet (30.4 m).
>
> 3. Automatic shutoff is not required for Group R, Division 3 and Group U Occupancies.
>
> 4. Automatic shutoff is not required for approved smoke-control systems or where analysis demonstrates shutoff would create a greater hazard, such as may be encountered in air-moving equipment supplying specialized portions of Group H Occupancies. Such equipment shall be required to have smoke detection with remote indication and manual shutoff capability at an approved location.

SECTION 609 — PRODUCT-CONVEYING DUCT SYSTEMS

609.1 Materials. Materials used in product-conveying duct systems shall be suitable for the intended use and shall be of metal.

> **EXCEPTIONS:** 1. Asbestos-cement, concrete, clay or ceramic materials may be used when it is shown that these materials will be equivalent to metal ducts installed in accordance with this chapter.
>
> 2. Ducts serving a Class 5 system may be constructed of approved nonmetallic material when the corrosive characteristics of the material being conveyed make a metal system unsuitable and when the mixture being conveyed is nonflammable.
>
> Approved nonmetallic material shall be either a listed product having a flame-spread index of 25 or less and a smoke-developed rating of 50 or less on both inside and outside surfaces without evidence of continued progressive combustion, or shall have a flame-spread index of 25 or less and shall be installed with an automatic fire-sprinkler protection system inside the duct.
>
> 3. Ducts used in central vacuum-cleaning systems within a dwelling unit may be of PVC pipe. Penetrations of fire walls and floor-ceiling or roof-ceiling assemblies shall comply with Sections 709 and 710 of the Building Code. Copper or ferrous pipes or conduits extending from within the separation between a garage and dwelling unit to the central vacuuming unit may be used.

609.1.1 Aluminum. Aluminum ducts shall not be used in systems conveying flammable vapors, fumes or explosive dusts nor in Class 2, 3 or 4 systems. Galvanized steel and aluminum ducts shall not be used when the temperature of the material being conveyed exceeds 400°F (204°C).

Aluminum construction may be used in Class 1 product-conveying duct systems only. The thickness of aluminum ducts shall be at least two B.&S. gages thicker than the gages required for steel ducts set forth in Tables 5-B and 5-C.

609.1.2 Linings. Metal ducts used in Class 5 systems that are not resistant to the corrosiveness of the product shall be protected with appropriate corrosion-resistant material.

609.2 Construction. Ducts used for conveying products shall be of substantial airtight construction and shall not have openings other than those required for operation and maintenance of the system. Ducts constructed of steel shall comply with Table 6-B or 6-C.

> **EXCEPTIONS:** 1. Class 1 product-conveying ducts that operate at less than 4 inches water column (995 kPa) negative pressure and convey noncorrosive, nonflammable and nonexplosive materials at temperatures not exceeding 250°F (121°C) may be constructed in accordance with Table 6-A, 6-B, 6-E or, with prior approval, UMC Standard 6-1.
>
> 2. Ducts used in central-vacuuming systems within a dwelling unit may be constructed of PVC pipe. Penetrations of fire-resistive walls and floor-ceiling or roof-ceiling assemblies shall comply with Sections 709 and 710 of the Building Code. Copper or ferrous pipes or conduit extending from within the separation between a garage and dwelling unit to the central vacuum unit may be used.

609.2.1 Rectangular sections. The use of rectangular ducts conveying particulates shall be subject to approval of the building official. The design of rectangular ducts shall consider the adhesiveness and buildup of products being conveyed within the duct.

609.3 Fittings. Fittings in Class 2, Class 3 and Class 4 product-conveying systems shall be at least two gages thicker than the thickness required for straight runs. Flexible metallic duct may be used for connecting ductwork to vibrating equipment. Duct systems subject to wide temperature fluctuations shall be provided with expansion joints.

Branches shall connect to main ducts at the large end of transitions at an angle not exceeding 45 degrees.

609.4 Cleanouts. Except for ducts used to convey noncorrosive vapors with no particulate, accessible cleanouts shall be provided at 10-foot (3048 mm) intervals and at changes in direction. Access openings shall also be provided for access to sprinklers and other equipment within the duct which requires servicing.

609.5 Explosion Venting. Ducts conveying explosive dusts shall have explosion vents, openings protected by antiflashback swing valves or rupture diaphragms. Openings to relieve explosive forces shall be located outside the building. When relief devices cannot provide sufficient pressure relief, ductwork shall be designed to withstand an internal pressure of not less than 100 pounds per square inch (689 kPa).

609.6 Supports. Spacing of supports for ducts shall not exceed 12 feet (3658 mm) for 8-inch (203 mm) ducts nor 20 feet (6096 mm) for larger ducts unless justified by the design. The design of supports shall assume that 50 percent of the duct is full of the particulate being conveyed.

609.7 Fire Protection. Sprinklers or other fire-protection devices shall be installed within ducts having a cross-sectional dimension exceeding 10 inches (254 mm) when the duct conveys flammable vapors or fumes. Sprinklers shall be installed at 12-foot (3658 mm) intervals in horizontal ducts and at changes in direction. In vertical runs, sprinklers shall be installed at the top and at alternate floor levels.

609.8 Clearances. Ducts conveying flammable or explosive vapors, fumes or dusts shall have a clearance from combustibles of not less than 18 inches (457 mm). This clearance may be reduced when the combustible construction is protected in accordance with Table 3-B.

609.8.1 Elevated temperatures. Ducts conveying products at temperatures exceeding 125°F (52°C) shall have a clearance to combustible materials not less than the following: 125°F to 250°F (52°C to 121°C)—1 inch (25 mm); 251°F to 600°F (122°C to 315°C)—8 inches (203 mm). For temperatures exceeding 600°F (315°C), the clearance shall not be less than required for chimneys in Table 8-D.

609.9 Protection from Physical Damage. Ducts installed in locations where they are subject to physical damage shall be protected by suitable guards.

TABLE 6-A

1997 UNIFORM MECHANICAL CODE

TABLE 6-A—CONSTRUCTION DETAILS FOR RECTANGULAR SHEET METAL DUCTS
FOR STATIC AIR PRESSURES UP TO 2 INCHES WC

For pressures in excess of 2-inch water column (498 Pa), duct wall thickness shall be
two gages (for sheet gage equivalents see Appendix D) heavier than set forth in this table.

Duct specifications shown here are applicable when ducts larger than 18 inches (457 mm) are cross broken. Where cross breaking is not used, duct wall thickness shall be two gages (for sheet gage equivalents see Appendix D) heavier on ducts 19 inches through 60 inches (483 mm through 1524 mm) wide unless longitudinal standing seams are used.

MINIMUM METAL GAGES				
Steel—U.S. Standard, inches (gage)	Aluminum B.&S., inches (gage)	Copper Cold Rolled	Duct Dimension (inches)	Permissible Girth Joints and Longitudinal Seams
× 25.4 for mm		× 0.0026 for kg/m²	× 25.4 for mm	× 25.4 for mm
0.019 (26)	0.020 (24)	16 oz.	Up through 12	Drive slip, plain "S" slip, or 1" pocket lock
0.024 (24)	0.025 (22)	24 oz.	13 through 18	Drive slip, plain "S" slip, or 1" pocket lock
			19 through 30	Hemmed "S" slip, 1" bar slip, or 1" pocket lock on 5' centers Hemmed "S" slip, 1" bar slip, or 1" pocket lock on 10' centers with 1" × 1" × $\frac{1}{8}$" angles on center line between Hemmed "S" slip, 1" bar slip, or 1" pocket lock on 10' centers with cross break 1" standing seam on 5' centers
0.030 (22)	0.032 (20)	32 oz.	31 through 42	1" bar slip, reinforced bar slip, or pocket lock, on 5' centers 1" bar slip, reinforced bar slip, or pocket lock on 10' centers with 1" × 1" × $\frac{1}{8}$" angles on center line between 1" standing seam on 5' centers Inside longitudinal standing seams with 1" × 1" × $\frac{1}{8}$" angles on 5' center on exterior
			43 through 54	$1\frac{1}{2}$" bar slip, reinforced bar slip, or pocket lock on 4' centers $1\frac{1}{2}$" bar slip, reinforced bar slip, or pocket lock on 8' centers with $1\frac{1}{2}$" × $1\frac{1}{2}$" × $\frac{1}{8}$" angles on center line between $1\frac{1}{2}$" bar slip, reinforced bar slip, or pocket lock on 4' centers with cross break
0.036 (20)	0.040 (18)	36 oz.	55 through 60	$1\frac{1}{2}$" standing steam on 3' centers Inside longitudinal standing seam with $1\frac{1}{2}$" × $1\frac{1}{2}$" × $\frac{1}{8}$" angles on 4' centers on exterior
			61 through 84	Reinforced bar slip, angle slip, alternate bar slip, or angle reinforced pocket lock on 4' centers using $1\frac{1}{2}$" × $1\frac{1}{2}$" × $\frac{1}{8}$" reinforcing angles and with $1\frac{1}{2}$" × $1\frac{1}{2}$" × $\frac{1}{8}$" angles on center line between Reinforced bar slip, angle slip, alternate bar slip, or angle reinforced pocket lock on 8' centers using $1\frac{1}{2}$" × $1\frac{1}{2}$" × $\frac{1}{8}$" reinforcing angles and with $1\frac{1}{2}$" × $1\frac{1}{2}$" × $\frac{1}{8}$" angles 2' on centers in between $1\frac{1}{2}$" angle reinforced standing seam on 2' centers using $1\frac{1}{2}$" × $1\frac{1}{2}$" × $\frac{1}{8}$" reinforcing angles Inside longitudinal standing seams with $1\frac{1}{2}$" × $1\frac{1}{2}$" × $\frac{1}{8}$" angles on 2' centers on exterior
0.047 (18)	0.050 (16)	48 oz.	85 through 96	Companion angles, angle slip, or angle reinforced pocket lock using $1\frac{1}{2}$" × $1\frac{1}{2}$" × $\frac{3}{16}$" companion or reinforcing angles on 4' centers with $1\frac{1}{2}$" × $1\frac{1}{2}$" × $\frac{3}{16}$" angles on center line between Companion angles, angle slip, or angle reinforced pocket lock using $1\frac{1}{2}$" × $1\frac{1}{2}$" × $\frac{3}{16}$" companion or reinforcing angles on 8' centers with $1\frac{1}{2}$" × $1\frac{1}{2}$" × $\frac{3}{16}$" angles on 2' centers in between $1\frac{1}{2}$" angle reinforced standing seam on 2' centers using $1\frac{1}{2}$" × $1\frac{1}{2}$" × $\frac{3}{16}$" reinforcing angles Inside longitudinal standing seams with $1\frac{1}{2}$" × $1\frac{1}{2}$" × $\frac{3}{16}$" angles on 2' centers on exterior
			Over 96	Companion angles, angle slip, or angle reinforced pocket using 2" × 2" × $\frac{1}{4}$" companion or reinforcing angles on 4' centers with 2" × 2" × $\frac{1}{4}$" angles on center line between Companion angles, angle slip, or angle reinforced pocket lock using 2" × 2" × $\frac{1}{4}$" companion or reinforcing angles on 8' centers with 2" × 2" × $\frac{1}{4}$" angles 2' on center line between $1\frac{1}{2}$" angle reinforced standing seam on 2' centers using 2" × 2" × $\frac{1}{4}$" reinforcing angles Inside longitudinal standing seams with 2" × 2" × $\frac{1}{4}$" angles on 2' centers on exterior

TABLE 6-B—CONSTRUCTION DETAILS FOR ROUND AND FLAT-OVAL DUCTS

DUCT DIAMETER MAXIMUM WIDTH (inches)	ALUMINUM B.&S. GAGE Pressure ≤ 2″ WC	STEEL—THICKNESS IN INCHES (STEEL—GALVANIZED SHEET GAGE)					GIRTH JOINTS[1]	
		Pressure ≤ 2″ WC[2] (498 Pa)		Pressure > 2″ ≤ 10″ WC (498 Pa ≤ 2.5 kPa)				Minimum Girth Reinforcing, Maximum Spacing and Angle Size
	Round	Round	Flat-Oval	Spiral Seam	Longitudinal Seam	Welded Fittings	Pressure > 2″ ≤ 10″ WC	
				× 25.4 for mm				
Up to 9	24	0.019 (26)	0.024 (24)	0.019 (26)	0.024 (24)	0.030 (22)	2″ slip	None
Over 9 Up to 14	24	0.019 (26)	0.024 (24)	0.024 (24)	0.030 (22)	0.036 (20)	4″ slip	None
Over 14 Up to 23	22	0.024 (24)	0.030 (22)	0.024 (24)	0.030 (22)	0.036 (20)	4″ slip	None
Over 23 Up to 37	20	0.030 (22)	0.036 (20)	0.030 (22)	0.036 (20)	0.036 (20)	4″ slip	None
Over 37 Up to 51	18	0.036 (20)	0.047 (18)	0.036 (20)	0.036 (20)	0.047 (18)	$1^1/_4″ \times 1^1/_4″ \times ^1/_8″$ flange	$1^1/_4″ \times 1^1/_4″ \times ^1/_8″$ on 72″
Over 51 Up to 61	16	0.047 (18)	0.058 (16)	X	0.047 (18)	0.047 (18)	$1^1/_4″ \times 1^1/_4″ \times ^1/_8″$ flange	$1^1/_4″ \times 1^1/_4″ \times ^1/_8″$ on 72″
Over 61 Up to 84	14	0.058 (16)	0.070 (14)	X	0.058 (16)	0.058 (16)	$1^1/_2″ \times 1^1/_2″ \times ^1/_8″$ flange	$1^1/_2″ \times 1^1/_2″ \times ^1/_8″$ on 48″

[1]For pressure ≤ 2 inches WC (498 Pa) any of the following joints are acceptable: butt slip, pipe slip, pipe lock, roll slip, snap slip, plenum lock and companion flange.
[2]Acceptable longitudinal seams for pressure ≤ 2 inches WC (498 Pa): Acme (grooved), snap lock, standing and spiral.

TABLE 6-C—THICKNESS OF METAL DUCTS AND PLENUMS USED FOR HEATING OR COOLING FOR A SINGLE DWELLING UNIT

SIZE AND SHAPE OF DUCT	GALVANIZED STEEL		APPROXIMATE ALUMINUM B.&S. GAGE
	Minimum Thickness (inches) × 25.4 for mm	Equivalent Galvanized Sheet Gage No.	
Round ducts and enclosed rectangular ducts			
14″ (356 mm) or less	0.013	30	26
Over 14″ (356 mm)	0.016	28	24
Exposed rectangular ducts			
14″ (356 mm) or less	0.016	28	24
Over 14″ (356 mm)	0.019	26	22

TABLE 6-D—INSULATION OF DUCTS

DUCT LOCATION	INSULATION TYPES MECHANICALLY COOLED	HEATING ZONE[1]	INSULATION TYPES HEATING ONLY
On roof on exterior of building	C, V[2] and W	I	A and W
		II	B and W
		III	C and W
Attics, garages and crawl spaces	A and V[2]	I	A
		II	A
		III	B
In walls,[3] within floor-ceiling spaces[3]	A and V[2]	I	A
		II	A
		III	B
Within the conditioned space or in basements; return ducts in air plenums	None required		None required
Cement slab or within ground	None required		None required

NOTE: Where ducts are used for both heating and cooling, the minimum insulation shall be as required for the most restrictive condition.

[1]Heating Degree Days:

Zone I	below 4,500 D.D.
Zone II	4,501 to 8,000 D.D.
Zone III	over 8,001 D.D.

[2]Vapor retarders shall be installed on supply ducts in spaces vented to the outside in geographic areas where the summer dew point temperature based on the $2^1/_2$ percent column of dry-bulb and mean coincident wet-bulb temperature exceeds 60°F (15.4°C).

[3]Insulation may be omitted on that portion of a duct which is located within a wall- or a floor-ceiling space where:

3.1 Both sides of the space are exposed to conditioned air.
3.2 The space is not ventilated.
3.3 The space is not used as a return plenum.
3.4 The space is not exposed to unconditioned air.
Ceilings which form plenums need not be insulated.

(Continued)

TABLE 6-D
TABLE 6-E

1997 UNIFORM MECHANICAL CODE

TABLE 6-D—INSULATION OF DUCTS—(Continued)

INSULATION TYPES[4]:

A— A material with an installed conductance of 0.48 (2.72 W/(m·K)] or the equivalent thermal resistance of 2.1 [0.367 (m·K)/W].
   Examples of materials capable of meeting the above requirements:
   1-inch (25 mm), 0.60 lb./cu. ft. (9.6 kg/m^3) mineral fiber, rock, slag or glass blankets.
   $^1/_2$-inch (13 mm), 1.5 to 3 lb./cu. ft. (24 to 48 kg/m^3) mineral fiber blanket duct liner.
   $^1/_2$-inch (13 mm), 3 to 10 lb./cu. ft. (48 to 160 kg/m^3) mineral fiber board.

B— A material with an installed conductance of 0.24 [1.36W/(m·K)] or the equivalent thermal resistance of 4.2 (0.735 m·K/w).
   Examples of materials meeting the above requirements:
   2-inch (51 mm), 0.60 lb./cu. ft. (9.6 kg/m^3) mineral fiber blankets.
   1-inch (25 mm), 1.5 to 3 lb./cu. ft. (24 to 48 kg/m^3) mineral fiber blanket duct liner.
   1-inch (25 mm), 3 to 10 lb./cu. ft. (48 to 160 kg/m^3) mineral fiber board.

C— A material with an installed conductance of 0.16 [0.9 W/(m·K)] or the
   equivalent thermal resistance of 6.3 [1.1 (m·K)/W].
   Examples of materials meeting the above requirements:
   3-inch (76 mm), 0.60 lb./cu. ft. (9.6 kg/m^3) mineral fiber blankets.
   $1^1/_2$-inch (38 mm), 1.5 to 3 lb./cu. ft. (24 to 48 kg/m^3) mineral fiber blanket duct liner.
   $1^1/_2$-inch (38 mm), 3 to 10 lb./cu. ft. (48 to 160 kg/m^3) mineral fiber board.

V— Vapor Retarders: Material with a perm rating not exceeding 0.5 perm [29 ng/(Pa·s·m^2)]. All joints to be sealed.

W— Approved weatherproof barrier.

[4]The example of materials listed under each type is not meant to limit other available thickness and density combinations with the equivalent installed conductance or resistance based on the insulation only.

TABLE 6-E—DUCT SUPPORTS

Part I—VERTICAL DUCTS

MAXIMUM SIDE OF RECTANGULAR DUCT	METAL STRAP OR ANGLE BRACKET	MAXIMUM DIAMETER OF ROUND DUCTS	STRAPS
		× 25.4 for mm	
24"	1" × $^1/_8$" (strap)[1]	10"	0.047" (No. 18 gage) galvanized steel 2" wide[1]
36"	1" × 1" × $^1/_8$" angle[1]	20"	0.058" (No. 16 gage) galvanized steel 2" wide[1]
48"	$1^1/_8$" × $1^1/_8$" × $^1/_8$" angle[1]	40"	$^1/_8$" steel × $1^1/_2$"[1]
60"	$1^1/_2$" × $1^1/_2$" × $^1/_8$" angle[1]	60"	$^1/_8$" steel × 2"[1]
Over 60"	2" × 2" × $^1/_8$" angle[1]	Over 60"	$^3/_{16}$" steel × 2"[1]

Part II—HORIZONTAL DUCTS

MAXIMUM SIDE OF RECTANGULAR DUCT	METAL STRAP OR ANGLE BRACKET	MAXIMUM DIAMETER OF ROUND DUCTS	STRAPS
18"	1" × 18 gage[2]	10"	Same gage as galvanized steel duct, 1" wide or (No. 18 gage galvanized steel wire) on 10' centers
30"	1" × 18 gage[2]		
48"	1" × $^1/_8$"[2]	20"	Same gage as galvanized steel duct, 1" wide or (No. 8 gage galvanized steel wire) tied to 1" galvanized steel band around duct on 10' centers
60"	1" × $^1/_8$"[2]	40"	
80"	1" × $^1/_8$"[2]	60"	Same gage as galvanized steel duct, $1^1/_2$" wide on 6' centers
		Over 60"	Same gage as galvanized steel duct, $1^1/_2$" wide on 4' centers

Part III—HORIZONTAL DUCTS—TRAPEZE-TYPE SUPPORTS

MAXIMUM DIAMETER OF ROUND DUCT OR SIDE OF RECTANGULAR DUCT	HORIZONTAL SUPPORT ANGLE[3]	HANGER
36"	$1^1/_2$" × $1^1/_2$" × $^1/_8$"	$^1/_4$" round rod or 1" × 1" × $^1/_8$" angle
48"	2" × 2" × $^1/_8$"	$^1/_4$" round rod or 1" × 1" × $^1/_8$" angle
60"	2" × 2" × $^1/_8$"	$^5/_{16}$" round rod or 1" × 1" × $^1/_8$" angle
84"	2" × 2" × $^1/_8$"	$^3/_8$" round rod or 1" × 1" × $^1/_8$" angle

[1]Spaced vertically not more than 12 feet (3658 mm) on centers.

[2]Spaced horizontally not more than 10 feet (3048 mm) on centers.

[3]Spaced not more than 8 feet (2438 mm) on centers.

Chapter 7
COMBUSTION AIR

SECTION 701 — GENERAL

701.1 Air Supply. Fuel-burning equipment shall be assured a sufficient supply of combustion air. The methods of providing combustion air in this chapter do not apply to direct-vent appliances, appliances listed as having separated combustion systems, listed cooking appliances, refrigerators and domestic clothes dryers.

701.2 Unusually Tight Construction. In buildings of unusually tight construction, combustion air shall be obtained from outside.

701.3 Ordinary Construction. In buildings of ordinary tightness insofar as infiltration is concerned, all or a portion of the combustion air for fuel-burning appliances may be obtained from infiltration when the requirement for 50 cubic feet per 1,000 Btu/h (4.831 L/W) input is met.

701.4 Existing Buildings. When fuel-burning appliances are installed in an existing building containing other fuel-burning appliances, the room or space shall be provided with combustion air as required by this chapter for all fuel-burning appliances contained therein.

SECTION 702 — COMBUSTION-AIR OPENINGS

702.1 Location. One opening shall be located within the upper 12 inches (304 mm) of the enclosure and one opening shall be located within the lower 12 inches (304 mm) of the enclosure.

> **EXCEPTION:** When all air is taken from the outdoors for an appliance with a minimum clearance of 1 inch (25 mm) on the sides and back and 6 inches (152 mm) on the front, one opening shall be permitted and located within the upper 12 inches (305 mm) of the enclosure.

702.2 Dampers Prohibited. Combustion-air ducts or plenums shall not be installed so as to require openings in or penetrations through construction where fire dampers are required. Manually operated dampers shall not be installed in combustion air openings. With prior approval, power-actuated movable louvers admitting combustion air may be used and, if installed, shall be electrically interlocked with the main burner fuel-supply valve so as to prevent fuel delivery unless the louvers are in the fully open position.

702.3 Louvers, Grilles and Screens. Combustion-air openings shall be covered with corrosion-resistant screen of $^1/_4$-inch (6.4 mm) mesh, except as provided in Section 704.3. In calculating the free area, consideration shall be given to the blocking effect of louvers, grilles and screens protecting openings. The free area through louvers, grilles and screens shall be used in calculating the size of opening required to provide the free area specified.

SECTION 703 — SOURCES OF COMBUSTION AIR

703.1 Air from Outside. Combustion air obtained from outside the building shall be supplied as follows:

1. Through permanent openings of the required area directly to the outside of the building through the floor, roof or walls of the appliance enclosure; or

2. Through continuous ducts of the required cross-sectional area extending from the appliance enclosure to the outside of the building. The required upper combustion-air duct shall extend horizontally or upwards to the outside of the building. Where not otherwise prohibited, combustion air may be obtained from an attic area, provided the attic ventilating openings are not subject to ice or snow blockage, and further provided:

   2.1 The attic has not less than 30 inches (762 mm) vertical clear height at its maximum point.

   2.2 Attic ventilation is sufficient to provide the required volume of combustion air and complies with the requirements of Section 706.

   2.3 The combustion-air opening is provided with a galvanized sleeve of not less than 0.019-inch (0.48 mm) (No. 26 gage) steel or other approved material extending from the appliance enclosure to at least 6 inches (153 mm) above the top of the ceiling joists and insulation.

703.2 Under-floor Supply. Lower combustion air openings may connect with under-floor areas conforming to the following requirements:

1. Under-floor spaces having unobstructed openings to the exterior at least twice the area of the required air openings.

2. The height of the under-floor space shall comply with the requirements of the Building Code and be without obstruction to the free flow of air.

703.3 Prohibited Sources. Openings and ducts shall not connect appliance enclosures with space in which the operation of a fan may adversely affect the flow of combustion air. Combustion air shall not be obtained from a hazardous location or from any area in which objectionable quantities of flammable vapor, lint or dust are released. Combustion air shall not be taken from a refrigeration machinery room.

703.4 Interior Spaces. In buildings of ordinary tightness, combustion air provided by infiltration may be obtained from freely communicating interior spaces, provided the combined volume in cubic feet complies with the following conditions:

703.4.1 Adequate volume—gas and liquid. If the volume of the room or space in which fuel-burning appliances are installed is equal to or greater than 50 cubic feet per 1,000 Btu/h (4.831 L/W) of aggregate input rating of appliances, infiltration may be regarded as adequate to provide combustion air. Exclude from the calculation the input ratings of listed direct-vent appliances, enclosed furnaces, cooking appliances, refrigerators and domestic clothes dryers.

703.4.2 Insufficient volume—gas and liquid. Rooms or spaces containing gas- or liquid-fuel-burning appliances which do not have the volume as specified above shall be provided with minimum unobstructed combustion-air openings as specified in Section 707 and arranged as specified in Section 702.

SECTION 704 — COMBUSTION-AIR DUCTS

704.1 General. Combustion-air ducts shall:

1. Be of galvanized steel complying with Chapter 6 or equivalent corrosion-resistant material approved for this use.

EXCEPTION: In Group R, Division 3 Occupancies, unobstructed stud and joist spaces may be used, provided not more than one required fire stop is removed.

2. Have a minimum cross-sectional dimension of 3 inches (76 mm).

3. Terminate in a space at least 3 inches (76 mm) in depth open to the front or firebox side of the appliance. Such space shall extend from the floor to the ceiling of the appliance compartment.

4. Have the same cross-sectional areas as the free area of the openings to which they connect.

5. Serve a single appliance compartment.

6. Serve only upper or lower combustion-air openings; the separation between ducts serving upper and lower combustion-air openings shall be maintained to the source of combustion air.

704.2 Dampers. Combustion-air ducts shall not be installed so as to pass through construction where fire dampers are required. Volume dampers shall not be installed in combustion-air ducts.

704.3 Screen. Neither end of ducts which terminate in an attic shall be screened.

SECTION 705 — COMBUSTION AIR FOR GRAVITY WARM-AIR FURNACES

Gravity-type warm-air furnaces shall be provided with combustion air as specified in Section 701, 702, 703 or 707 of this code.

Combustion and cold-air return for gravity-type warm-air furnaces may be obtained from the same area.

SECTION 706 — CONDITIONS CREATED BY MECHANICAL EXHAUSTING

Operation of exhaust fans, kitchen ventilation systems, clothes dryers or fireplaces shall be considered in determining combustion air requirements to avoid unsatisfactory operation of installed gas appliances.

SECTION 707 — AREA OF COMBUSTION-AIR OPENINGS

707.1 General. The net free area of openings, ducts or plenums supplying combustion air to an area containing fuel-burning appliances shall be as specified in Table 7-A. When grilles, screens or louvers are inserted in combustion-air openings, the provisions of Section 702.3 apply. Permanent mechanically pressurized combustion-air facilities in central heating plants, fossil-fueled steam electric generating plants, district heating plants, industrial facilities and power boiler plants are exempt from the requirements of Table 7-A.

707.2 Designed Installations. Compliance with Table 7-A is not required for an installation which has been professionally designed to ensure an adequate supply of combustion air.

TABLE 7-A—SIZE OF COMBUSTION-AIR OPENINGS OR DUCTS[1]

COLUMN I		COLUMN II	
Buildings of Ordinary Tightness		**Buildings of Unusually Tight Construction[2]**	
	Size of Openings or Ducts		**Size of Openings or Ducts**
Condition	× 0.293 for W × 645.2 for mm²	**Condition**	× 0.293 for W × 645.2 for mm²
Appliance in unconfined[2] space:	May rely on infiltration alone.	Appliance in unconfined[2] space: Obtain combustion air from outdoors or from space freely communicating with outdoors.	Provide two openings, each having 1 sq. in. per 5,000 Btu/h input. Ducts admitting outdoor air may be connected to the cold-air return.
Appliance in confined[3] space: 1. All air from inside building.	Provide two openings into enclosure each having 1 sq. in. per 1,000 Btu/h input freely communicating with other unconfined interior spaces. Minimum 100 sq. in. each opening.[4]	Appliance in confined[3] space: Obtain combustion air from outdoors or from space freely communicating with outdoors.	1. Provide two vertical ducts or plenums; 1 sq. in. per 4,000 Btu/h input each duct or plenum. 2. Provide two horizontal ducts or plenums; 1 sq. in. per 2,000 Btu/h input each duct or plenum.
2. Part of air from inside building.	Provide two openings into enclosure[4] from other freely communicating unconfined[2] interior spaces each having an area of 100 sq. in. plus one duct or plenum opening to outdoors having an area of 1 sq. in. per 5,000 Btu/h input rating. The outdoor duct or plenum opening may be connected to the cold-air return.		3. Provide two openings in an exterior wall of the enclosure; each opening 1 sq. in. per 4,000 Btu/h input. 4. Provide one ceiling opening to ventilated attic and one vertical duct to attic; each opening 1 sq. in. per 4,000 Btu/h input. 5. Provide one opening or one vertical duct or one horizontal duct in the enclosure; 1 sq. in. per 3,000 Btu/h input but no smaller than vent flow area.
3. All air from outdoors. Obtain from outdoors or from space freely communicating with outdoors.	Use any of the methods listed for confined space in unusually tight construction as indicated in Column II.		6. Provide one opening in enclosure ceiling to ventilated attic and one opening in enclosure floor to ventilated crawl space; each opening 1 sq. in. per 4,000 Btu/h input.

[1]For location of openings, see Section 702.

[2]As defined in Section 223.

[3]As defined in Section 205.

[4]When the total input rating of appliances in enclosure exceeds 100,000 Btu/h (29.3 kW), the area of each opening into the enclosure must be increased 1 square inch (645 mm²) for each 1,000 Btu/h (293 W) over 100,000 (29.3 kW).

Chapter 8
CHIMNEYS AND VENTS

SECTION 801 — VENTING SYSTEMS—GENERAL

801.1 Venting System Required. Appliances designed to be vented shall be connected to a venting system as specified in Section 802 and the venting system shall comply with the provisions of this chapter, except as provided in this section.

Venting systems shall consist of approved chimneys, Type B vents, Type BW vents, Type L vents, plastic pipe recommended by the manufacturer of listed condensing appliances for use with specified models, or a venting assembly which is an integral part of a listed appliance.

801.2 Standards of Quality. The standard listed below is a recognized standard (see UMC Sections 1602 and 1603, and UBC Sections 3503 and 3504).

801.2.1 Fireplace refractories. Fireclay Refractories, ASTM C 27-60.

801.3 Positive Flow. Venting systems shall be designed and constructed so as to develop a positive flow adequate to convey all combustion products to the outside atmosphere.

Venting systems may be designed in accordance with accepted engineering methods when the design method has been approved by the building official.

801.4 Integral Venting Systems. A venting system which is an integral part of the vented appliance and plastic pipe recommended by the manufacturer in installation instructions as suitable for use with listed condensing appliances shall be installed in accordance with the appliance listing, manufacturer's installation instructions and applicable requirements of this code.

801.5 Appliance Designed for Type B Vents. Gas venting systems serving appliances equipped with draft hoods and appliances listed for use with Type B vents may be designed in accordance with tables in Appendix C, Chapter 8, when the design method has been approved by the building official.

SECTION 802 — TYPES OF VENTING SYSTEMS REQUIRED

802.1 General. The type of venting system required to serve various classifications of appliances shall be as set forth in Tables 8-B and 8-C.

802.2 Limitations. Type B vents shall not be used for venting the following:

1. Appliances which may be converted readily to the use of solid or liquid fuels;

2. Combination gas-oil-burning appliances; and

3. Appliances listed for use with chimneys only.

802.3 Vent Connector. Connectors used for gas appliances having draft hoods for listed conversion-burner-equipped appliances having draft hoods may be constructed of materials having resistance to corrosion and heat not less than that specified in Section 816 or they may be of Type B or Type L vent material.

802.4 Solid Fuel. Solid-fuel-burning appliances shall not be connected to a venting system which serves gas- or oil-burning appliances.

802.5 Plastic Venting Systems for Use with Listed Condensing Appliances. Condensing appliances which cool flue gases nearly to the dewpoint within the appliance resulting in low vent gas temperatures may use plastic venting materials and vent configurations unsuitable for noncondensing appliances. Listed condensing appliances shall be considered properly vented when installed in accordance with the terms of listing and the manufacturer's installation instructions.

SECTION 803 — INSTALLATION AND CONSTRUCTION REQUIREMENTS

803.1 General. Factory-built chimneys, Type L vents, Type B gas vents or Type BW gas vents shall be installed in accordance with the manufacturer's installation instructions, the terms of listing and the applicable requirements of this code.

803.2 Smokestack and Masonry Chimneys. Smokestacks shall be installed according to the applicable requirements of Section 814. For masonry chimneys, see Section 813.

803.3 Dampers. Manually operated dampers shall not be placed in chimneys, vents or chimney or vent connectors of liquid- or gas-burning appliances. Fixed baffles on the appliance side of draft hoods and draft regulators shall not be classified as dampers.

Automatically operated vent damper devices shall be listed and installed in accordance with the terms of the listing. Electrically and mechanically operated vent damper devices shall be arranged to prevent firing of the burner unless the damper is opened to a safe position.

803.4 Unused Openings. Unused openings in a venting system shall be closed or capped to the satisfaction of the building official.

SECTION 804 — LOCATION AND SUPPORT OF VENTING SYSTEMS, INCLUDING MASONRY VENTING SYSTEMS

804.1 Penetrations into Air Ducts and Plenums. A combustion products vent, vent connector, chimney or chimney connector shall not extend into or through an air duct or plenum.

> **EXCEPTION:** A venting system may pass through a combustion air duct.

804.2 Enclosure and Support. Portions of venting systems which extend through occupied and storage spaces shall be enclosed to avoid contact with or damage to the installation.

The base of a vent which extends to the ground shall rest on a solid masonry or concrete base at least 2 inches (51 mm) in thickness. The base of a vent which does not extend to the ground and is not self-supporting shall rest on a firm metal or masonry support.

Venting systems shall be adequately supported for the weight and the design of the material used.

804.3 Venting into a Fireplace Chimney. Appliances shall not be vented into a fireplace or into a chimney serving a fireplace.

SECTION 805 — GRAVITY VENTING SYSTEMS—LENGTH, PITCH AND CLEARANCES

805.1 Offsets in a Gravity Vent. Except as provided in Sections 801 and 807, gravity vents shall extend in a generally vertical direction with offsets not exceeding 45 degrees, except that a gravity vent system having not more than one 60-degree offset may be allowed.

An angle greater than 45 degrees from the vertical is considered a horizontal run. The total horizontal run of a vent plus the length of horizontal vent connector shall not exceed 75 percent of the vertical height of the vent.

Vent offsets shall be supported for their weight and shall be installed to maintain proper clearance, to prevent physical damage, and to prevent separation of the joints.

805.2 Vent Connector Rise. A vent connector which is a part of a gravity-type venting system shall have a continuous rise of not less than $^1/_4$ unit vertical in 12 units horizontal (2% slope) measured from the appliance vent collar to the vent.

805.3 Clearance. Single-wall metal vent connectors, when permitted to be used by Section 802.3, shall be provided with clearances from combustible material of not less than that set forth in Table 3-C.

SECTION 806 — VENT TERMINATION

806.1 General. Vents shall extend above the roof surface, through a flashing, and terminate in a listed vent cap installed in accordance with its listing and the manufacturer's installation instructions.

806.2 Gravity-type Venting Systems. Gravity-type venting systems, other than a Type BW gas-venting system or a venting system which is an integral part of a listed appliance shall terminate not less than 5 feet (1524 mm) above the highest vent collar which it serves.

806.3 Wall Furnace. A Type BW gas vent serving a vented wall furnace shall terminate at least 12 feet (3658 mm) in vertical height above the bottom of the furnace, except as provided in Section 807.

806.4 Type B or BW Gas Vents. Type B or BW gas vents with listed vent caps 12 inches (305 mm) in size or smaller shall be permitted to be terminated in accordance with Table 8-A, provided they are located at least 8 feet (2438 mm) from a vertical wall or similar obstruction. All other Type B gas vents shall terminate not less than 2 feet (610 mm) above the highest point where they pass through the roof and at least 2 feet (610 mm) higher than any portion of a building within 10 feet (3048 mm).

806.5 Type L Venting Systems. Type L venting systems shall terminate not less than 2 feet (610 mm) above the highest point where the vent passes through the roof of the building and at least 2 feet (610 mm) higher than any portion of the building within 10 feet (3048 mm) of the vent.

806.6 Vent Terminals. Venting systems shall terminate not less than 4 feet (1219 mm) below or 4 feet (1219 mm) horizontally from, and not less than 1 foot (305 mm) above a door, an openable window or a gravity air inlet into a building.

> **EXCEPTION:** Vent terminals of direct-vent appliances with inputs of 50,000 Btu/h (14.7 kW) or less shall be located at least 9 inches (229 mm) from an opening through which combustion products could enter a building. Appliances with inputs exceeding 50,000 Btu/h (14.7 kW) but not exceeding 65,000 Btu/h (19 kW) shall require 12-inch (305 mm) vent termination clearances. The bottom of the vent terminal and the air intake shall be located at least 12 inches (305 mm) above grade.

806.6.1 Separation from inlets. Venting systems shall terminate at least 3 feet (914 mm) above an outside- or makeup-air inlet

located within 10 feet (3048 mm) and at least 4 feet (1219 mm) from a property line except a public way.

> **EXCEPTION:** Vent terminations of direct-vent appliances with inputs not exceeding 50,000 Btu/h (19 kW) shall be permitted to terminate at least 2 feet (610 mm) from a property line except a public way.

806.7 Outdoor Appliances with Integral Vents. Appliances listed for outdoor installation incorporating integral venting means shall be considered as being properly vented when they are installed in accordance with their listings and the manufacturer's instructions. Venting systems shall terminate at least 4 feet (1219 mm) below or 4 feet (1219 mm) horizontally from, and at least 1 foot (305 mm) above a door, an openable window or a gravity-air inlet into building. Venting systems shall terminate not less than 3 feet (914 mm) above a forced-air inlet located within 10 feet (3048 mm) and at least 4 feet (1219 mm) from a property line, except a public way.

SECTION 807 — VENTED WALL FURNACE (TYPE BW) SYSTEMS

In addition to other requirements specified in this chapter, gas-burning vented wall furnaces requiring a Type BW gas vent shall be vented to comply with the following requirements:

1. Type BW gas vents shall be attached to a solid header plate designed for the vented wall furnace installed. This attachment shall be made by a base plate furnished with the gas vent used.

2. The stud space in which a Type BW gas vent is installed shall be free of obstructions, except for fire-stop spacers that are required for multistory Type BW gas vents. All ceiling plates and floor plates through which the gas vent passes shall be cut flush with the adjacent wall studs.

3. Clearance of a Type BW gas vent from any material shall be that space provided by the base plate, ceiling plate spacer straps and fire-stop spacers, furnished with the gas vent used. When a Type BW gas vent is located in a stud space, care shall be exercised so that clearances provided by spacers are maintained after application of wall coverings and other parts of the construction. A sheet metal barrier shall be installed between a Type BW gas vent located in a stud space and wall covering constructed of perforated lath, metal lath or building paper.

4. A Type BW gas vent listed only for single-story use shall be installed only in a single-story building or on the top story of a multistory building. A Type BW gas vent listed for multistory use may be installed in single- or multistory buildings.

5. A stud space that contains a Type BW gas vent, which is serving a vented wall furnace installed in a single-story building or in the top story of a multistory building, shall be open to an attic space or to a ventilated roof flashing equipped with a storm collar.

> **EXCEPTION:** In lieu of a ventilated roof flashing, this stud space may be ventilated by providing an opening in the wall covering, within 12 inches (305 mm) of the upper portion of the stud space, opening into a room served by the wall furnace.

Where a Type BW gas vent extends into an attic space, a metal sleeve not less than 0.016 inch (0.48 mm) (No. 26 manufacturer's standard gage) steel, having the same area as the opening through the ceiling plate, shall extend around the gas vent from the top of the ceiling plate into the attic at least 12 inches (305 mm) or to a point 2 inches (51 mm) below the roof sheathing, whichever is the lesser. This sleeve shall be securely fixed in position.

> **EXCEPTION:** The metal sleeve will not be required if fire-stop spacers are required at the ceiling plate by Item 6 of this section.

6. The stud space in which a vented recessed wall furnace is installed shall be ventilated at the first ceiling plate level above the furnace by the ceiling plate spacer furnished with the gas vent

used. Fire-stop spacers furnished with the gas vent used shall be installed at each subsequent ceiling plate through which the gas vent passes.

7. A suitable metal guard shall be installed at the floor line of each floor through which the gas vent passes to ensure required clearance from combustible material and to prevent damage to the vent.

8. When a Type BW gas vent is installed in an existing building, the wall covering one side of the vent shall be completely open for installation and inspection.

9. Type BW gas vents shall extend from the header plate of the vented wall furnace to a point above the highest ceiling plate through which the vent passes, without offsets or crossovers therein. After a Type BW gas vent passes through the highest ceiling plate above the furnace which it serves, the vent system may be completed with Type B gas vents of the same manufacturer, and offsets or breakovers shall be limited to those specified in Section 805.

SECTION 808 — SIZE OF GRAVITY VENTING SYSTEMS

808.1 Area Required. Gravity venting systems shall have an internal cross-sectional area equivalent to the area of the vent collar on the appliance.

> **EXCEPTION:** Pressurized venting systems which are an integral part of a listed appliance employing plastic pipe are regulated under the fourth paragraph of Section 801 and Column IV of Table 8-C.

808.2 Minimum Area. Gravity venting systems shall have an area of at least 7 square inches (4516 mm^2) unless the venting system is an integral part of a listed appliance.

SECTION 809 — COMMON VENTING SYSTEM

Two or more oil- or gas-burning appliances may be connected to a common venting system, or automatically controlled gas appliances may be vented into the same chimney serving liquid-fuel-fired appliances, provided: (1) the gas appliances are each equipped with a safety shutoff device, (2) each oil appliance is equipped with a primary safety control, and (3) the venting system is designed to meet the requirements of Section 801 of this code, or the venting system complies with the following requirements:

1. Appliances which are connected to a common venting system shall be located within the same story of the building, except designed vent systems as provided by Section 801.

2. Two or more connectors shall not enter a common venting system unless the inlets are offset in such a manner that no portion of an inlet is opposite the other inlets.

3. When two or more appliances are connected to one venting system, the venting system area shall not be less than the area of the largest vent connector plus 50 percent of the areas of the additional vent connectors.

4. Each vent connector of a multiple-venting system shall have the greatest possible rise consistent with the headroom available between the draft hood outlet, the barometric damper or the flue collar and the point of interconnection to a manifold, to a common vent or to a chimney.

SECTION 810 — EXISTING VENTING SYSTEMS

An existing venting system shall not be connected to a replaced appliance unless the venting system complies with all the following requirements:

1. The venting system shall have been lawfully installed in compliance with the code in effect at the time of its installation and shall be in a safe condition.

2. The internal area of the venting system shall comply with Section 808 for a single-appliance venting system and Section 809 for multiple-appliance venting systems.

3. The venting system shall be connected to the appliance in a safe manner.

SECTION 811 — DRAFT HOODS

An appliance draft hood shall be located in the same room or space as the combustion air opening of the appliance.

A draft hood shall be installed in the position for which it was designed, and shall be located so that the draft hood relief opening is at least 6 inches (152 mm) from any surface other than the appliance it serves, measured in a direction 90 degrees to the plane of the relief opening. When a greater clearance is indicated by the appliance approval, as shown on the appliance label, the greater clearance shall be provided.

SECTION 812 — TYPES OF CHIMNEYS

812.1 Factory-built Chimneys. Factory-built chimneys shall be installed in accordance with the terms of their listing, the manufacturer's installation instructions and the applicable requirements of this code. Factory-built chimneys shall terminate as required for unlisted single-wall metal chimneys in Table 8-D.

Chimneys used with fireplaces or heating appliances in which solid or liquid fuel is used shall be maintained with a spark arrester as required for incinerators.

> **EXCEPTION:** Chimneys which are located more than 200 feet (61 m) from any mountainous, brush-covered or forest-covered land or land covered with flammable material and are not attached to a structure having less than a Class C roof covering, as set forth in the Building Code.

812.2 Masonry Chimneys. Masonry chimneys shall be constructed to meet the requirements of Section 813.

812.3 Unlisted Smokestacks. Unlisted metal chimneys shall be constructed to meet the requirements of Section 814.

SECTION 813 — EXISTING MASONRY CHIMNEYS FOR GAS VENTING

813.1 Design. Masonry chimneys shall be designed, anchored, supported and reinforced as required in Chapters 16, 18 and 31 of the Building Code.

813.2 Gas Venting into Existing Masonry Chimneys. Existing lined masonry chimneys and unlined chimneys with not more than one side exposed to the outside may be used to vent gas appliances, provided:

1. An approved liner shall be installed in an existing unlined masonry chimney when deemed necessary by the building official considering local problems of vent gas condensate.

2. The effective cross-sectional area is not more than four times the cross-sectional area of the vent and chimney connectors entering the chimney.

3. The effective area of the chimney when connected to more than one appliance shall not be less than the area of the largest vent

or chimney connector plus 50 percent of the area of the additional vent or chimney connectors.

4. Automatically controlled gas appliances connected to a chimney which also serves equipment burning liquid fuel shall be equipped with an automatic pilot. A gas appliance vent connector and a chimney connector from an appliance burning liquid fuel may be connected into the same chimney through separate openings, provided the gas appliance is vented above the liquid fuel-burning appliance, or both may be connected through a single opening if joined by a suitable fitting located at the chimney.

5. The chimney passageway shall be examined to ascertain that it is clear and free of obstructions and shall be cleaned if previously used for venting solid- or liquid-fuel-burning appliances.

6. The vent or chimney connector shall enter the chimney at least 6 inches (152 mm) from the bottom of the chimney. The chimney shall be provided with a cleanout. If 6 inches (152 mm) are not available, a cleanout shall be provided by installing a capped tee in the vent connector next to the chimney.

Unlined chimneys with more than one side exposed to the outside shall be lined with an approved liner unless otherwise approved by the building official.

When inspection reveals that an existing chimney is not safe for the intended application, it shall be rebuilt to conform to chimney standards of the Building Code or replaced with an approved gas vent or factory-built chimney complying with Section 812.1.

SECTION 814 — UNLISTED SMOKESTACKS

814.1 Prohibited Use.

814.1.1 Limitations. Unlisted single-wall metal chimneys (smokestacks) shall not be installed within a dwelling unit of a Group R Occupancy.

814.1.2 Location. Metal chimneys shall not be carried up inside ventilating ducts unless such ducts are constructed and installed as required by this code for chimneys and are used solely for exhaust of air from the room or space in which the appliances served by the metal chimneys are located.

814.1.3 Design. Metal chimneys shall have a minimum thickness of 0.127 inch (3.23 mm) (No. 10 manufacturer's standard gage) steel and shall be designed and constructed as specified in this chapter and Chapters 16 and 22 of the Building Code.

814.1.4 Construction. Unlisted metal chimneys shall be riveted or welded and, unless structurally self-supporting, shall be guyed securely or firmly anchored to or otherwise supported by the building or structure served thereby. All joints shall be liquid tight or of such a design that liquid will drain to the interior of the chimney.

814.1.5 Lining. Metal chimneys shall be lined as required by Table 8-D.

814.1.6 Termination. Metal chimneys shall terminate as required by Table 8-D.

814.1.7 Clearance. Clearance from combustible construction shall be in accordance with Table 8-D and the applicable requirements for each classification of chimney as required by this chapter.

When a metal chimney passes through a ceiling or roof constructed of combustible materials, it shall be protected by an approved ventilating thimble extending not less than 9 inches (229 mm) below and 9 inches (229 mm) above the ceiling or roof con-

struction. Thimbles shall be of a size to provide a clearance on all sides of the chimney at least 18 inches (457 mm), except that for chimneys of low-heat appliances the clearance may be reduced to at least 6 inches (152 mm).

814.1.8 Support. Metal chimneys shall be supported on properly designed foundations of masonry or reinforced concrete or on noncombustible material having a fire-resistance rating of not less than three hours, provided such supports are independent of the building construction and the load is transferred to the ground.

814.1.9 Enclosure required for interior chimneys. Metal chimneys or parts thereof in a building exceeding one story in height shall be enclosed above the story in which the appliance served is located, in walls of noncombustible construction having a fire-resistive rating of not less than one hour if the building is less than four stories in height, and not less than two hours if the building is four stories or more in height, with a space on all sides between the chimney and the enclosing walls sufficient to render the entire chimney accessible for examination and repair. The enclosing walls shall be without openings.

> **EXCEPTION:** Doorways equipped with a fire assembly having a one-hour fire-resistive rating may be permitted at each floor level for inspection purposes.

814.2 Metal Chimneys for Building Heating and Industrial-type Low-heat Appliances. When a metal chimney used for building heating and industrial-type low-heat appliances is located in the same story of a building as that in which the appliances connected thereto are located, it shall have a clearance of not less than 18 inches (457 mm) from any combustible material. Interior metal chimneys over 18 inches (457 mm) in diameter shall have a clearance of not less than 4 inches (102 mm); those less than 18 inches (457 mm) in diameter shall have a clearance of at least 2 inches (51 mm) from noncombustible construction.

814.2.1 Roof penetration. When a metal chimney serving only building heating and industrial-type or low-heat appliances passes through a roof constructed of combustible material, the roof shall be guarded by a ventilating thimble of galvanized steel or approved corrosion-resistant metal extending at least 9 inches (229 mm) below and 9 inches (229 mm) above the roof construction, and of a size to provide not less than 6-inch (152 mm) clearance on all sides of the chimney; or the combustible material in the roof construction shall be cut away so as to provide not less than 18-inch (457 mm) clearance on all sides of the chimney, with any material used to close up such opening entirely noncombustible.

814.3 Metal Chimneys for Medium-heat Appliances. Metal chimneys for medium-heat appliances and producing flue gases having a temperature above 1,000°F (538°C), measured at the entrance to the chimney, shall be lined with medium-duty firebrick which is in accordance with recognized standards listed in Part III of Chapter 16 of this code, or the equivalent, laid in fireclay mortar. The lining shall be at least $2^1/_2$ inches (64 mm) thick for chimneys having a diameter or greatest cross-section dimension of 18 inches (457 mm) or less and shall have a thickness of not less than $4^1/_2$ inches (114 mm) laid on a $4^1/_2$-inch (114 mm) bed for chimneys having a diameter or greatest cross-section dimension greater than 18 inches (457 mm). The lining shall start 2 feet (610 mm) or more below the lowest chimney connector entrance and shall extend to a height of at least 25 feet (7620 mm) above the highest chimney connector entrance.

814.3.1 Roof penetration. When a metal chimney serving a medium-heat appliance passes through a roof constructed of combustible material, the roof shall be guarded by a ventilating thimble of galvanized iron or approved corrosion-resistant metal extending not less than 9 inches (229 mm) below and 9 inches (229 mm) above the roof construction and of a size to provide not less than 18-inch (457 mm) clearance on all sides of the chimney.

814.3.2 Clearances. When a metal chimney used for medium-heat appliances is located in the same story of a building as that in which the appliances connected are located, it shall have a clearance of not less than 36 inches (914 mm) from any combustible material. Such interior metal chimneys over 18 inches (457 mm) in diameter shall have a clearance of not less than 4 inches (102 mm), and those 18 inches (457 mm) or less in diameter a clearance of not less than 2 inches (51 mm) from noncombustible construction.

814.4 Metal Chimneys for High-heat Appliances. Metal chimneys for high-heat appliances shall be lined with high-duty firebrick as specified in recognized standards listed in Part III of Chapter 16 of this code, or the equivalent, not less than $4^1/_2$ inches (114 mm) thick laid on the $4^1/_2$-inch (114 mm) bed in refractory mortar as specified in recognized standards listed in Part III of Chapter 35 of the Building Code, or the equivalent. The lining shall start 2 feet (610 mm) or more below the lowest chimney connector entrance and shall extend to a height of at least 25 feet (7620 mm) above the highest chimney connector entrance. Chimneys terminating 25 feet (7620 mm) or less above a chimney connector entrance shall be lined to the top.

814.5 Metal Chimneys for Residential-type Incinerators. Galvanized steel pipe not less than 0.129-inch (3.2 mm) (No. 10 galvanized-sheet gage number) or other equivalent noncombustible, fire- and corrosion-resistant material may be used for residential-type incinerators installed in locations such as open sheds, breezeways or carports, provided the pipe is exposed and readily examinable for its full length and clearance not less than 18 inches (457 mm) is maintained from combustible material. The pipe shall extend at least 3 feet (914 mm) above the highest point where it passes by or through a roof and at least 2 feet (610 mm) higher than any portion of a building within 10 feet (3048 mm). If the pipe passes through a roof constructed of combustible material, it shall be guarded by a ventilating thimble of galvanized sheet steel or approved corrosion-resistant noncombustible material extending not less than 9 inches (229 mm) below and 9 inches (229 mm) above the roof construction and of a size to provide not less than 6-inch (152 mm) clearance on all sides of the pipe; or the combustible material in the roof construction shall be cut away so as to provide not less than 18-inch (457 mm) clearance on all sides of the pipe, with any material used to close up such opening entirely noncombustible.

814.6 Commercial and Industrial-type Incinerators. Metal chimneys for commercial and industrial-type incinerators shall be lined with medium-duty firebrick as specified in recognized standards listed in Part III of Chapter 35 of the Building Code, or the equivalent, not less than $4^1/_2$ inches (114 mm) thick laid on the $4^1/_2$-inch (114 mm) bed in refractory mortar, medium duty as specified in recognized standards listed in Part III of Chapter 16 of this code, or the equivalent. The lining shall start at the base of the chimney and extend continuously to the top.

814.6.1 Termination. Metal chimneys of commercial and industrial-type incinerators shall extend at least 3 feet (914 mm) above roofs measured from the highest point at which the metal chimney passes through the roof. In any case, the chimney shall extend at least 10 feet (3048 mm) higher than any portion of a building within 25 feet (7620 mm).

814.6.2 Clearances. Metal chimneys for commercial and industrial incinerators shall be installed to provide clearances as specified in Section 814.3.2.

814.7 Spark Arrestors. Chimneys serving incinerators shall terminate in a substantially constructed spark arrestor having an area not less than four times the net free area of the chimney it serves. Openings shall not permit the passage of a sphere having a diameter larger than $1/_2$ inch (13 mm) nor block the passage of a sphere having a diameter less than $3/_8$ inch (9.5 mm). Spark arrestors shall be adequately supported and secured.

814.8 Enclosures. Metal chimneys serving flue-fed, chute-fed, commercial or industrial-type incinerators, extending through any story of a building above that in which the incinerator is located, shall be enclosed in the upper stories within a continuous enclosure constructed of materials which are not combustible, such as masonry. The enclosure shall extend from the ceiling of the incinerator room to or through the roof so as to retain the integrity of the fire separations as required by applicable Building Code provisions. The enclosure shall have a fire-resistance rating of not less than one hour if the building is less than four stories in height, and not less than two hours if the building is four or more stories in height. All openings into the enclosing walls shall be protected with a self-closing fire assembly having a fire-resistive rating of not less than one and one-half hours.

SECTION 815 — CONNECTORS

815.1 General. Connectors shall be used to connect fuel-burning appliances to a vertical chimney or vent unless the chimney or vent is attached directly to the appliance. Such connectors shall be installed within the space or area in which the appliance is located and shall be connected to a chimney or vent in such a manner as to maintain the clearance to combustibles as required in Table 3-C. Chimney connectors shall be attached to factory-built chimneys as required by the listing and the manufacturer's installation instructions.

> **EXCEPTION:** Listed appliances with integral venting systems such as direct-vent appliances need not comply.

815.1.1 Using power exhauster. Connectors serving gravity-vent-type appliances shall not be connected to a venting system served by a power exhauster unless the connection is made on the negative pressure side of the power exhauster.

815.1.2 Configuration. Connectors shall be as short and straight as possible.

815.1.3 Proximity. An appliance shall be located as close as practical to the venting system.

815.1.4 Concealment. Connectors shall not be concealed by building construction. Connectors made of Type B or Type L materials may be enclosed following inspection, provided the installation meets the provisions of Section 815.2.

815.1.5 Penetrations. Connectors shall not pass through an area or occupancy separation. Connectors may pass through other walls or partitions in accordance with the provisions of Section 815.10.

815.1.6 Single-wall connectors. Single-wall metal pipe used as a connector shall not originate in an unoccupied attic or concealed space and shall not pass through an attic, inside wall or concealed space.

815.1.7 Passage through cold areas. When the connector used for a gas appliance having a draft hood must be located within or pass a crawl space or other cold area, that portion of the connector shall be listed Type B or Type L vent material or be provided with equivalent means of insulation.

815.1.8 Minimize flow resistance. Connectors shall be installed so as to avoid sharp turns or other construction features which would create excessive resistance to the flow of flue gases. Devices which will obstruct the free flow of flue gases shall not be installed in a connector. This provision shall not be construed to prohibit the use of devices specifically listed or approved for installation in a connector, such as heat reclaimers, draft regulators and safety controls.

815.1.9 Support and fasteners. Connectors shall be securely supported and joints fastened with sheet metal screws, rivets or other approved means. At the point of connection of the single-wall connector to the double-wall gas vent, three sheet metal screws or rivets may be used as an approved means.

Connectors shall be adequately supported for the design and weight of the materials employed to maintain proper clearances, to prevent physical damage and to prevent separation of the joints.

815.1.10 Automatically operated dampers. Automatically operated dampers shall be listed and installed in accordance with the terms of the listing and arranged to prevent the initiation or increase of firing unless the damper is opened to a safe position.

815.1.11 Manually operated dampers. Manually operated dampers shall not be placed in connectors of stoker-fired, liquid- or gas-burning appliances. Fixed baffles on the appliance side of draft hoods and draft regulators shall not be classified as dampers.

815.2 Chimney Connector Materials. Chimney connectors shall be constructed of single-wall metal conforming with Sections 815.2.1 and 815.3, of Type L vent material or of other materials approved for the use intended. Chimney connectors used for listed gas appliances with draft hoods may be installed in accordance with the provisions of Section 816.

815.2.1 Residential and low-heat appliances. If serving residential building-heating appliances and low-heat appliances, chimney connectors made of single-wall steel pipe shall be of at least the thickness indicated.

MINIMUM DIAMETER OF CONNECTOR (inches)	THICKNESS (inches)	(GALVANIZED SHEET GAGE NO.)
	× 25.4 for mm	
5 or less	0.016	(28)
Over 5 to 9	0.019	(26)
Over 9 to 12	0.030	(22)
Over 12 to 16	0.036	(20)
Over 16	0.058	(16)

815.2.2 Breeching for medium- and high-heat appliances. Breeching for medium-heat and high-heat appliances shall be fabricated of black hot-rolled steel with welded seams and shall be of at least the following thickness:

DIAMETER OF CONNECTOR (inches)	MINIMUM THICKNESS (inches)	(MANUFACTURER'S STANDARD GAGE NO.)
	× 25.4 for mm	
12 or less	0.044	(18)
Over 12 to 24	0.055	(16)
Over 24 to 36	0.068	(14)
Over 36 to 60	0.097	(12)
Over 60	0.127	(10)

815.2.3 Joints in breechings. End joints of breechings may be welded, lapped, bolted or made with companion end flanges. Long breechings shall be provided with expansion joints.

815.3 Medium-heat Appliances and Industrial Incinerators. Metal connectors for medium-heat appliances and industrial incinerators shall be lined with firebrick not less than $2^1/_2$ inches (64 mm) thick when the appliance flue collar is not larger than 18 inches in diameter or greatest dimension, and $4^1/_2$ inches (114 mm) thick when the flue collar is larger than 18 inches (457 mm) in diameter. Firebrick shall be laid in fireclay, such connectors shall maintain a free area equal in size to the flue collar.

815.4 High-heat Appliances. Metal connectors for high-heat appliances shall be lined with high-duty firebrick having a thickness of at least $4^1/_2$ inches (114 mm) laid on the $4^1/_2$-inch (114 mm) bed in fireclay mortar.

815.5 Installation.

815.5.1 Sizing. The connector, for its entire length, shall not be smaller than the flue collar of the appliance unless otherwise recommended by the appliance, chimney or vent manufacturer.

815.5.2 Joining two chimney connectors. Two or more chimney connectors shall not be joined unless the common connector, the manifold and the chimney are sized properly to serve the appliances connected thereto and adequate draft is available to remove all products of combustion to the outdoors.

815.6 Clearance. Single-wall metal connectors shall be installed with clearance to combustibles as set forth in Table 3-C.

815.7 Draft Regulators. A draft regulator shall be installed in the connector serving a liquid-fuel-burning appliance unless the appliance is approved for use without a draft regulator.

815.7.1 On gas-fired incinerators. A draft regulator may be installed in the connector serving a listed gas incinerator when recommended by the incinerator manufacturer. Draft regulators shall be installed in accordance with the installation instructions accompanying the incinerator.

815.7.2 Same room or enclosure. A draft regulator when used, shall be installed in the same room or enclosure as the appliance in such a manner that no difference in pressure between air in the vicinity of the regulator and the combustion air will be permitted.

815.8 Pitch. Chimney connectors shall have a rise of not less than $1/_4$ unit vertical in 12 units horizontal (2% slope).

815.9 Entering Masonry Chimneys. A connector entering a masonry chimney shall extend through the wall to the inner face of the liner, but not beyond, and shall be firmly cemented to masonry. A thimble may be used to facilitate removal of the connector for cleaning, in which case the thimble shall be permanently cemented in place with high-temperature cement. The chimney connector shall enter the chimney not less than 6 inches (152 mm) from the bottom of the chimney. The chimney shall be provided with a cleanout. If 6 inches (152 mm) are not available, a cleanout shall be provided by installing a capped tee in the connector next to the chimney.

815.10 Passage through Walls or Partitions. The connector of a medium- or high-heat appliance as classified in Table 8-A shall not pass through any wall or partition constructed of combustible material.

Connectors for listed gas appliances with draft hoods, except incinerators and oil appliances listed for Type L vents, may pass through walls or partitions constructed of combustible materials if:

1. Made of Type B or Type L material and installed with at least the listed clearances to combustible material.

2. Made of single-wall metal pipe and guarded by a ventilated thimble at least 4 inches (102 mm) larger in diameter than the vent connector.

815.10.1 Residential appliances. Connectors for residential-type appliances may pass through walls or partitions constructed of combustible materials to reach a masonry chimney if:

1. The connector is listed for wall pass through and installed according to the listing.

2. The connector is put through a device listed for wall pass through.

3. The connector is 10 inches (254 mm) or less in diameter and is installed according to one of the methods specified in Table 8-E. Concealed metal parts of the pass-through system in contact with flue gases shall be of stainless steel or equivalent material that resists corrosion, softening or cracking up to 1,800°F (982°C).

815.10.2 Alternate protection. In lieu of thimbles or other wall pass-through systems, combustible material in the wall or partition shall be cut away from the connector a sufficient distance to provide the clearance required from the connector. A material used to close up the openings shall be noncombustible material conforming to part 1 of the definition for "noncombustible" in Section 216.

815.11 Length. A connector shall be as short and straight as possible. The appliance shall be located as close as practicable to the chimney. The horizontal run of an uninsulated connector to a natural draft chimney shall not be more than 75 percent of the height of the vertical portion of the chimney above the connector, unless part of an engineered system.

The horizontal run of an insulated connector to a natural draft chimney serving a single fuel-fired appliance shall not be more than 100 percent of the height of the vertical portion of the chimney above the connector, unless part of an engineered system. The horizontal length, design and construction of combined connectors, or connectors to a manifold joining two or more appliances to a chimney, shall be determined in accordance with approved engineering methods.

815.12 Access. The entire length of a connector shall be accessible for inspection, cleaning and replacement, unless listed materials are used and approval has been obtained from the building official.

815.13 Fireplace Connection. A chimney connector shall not be connected to a chimney flue serving a fireplace unless the fireplace opening is sealed or the chimney flue which vents the fireplace is permanently sealed below the connection.

SECTION 816 — VENT CONNECTORS

816.1 Materials. Vent connectors used for gas appliances having draft hoods, for listed conversion-burner-equipped appliances having draft hoods and for other gas appliance(s) listed for use with Type B venting systems may be constructed of Type B or Type L vent material or of noncombustible corrosion-resistant material capable of withstanding the flue gas temperatures produced by the appliance, such as 0.016-inch (0.48 mm) (No. 28 galvanized sheet gage) steel, No. 26 B.&S. gage (0.40 mm) copper or No. 24 B.&S. gage (0.51 mm) aluminum.

816.2 Size. Vent connectors shall be sized in accordance with the requirements of Section 815.5.1.

816.3 Clearance. Single-wall metal vent connectors, where permitted to be used by Section 802, shall be provided with clearances from combustible material of not less than that set forth in Table 3-C.

> **EXCEPTION:** A lesser clearance is acceptable if protection is provided according to the requirements of Tables 3-A and 3-B of Chapter 3 of this code.

816.4 Length. The maximum permissible length of a vent connector shall be in accordance with Section 815.11.

816.5 Pitch. Vent connectors shall be installed without any downward pitch from the appliance and without any dips or sags.

Vent connectors shall be pitched upwards from the appliance at least $1/4$ unit vertical in 12 units horizontal (2% slope).

816.6 Access. The entire length of vent connectors shall be accessible for inspection, cleaning and replacement, unless listed materials are used and approval has been obtained from the building official.

816.7 Limited Passage through Walls or Partitions. The passage of vent connectors through walls or partitions shall be limited to the conditions specified in Section 815.10.

816.8 Two or More Appliances Connected to a Single Vent. Two or more vent connectors shall not be joined unless the common connector, the manifold and the vent are sized properly to serve the appliances connected thereto and adequate draft is available to remove all products of combustion to the outdoors.

Each vent connector of a multiple venting system shall have the greatest possible rise consistent with the headroom available between the draft hood outlet or the flue collar and the point of interconnection to a manifold or to a common vent.

SECTION 817 — MECHANICAL DRAFT SYSTEMS

817.1 Forced- or Induced-Draft Systems. Appliances, except incinerators, requiring venting also may be vented by means of mechanical draft systems of either forced- or induced-draft design.

817.2 Positive-pressure Systems. Forced draft systems and all portions of induced draft systems under positive static pressure during operation shall be designed and installed so as to be gastight or as to prevent leakage of combustion products into a building.

817.3 Interconnected Systems. Vent connectors serving gas appliances vented by natural draft shall not be connected into any portion of a mechanical draft system operating under positive pressure.

817.4 Interlock Controls. When a forced-draft or induced-draft system is employed, provision shall be made to prevent the flow of gas to the main burner when the draft system is not performing so as to satisfy the operating requirements of the appliance for safe performance.

817.5 Exit Terminals. The exit terminals of forced-draft and induced-draft systems shall be located not less than 12 inches (305 mm) from any opening through which combustion products could enter the building, nor less than 2 feet (610 mm) from an adjoining building, and not less than 7 feet (2134 mm) above grade when located adjacent to public walkways.

SECTION 818 — VENTING THROUGH VENTILATING HOODS AND EXHAUST SYSTEMS

818.1 Commercial Applications. Ventilating hoods and exhaust systems may be used to vent gas-burning appliances installed in commercial applications.

818.2 Dampers. When automatically operated appliances such as water heaters are vented through natural draft ventilating hoods, dampers shall not be installed in the ventilating system. When the ventilating hood or exhaust system is equipped with power means of exhaust, the appliance control system shall be interlocked so as to permit appliance operation only when the power means of exhaust is in operation.

TABLE 8-A
TABLE 8-B

1997 UNIFORM MECHANICAL CODE

TABLE 8-A—VENT TERMINATION ABOVE ROOF

ROOF SLOPE	MINIMUM HEIGHT FROM ROOF TO LOWEST DISCHARGE OPENING	
	feet-inches	mm
Flat to 6/12	1-0	305
Over 6/12 to 7/12	1-3	406
Over 7/12 to 8/12	1-6	457
Over 8/12 to 9/12	2-0	610
Over 9/12 to 10/12	2-6	762
Over 10/12 to 11/12	3-3	991
Over 11/12 to 12/12	4-0	1219
Over 12/12 to 14/12	5-0	1524
Over 14/12 to 16/12	6-0	1829
Over 16/12 to 18/12	7-0	2134
Over 18/12 to 20/12	7-6	2286
Over 20/12 to 21/12	8-0	2438

TABLE 8-B—CHIMNEY SELECTION CHART

CHIMNEYS FOR RESIDENTIAL APPLIANCES	CHIMNEYS FOR LOW-HEAT APPLIANCES		CHIMNEYS FOR MEDIUM-HEAT APPLIANCES	CHIMNEYS FOR HIGH-HEAT APPLIANCES
	Building-Heating Appliances	Industrial-Type Low-Heat Appliances		
1. Factory-built (residential) 2. Masonry (residential) 3. Metal (residential)	1. Factory-built (low-heat type) 2. Masonry (low-heat type) 3. Metal (smokestack)	1. Factory-built (industrial low-heat type) 2. Masonry (low-heat type) 3. Metal (smokestack)	1. Factory-built (medium-heat type) 2. Masonry (medium-heat type) 3. Metal (smokestack)	1. Masonry (high-heat type) 2. Metal (smokestack)

TYPES OF APPLIANCES TO BE USED WITH EACH TYPE CHIMNEY

Column I	Column II	Column III	Column IV	Column V
A. Residential-type appliances, such as: 1. Ranges 2. Warm-air furnaces 3. Water heaters 4. Hot-water-heating boilers 5. Low-pressure steam-heating boilers [not over 15 psig (103.4 kPa)] 6. Domestic incinerators 7. Floor furnaces 8. Wall furnaces 9. Room heaters 10. Fireplace stoves 11. Closed-combustion-type solid-fuel-burning stoves or room heaters.[1] B. Fireplaces	A. All appliances shown in Column I B. Nonresidential-type building-heating appliances for heating a total volume of space exceeding 25,000 cubic feet (707.75 m³) C. Steam boilers operating at not over 1,000°F (538°C) flue gas temperature; pressing machine boilers	All appliances shown in Columns I and II, and appliances such as: 1. Annealing baths for hard glass (fats, paraffin, salts or metals) 2. Bake ovens (in bakeries) 3. Boiling vats, for wood fibre, straw, lignin, etc. 4. Candy furnaces 5. Coffee roasting ovens 6. Core ovens 7. Cruller furnaces 8. Feed drying ovens 9. Fertilizer drying ovens 10. Fireplaces, other than residential type 11. Forge furnaces (solid fuel) 12. Gypsum kilns 13. Hardening furnaces (below dark red) 14. Hot-air engine furnaces 15. Ladle-drying furnaces 16. Lead-melting furnaces 17. Nickel plate (drying) furnaces 18. Paraffin furnaces 19. Recuperative furnaces (spent materials) 20. Rendering furnaces 21. Restaurant-type cooking appliances using solid or liquid fuel 22. Rosin-melting furnaces 23. Stereotype furnaces 24. Sulphur furnaces 25. Tripoli kilns (clay, coke and gypsum) 26. Type foundry furnaces 27. Wood-drying furnaces 28. Wood-impregnating furnaces 29. Zinc-amalgamating furnaces	All appliances shown in Columns I, II and III, and appliances such as: 1. Alabaster gypsum kilns 2. Annealing furnaces (glass or metal) 3. Charcoal furnaces 4. Cold stirring furnaces 5. Feed driers (direct-fire-heated) 6. Fertilizer driers (direct-fire-heated) 7. Galvanizing furnaces 8. Gas producers 9. Hardening furnaces (cherry to pale red) 10. Incinerators, commercial and industrial-type 11. Lehrs and glory holes 12. Lime kilns 13. Linseed-oil-boiling furnaces 14. Porcelain biscuit kilns 15. Pulp driers (direct-fire-heated) 16. Steam boilers operating at over 1,000°F (538°C) flue gas temperature 17. Water-glass kiln 18. Wood-distilling furnaces 19. Wood-gas retorts	All appliances shown in Columns I, II, III and IV, and appliances such as: 1. Bessemer retorts 2. Billet and bloom furnaces 3. Blast furnaces 4. Bone calcining furnaces 5. Brass furnaces 6. Carbon point furnaces 7. Cement brick and tile kilns 8. Ceramic kilns 9. Coal and water gas retorts 10. Cupolas 11. Earthenware kilns 12. Glass blow furnaces 13. Glass furnaces (smelting) 14. Glass kilns 15. Open hearth furnaces 16. Ore-roasting furnaces 17. Porcelain-baking and glazing kilns 18. Pot-arches 19. Puddling furnaces 20. Regenerative furnaces 21. Reverberatory furnaces 22. Stacks, carburetor or superheating furnaces (in water-gas works) 23. Vitreous enameling oven (ferrous metals) 24. Wood-carbonizing furnaces

[1]When this appliance is vented with a factory-built chimney, the chimney must be a listed Type HT chimney.

TABLE 8-C—VENT SELECTION CHART

COLUMN I TYPE B, GAS Round or Oval	COLUMN II TYPE BW GAS	COLUMN III TYPE L	COLUMN IV PLASTIC PIPE
All listed gas appliances with draft hoods such as: 1. Central furnaces 2. Floor furnaces 3. Heating boilers 4. Ranges and ovens 5. Recessed wall furnaces (above wall section) 6. Room and unit heaters 7. Water heaters	1. Gas-burning wall heaters listed for use with Type BW vents	1. Oil-burning appliances listed for use with Type L vents 2. Gas appliances as shown in first column	1. Condensing appliances listed for use with a specific plastic pipe recommended and identified in the manufacturer's installation instructions

TABLE 8-D—CONSTRUCTION, CLEARANCE AND TERMINATION REQUIREMENTS FOR UNLISTED SINGLE-WALL METAL CHIMNEYS

CHIMNEYS SERVING $0.556 \times (t_{°F} - 32)$ for °C	MINIMUM THICKNESS × 25.4 for mm		TERMINATION × 304.8 for mm				CLEARANCE × 25.4 for mm			
				Above Any Part of Building Within			Combustible Construction		Noncombustible Construction	
	Wall	Lining	Above Roof Opening	10'	25'	50'	Interior Inst.	Exterior Inst.	Interior Inst.	Exterior Inst.
Building-heating and industrial-type low-heat appliances (1,000°F operating-1,400°F temp. maximum)[1]	0.127" (Mfrs. Std. 10 ga.)	None	3'	2'			18"	6"	Up to 18" diameter, 2" Over 18" diameter, 4"	
Medium-heat industrial-type appliances (2,000°F maximum)[1,3]	0.127" (Mfrs. Std. 10 ga.)	Up to 18" dia.—2½" Over 18" 4½" on 4½" bed	10'		10'		36"	24"		
High-heat industrial-type appliances (over 2,000°F)[1,2]	0.127" (Mfrs. Std. 10 ga.)	4½" laid on 4½" bed	20'			20'	See Footnote 4			
Residential-type incinerator[4]	0.127" (Mfrs. Std. 10 ga.)	None	3'	2'			Not permitted	18"	Not permitted	4"
Chute-fed, flue-fed commercial or industrial-type incinerators[2,5]	0.127" (Mfrs. Std. 10 ga.)	4½" laid on 4½" bed	3' above sloping roof or 8' above flat roof		10'		36"	24"	Up to 18" diameter, 2" Over 18" diameter, 4"	

[1]See Table 8-B for types of appliances to be used with each type of chimney.

[2]Lining shall extend from bottom to top of chimney.

[3]Lining shall extend from 24 inches (610 mm) below connector to 24 feet (7315 mm) above.

[4]Clearance shall be as specified by the design engineer and shall have sufficient clearance from buildings and structures to avoid overheating combustible materials [maximum 160°F (71°C)].

[5]Spark arrestors shall be provided in accordance with Section 814.7.

TABLE 8-E   **1997 UNIFORM MECHANICAL CODE**

TABLE 8-E—CHIMNEY CONNECTOR SYSTEMS AND CLEARANCES FROM ROOM WALL COMBUSTIBLES FOR RESIDENTIAL HEATING APPLIANCES

System A [12-inch (305 mm) clearance]	A $3^1/_2$-inch-thick (89 mm) brick wall may be framed into the combustible wall. A $^5/_8$-inch-thick (16 mm) fire clay liner must be firmly cemented in the center of the brick wall maintaining a 12-inch clearance to combustibles. The clay liner must run from the outer surface of the bricks to the inner surface of the chimney liner, but it shall not protrude into the chimney liner.
System B [9-inch (229 mm) clearance]	A listed solid insulated factory-built chimney section [1-inch (25.4 mm) insulation] the same inside diameter as the connector may be used. Sheet metal supports cut to maintain a 9-inch (229 mm) clearance to combustibles must be fastened to the wall surface and to the chimney section. Fasteners shall not penetrate the chimney flue liner. The chimney length must be flush with the masonry chimney liner and sealed to the masonry with water-insoluble refractory cement. Chimney manufacturer's parts must be used to securely fasten the chimney connector to the chimney section.
System C [6-inch (153 mm) clearance]	A sheet metal (minimum 24 gage) ventilated thimble having two 1-inch (25 mm) air channels must be used with a sheet steel chimney connector (minimum 24 gage). Sheet steel supports (minimum 24 gage) shall be cut to maintain a 6-inch (153 mm) clearance between the thimble and combustibles. One side of the support must be fastened to the wall on all sides. Glass fiber insulation shall fill the 6-inch (153 mm) space between the thimble and the supports. The chimney section shall be secured to the support. Fasteners used shall not penetrate the liner of the chimney section.
System D [2-inch (51 mm) clearance]	A listed solid insulated factory-built chimney section [1-inch (25.4 mm) insulation] with a diameter 2 inches (51 mm) larger than the chimney connector shall be used with a sheet steel chimney connector (minimum 24 gage). Sheet metal supports shall be positioned to maintain a 2-inch (51 mm) clearance to combustibles and to hold the chimney connector to ensure that a 1-inch (25.4 mm) air space surrounds it as it passes through the chimney section. The steel support shall be fastened to the wall on all sides and the chimney section shall be fastened to the supports. Fasteners used shall not penetrate the liner of the chimney section.

Requirements for systems in Table 8-E:

1. Insulation material used as a part of a wall pass through shall be noncombustible and shall have a thermal conductivity of 1.0 Btu-in./ft.^{2}°F (1.73 W/m·K) or less.
2. All clearances and thicknesses are minimums.
3. Materials used to close up openings for the connector shall be noncombustible.
4. Connectors for all systems except System B shall extend through the wall pass-through system to the inner face of the flue liner.

Chapter 9
SPECIAL FUEL-BURNING EQUIPMENT

Part I—Factory-built and Masonry Fireplaces

SECTION 901 — VENTED DECORATIVE APPLIANCES, DECORATIVE GAS APPLIANCES FOR INSTALLATION IN SOLID-FUEL-BURNING FIREPLACES AND GAS-FIRED LOG LIGHTERS

901.1 Vented Decorative Appliances. Vented decorative appliances shall be installed in accordance with the manufacturer's installation instructions.

901.2 Decorative Gas Appliances for Installation in Solid-fuel-burning Fireplaces. In addition to the general requirements specified in Section 309, approved gas logs may be installed in solid-fuel-burning fireplaces, provided:

1. The gas log is installed in accordance with the manufacturer's installation instructions.

2. If the fireplace is equipped with a damper, it shall be permanently blocked open to a sufficient amount to prevent spillage of combustion products into the room.

3. The minimum flue passageway shall be not less than 1 square inch per 2,000 Btu/h input (1.09 mm^2/W).

4. Gas logs, when equipped with a pilot, shall have a listed safety shutoff valve.

901.3 Gas-fired Log Lighters. Approved gas-fired log lighters shall be installed in accordance with the manufacturer's installation instructions.

Part II—Incinerators

SECTION 902 — INCINERATORS, GENERAL

902.1 Scope. Incinerators for the reduction of refuse, garbage or other waste materials shall be installed in accordance with the provisions of this chapter. Materials and structural design shall meet the requirements of the Building Code.

902.2 Small Domestic-type Incinerators. Incinerators of small uninsulated domestic type installed indoors shall be constructed, mounted, installed and vented according to the applicable requirements for room heating stoves burning solid fuel and room heaters burning liquid fuel as specified in Chapters 3, 7 and 8 of this code, except that mounting shall be on a noncombustible and fire-resistive floor, and minimum clearances to combustible materials shall be 36 inches (914 mm) above, 48 inches (1219 mm) in front and 36 inches (914 mm) in back and at sides. The requirements of this section also apply to incinerators installed as a part of other appliances.

902.2.1 Listed units. Incinerators of small domestic type, or those that are a part of another appliance, which have been tested and listed by an approved agency which are listed for installation on a combustible floor or with lesser clearances may be installed in accordance with the conditions of their listing and shall be connected to a chimney complying with the requirements of Chapter 8.

EXCEPTION: Existing unlined chimneys having at least 4-inch (102 mm) nominal brick walls may be used for the venting of domestic gas-fired freestanding incinerators when such chimneys meet the other requirements of this chapter and have been approved and inspected by the building official.

902.2.2 Outdoor installations. Outdoor incinerators of small domestic type and their location on property shall be approved.

SECTION 903 — INCINERATORS USING THE FLUE AS A REFUSE CHUTE

903.1 Construction. Incinerators in which no fuel other than normal refuse, except a gas flame or similar means to accomplish ignition, is used for combustion, and in which the chute and smoke flue are identical, shall have the enclosing walls of the combustion chamber constructed of clay or shale brickwork not less than 4 inches (102 mm) thick when there is a horizontal grate area of not more than 9 square feet (0.8 m^2) and not less than 8 inches (203 mm) thick when there is a horizontal grate area exceeding 9 square feet (0.8 m^2) and, in each case, a lining of firebrick not less than 4 inches (102 mm) thick, with an air space, in the case of the thicker wall, between the clay or shale brick and the firebrick sufficient to provide for expansion and contraction.

The combined chute and flue shall be constructed as required for incinerator chimneys in Chapter 31 of the Building Code. The chute and flue shall be constructed straight and plumb, and finished smooth on the inside. All flues shall terminate in a substantially constructed spark arrestor having a mesh not exceeding $1/2$ inch (13 mm).

Firebrick shall be laid in fireclay mortar.

903.2 Service Openings. Service openings into the chute shall be equipped with approved self-closing hoppers so constructed that the openings are closed off while the hopper is being charged and no part will project into the chute or flue. The area of the service opening shall not exceed one third of the area of the chute or flue.

SECTION 904 — COMMERCIAL AND INDUSTRIAL INCINERATORS

904.1 Capacity 250 Pounds (113 kg) per Hour or Less. Commercial- and industrial-type incinerators designed to burn not more than 250 pounds (113 kg) of refuse per hour and having a horizontal grate area not exceeding 9 square feet (0.8 m^2) shall have enclosing walls of the combustion chamber constructed of clay or shale brick not less than 8 inches (203 mm) thick, with a lining of firebrick not less than 4 inches (102 mm) thick, provided that the outer 4 inches (102 mm) of clay or shale brickwork may be replaced by a steel plate casing not less than $3/16$ inch (5 mm) in thickness.

904.2 Capacity Greater than 250 Pounds (113 kg) per Hour. Commercial and industrial types of incinerators of a size designed to burn more than 250 pounds (113 kg) of refuse per hour and having a grate area exceeding 9 square feet (0.8 m^2) shall have enclosing walls of the combustion chamber constructed of clay or shale brick not less than 8 inches (203 mm) thick with a lining of firebrick not less than 8 inches (203 mm) thick, provided that the outer 4 inches (102 mm) of clay or shale brickwork may be replaced by a steel plate casing not less than $3/16$ inch (5 mm) in thickness.

904.3 Location. Incinerators with their waste material bins or containers shall be located in a room or compartment used for no other purpose, or in a room devoted exclusively to boilers and heating plants. In either case, such room shall be separated from the rest of the building by a one-hour fire-resistive occupancy separation.

904.4 Venting System. The flue connections or breechings from the combustion chamber shall be constructed of 0.055-inch-thick (1.40 mm) (No. 16 U.S. gage) steel when they do not exceed 12 inches in diameter or greater dimension and of 0.097-inch-thick (2.46 mm) (No. 12 U.S. gage) steel when they exceed 12 inches (305 mm) in diameter or greatest dimension. In addition they shall be lined with firebrick laid in fireclay mortar not less than $2^{1}/_{2}$ inches (64 mm) thick when they are between 12 inches (305 mm) and 18 inches (475 mm) in diameter or greatest dimension, and not less than $4^{1}/_{2}$ inches (114 mm) thick when they are larger. If they lead into and combine with flue connections or breechings from other appliances, such other connections or breechings shall also be lined as required for direct flue connections, unless the cross-sectional area of the connection into which they lead is at least four times the area of the incinerator connection.

904.5 Clearances. The clearance to woodwork or other combustible material or construction on all sides of flue connections or breechings shall not be less than 36 inches (914 mm), provided that clearances may be reduced as set forth in Table 3-B.

904.6 Chutes. Refuse chutes shall not feed directly to the combustion chamber but shall discharge into a room or bin enclosed and separated from the incinerator room by floors, ceilings and walls of not less than two-hour fire-resistive construction. The opening through which material is transferred from such room or bin to the incinerator room shall be equipped with a fire assembly having a three-hour fire-resistive rating.

Refuse chutes shall rest on substantial noncombustible foundations. The enclosing walls of such chutes shall consist of clay or shale brickwork not less than 8 inches (203 mm) thick or of reinforced concrete not less than 6 inches (152 mm) thick. Such chutes shall extend at least 4 feet (1219 mm) above the roof and shall be covered by a metal skylight glazed with single thick plain glass.

904.7 Service Openings. Service openings for chutes shall be located, constructed and protected as required by the Building Code. Refuse chutes require automatic sprinkler systems for protection.

SECTION 905 — OTHER TYPES OF INCINERATORS

905.1 Design. Incinerators of types other than those regulated above shall be constructed and installed in accordance with the structural requirements of the Building Code, except that special large-capacity incinerators and refuse burners used in connection with sawmills and woodworking plants and other applications shall have special approval of the building official.

Part III—Miscellaneous Heat-producing Appliances

SECTION 906 — DOMESTIC RANGE AND COOK TOP UNIT INSTALLATION

906.1 Vertical Clearance above Cooking Top. Domestic free-standing or built-in ranges shall have a vertical clearance above the cooking top of not less than 30 inches (762 mm) to unprotected combustible material. When the underside of such combustible material is protected with insulating millboard at least $1/4$ inch (6 mm) thick covered with 0.021-inch-thick (0.41mm) (No. 28 U.S. gage) or a metal ventilating hood, the distance shall not be

less than 24 inches (610 mm). For ducts serving domestic range hoods, see Section 504.

906.2 Horizontal Clearance of Built-in Top Cooking Units. The minimum horizontal distance from the center of the burner heads of a top (or surface) cooking unit to adjacent vertical combustible surfaces extending immediately above the counter top shall be at least the distance specified by the permanent marking on the unit.

906.3 Installation of a Listed Cooking Appliance or Microwave Oven above a Listed Cooking Appliance. The installation of a listed cooking appliance or microwave oven over a listed cooking appliance shall conform to the conditions of the upper appliance's listing and the manufacturers' installation instructions.

SECTION 907 — DOMESTIC OPEN-TOP BROILER UNITS AND HOODS

907.1 General. Listed open-top broiler units and hoods shall be installed in accordance with their listing and the manufacturer's installation instructions.

907.2 Hoods, Ducts and Fans. An exhaust duct and fan having a minimum capacity of 100 cfm per square foot [508 L/(s•m^2)] of hood intake area shall be installed for a barbecue unit and, when the duct penetrates a ceiling or a floor, it shall be enclosed in a fire-resistive shaft covered on one side as required for one-hour fire-resistive construction with no combustible material used inside the fire protection. The shaft shall be separated from the duct by a minimum 1-inch (25 mm) air space vented to the outside air, and the duct shall terminate not less than 18 inches (457 mm) above the roof surface. A minimum clearance of 24 inches (610 mm) shall be maintained between the cooking top and the combustible material and the hood shall be as wide as the open-top broiler and be centered over the unit.

SECTION 908 — CLOTHES DRYERS

908.1 Domestic Clothes Dryers. When a compartment or space for a domestic clothes dryer is provided, a minimum 4-inch-diameter (102 mm) moisture exhaust duct of approved material shall be installed in accordance with this section and Section 504.

908.2 Makeup Air. When a closet is designed for the installation of a clothes dryer, a minimum opening of 100 square inches (0.0645 m^2) for makeup air shall be provided in the door or by other approved means.

908.3 Commercial Clothes Dryers. The installation of commercial clothes-dryer exhaust ducts shall comply with the appliance manufacturer's installation instructions.

SECTION 909 — DIRECT GAS-FIRED MAKEUP AIR HEATERS AND INDUSTRIAL AIR HEATERS

909.1 General. Direct gas-fired makeup air heaters may be installed in commercial and industrial occupancies for heating incoming outside air for the purpose of replacing air exhausted from the space. Direct gas-fired industrial air heaters may be installed in commercial and industrial occupancies to offset building heat loss. Such equipment may be used to provide fresh air ventilation. Such equipment shall not supply an occupancy containing sleeping quarters.

909.2 Relief Openings. The design of the installation shall include adequate provision to permit the equipment to operate at rated capacity by taking into account the structure's designed infiltration rate, providing properly designed relief openings, or an interlocked power exhaust system, or a combination of these methods.

Relief openings may be louvers or counterbalanced gravity dampers or, if motorized dampers, shall be interlocked so as not to permit equipment blower and main burner operation until the motorized dampers are proved in the open position.

909.3 Clearance. Such equipment shall be installed so as not to raise the temperature of surrounding combustible material more than 90°F (50°C) above ambient.

SECTION 910 — SMALL CERAMIC KILNS

910.1 General. The provisions of this section apply to kilns used for ceramics that have a maximum interior volume of 20 cubic feet (0.56 m^3) and are used for hobby or noncommercial purposes.

910.2 Installation. Kilns shall be installed in accordance with the manufacturer's instructions and the provisions of this code.

910.3 Installations inside Buildings. In addition to other requirements specified in this section, interior installation shall meet the following requirements:

910.3.1 Clearances for interior installation. The sides and tops of kilns shall be located a minimum of 18 inches (457 mm) from any noncombustible wall surface and 3 feet (914 mm) from any combustible wall surface. Kilns shall be installed on noncombustible flooring consisting of at least 2 inches (51 mm) of solid masonry or concrete extending at least 12 inches (305 mm) beyond the base or supporting members of the kiln.

> **EXCEPTION:** These clearances may be reduced, provided the kiln is installed in accordance with its listing or to acceptable conclusions of testing reports submitted to the building official.

910.3.2 Control side clearance. The clearance on the gas or electrical control side of a kiln shall not be reduced to less than 30 inches (762 mm).

910.3.3 Hood and duct clearances. Hoods and ducts serving a fuel-burning kiln shall have a clearance from combustible construction of at least 18 inches (457 mm). This clearance may be reduced in accordance with Table 3-B.

910.3.4 Exterior Installations. Kilns shall be installed with minimum clearances as specified in Section 910.3.1. Where a kiln is located under a roofed area and is partially enclosed by more than two vertical wall surfaces, hood and gravity ventilation duct shall be installed to comply with Sections 505.8.1, 505.8.2 and 910.3.3.

Chapter 10
BOILER/WATER HEATERS

**NOTE: Portions of this chapter have been moved from
Appendix B and the numbering has been revised.**

See Appendix B, Section 1501 for heating sources for hydronic panel heating systems.

Part I — Water Heaters

SECTION 1001 — SCOPE

1001.1 Applicability. Provisions of Part I apply to water heaters. In addition to the general requirements of Chapter 3, water heaters shall be installed to conform to the requirements of this part.

SECTION 1002 — GENERAL

1002.1 Potable Water System Connection. Connections to the potable water system shall conform to the requirements in the Plumbing Code.

1002.2 Water Heater Used for Space Heating. The potability of the domestic water system shall be maintained when a water heater is used as a part of a space heating system.

1002.3 Drain Valves. Drain valves for emptying shall be installed at the bottom of each tank-type water heater and hot-water storage tank.

1002.4 Combustion Air. A fuel-burning water heater shall be provided with combustion air as specified in Chapter 7.

1002.5 Venting. Fuel-burning water heaters shall be vented as specified in Chapter 8.

1002.6 Location in Garages and Warehouses. Water heaters shall be installed as specified in Section 303.1.3.

SECTION 1003 — PROHIBITED INSTALLATIONS

1003.1 Bathrooms, Bedrooms and Closets. Fuel-burning water heaters shall not be installed in bathrooms and bedrooms or in a closet with access only through a bedroom or bathroom.

> **EXCEPTIONS:** 1. Water heaters having direct vent systems.
>
> 2. Water heaters installed in a closet that has a weather-stripped solid door with an approved door closing device, and designed exclusively for the water heater and where all air for combustion and ventilation is supplied from the outdoors.
>
> 3. Water heaters of the automatic storage type installed as a replacement in a bathroom, when specifically approved, properly vented and supplied with adequate combustion air.

1003.2 Rooms Used as a Plenum. Fuel-burning water heaters shall not be installed in a room containing air-handling machinery when such room is used as a plenum.

SECTION 1004 — SAFETY DEVICES

1004.1 Relief Valve. All storage water heaters operating above atmospheric pressure shall be provided with an approved, self-closing (levered) pressure relief valve and temperature relief valve or combination thereof. The relief valve shall conform to the applicable recognized standard listed in Part III of Chapter 16.

1004.1.1 Installation. Relief valves shall be installed in the shell of the water heater tank or in the hot water outlet. Where installed in the hot water outlet, the thermo-bulb shall extend into the shell of the tank. Temperature relief valves shall be so located in the tank as to be actuated by the water in the top 6 inches (152 mm) of the tank served. For installations with separate storage tanks, the valves shall be installed on the tank and there shall not be any type of valve installed between the water heater and the storage tank. There shall not be a check valve or shutoff valve between a relief valve and the heater or tank served.

1004.2 Relief Outlet Waste. The outlet of a pressure, temperature or other relief valve shall not be directly connected to the drainage system.

1004.2.1 Discharge. The discharge shall be installed in a manner that does not cause personal injury or property damage and that is readily observable by the building occupants. The discharge from a relief valve shall not be trapped. The discharge piping shall be the same diameter as the relief valve outlet, installed so as to drain by gravity flow and shall terminate atmospherically not more than 6 inches (152 mm) above the floor. The end of the discharge pipe shall not be threaded.

1004.2.2 Location. In addition to all other requirements, if the relief outlet discharge piping is installed so that it leaves the room or enclosure in which the water heater and relief valve are located and discharges to an indirect waste receptor, there shall be an air gap installed before or at the point of leaving the room or enclosure.

1004.3 Required Pan. Where water heaters or hot water storage tanks are installed in a location where leakage of the tanks or connections will cause damage, such as in suspended ceiling spaces, furred spaces or attics, the tank or water heater shall be installed in a galvanized steel or other metal pan of equal corrosive resistance having a minimum thickness of 0.0276 inch (0.7 mm).

1004.3.1 Pan size and drain. The pan shall be no less than $1^1/_2$ inches (38 mm) deep and shall be of sufficient size and shape to receive all dripping or condensate from the tank or water heater. The pan shall be drained by an indirect waste pipe having a minimum diameter of 1 inch (25 mm) or the outlet diameter of the required relief valve, whichever is larger.

1004.3.2 Pan drain termination. The pan drain shall extend full size and terminate over a suitably located indirect waste receptor or floor drain or extend to the exterior of the building and terminate no less than 6 inches (152 mm) or more than 24 inches (610 mm) above the adjacent ground surface.

Part II — Steam and Hot-water Boilers

SECTION 1005 — PURPOSE

The purpose of this chapter is to establish and provide minimum standards for the protection of public welfare, health, safety and property by regulating and controlling the quality, location and installation of steam and hot-water boilers.

SECTION 1006 — SCOPE

The requirements of this chapter shall apply to the construction, installation, operation, repair and alteration of boilers and pressure vessels.

> **EXCEPTIONS:** 1. Listed and approved potable water heaters with a nominal capacity of 120 gallons (454 L) or less having a heat input of 200,000 Btu/h (58.58 kW) or less used for hot-water supply at pressure of 160 pounds per square inch (psi) (1103 kPa) or less and at temperatures not exceeding 210°F (99°C) as regulated by the Plumbing Code.
>
> 2. Pressure vessels used for unheated water supply, including those containing air which serves only as a cushion and is compressed by the introduction of water and tanks connected to sprinkler systems.
>
> 3. Portable unfired pressure vessels and I.C.C. containers.
>
> 4. Containers for liquefied petroleum gases, bulk oxygen and medical gas, which are regulated by the Fire Code.
>
> 5. Unfired pressure vessels in Groups B, F, H, M, R, S and U Occupancies having a volume of 5 cubic feet (0.14 m^3) or less and operated at pressures not exceeding 250 psi (1724 kPa).
>
> 6. Pressure vessels used in refrigeration systems which are regulated by Chapter 11 of this code.
>
> 7. Pressure tanks used in conjunction with coaxial cables, telephone cables, power cables, and other similar humidity-control systems.
>
> 8. Any boiler or pressure vessel subject to regular inspection by federal inspectors or licensed by federal authorities.

SECTION 1007 — WORKMANSHIP

Equipment, appurtenances, devices and piping shall be installed in a workmanlike manner in conformity with the provisions and intent of this chapter.

SECTION 1008 — PERMIT REQUIRED

Except for work exempted by Section 112.2 of this code, a permit shall be obtained from the building official prior to installation, alteration, repair or replacement of boilers and pressure vessels. Alteration of control systems on automatic boilers and the conversion of solid-fuel-fired boilers as permitted by Section 1016 shall also require a permit. See Section 112 for requirements for obtaining permits.

SECTION 1009 — DETAILED REQUIREMENTS

1009.1 Safety Requirements. The construction of boilers and pressure vessels and the installation thereof shall conform to minimum requirements for safety from structural and mechanical failure and excessive pressures, established by the building official in accordance with nationally recognized standards.

1009.2 Controls. Required electrical, mechanical, safety and operating controls shall carry approval of an approved testing agency. Electrical controls shall be of such design and construction as to be suitable for installation in the environment in which they are located.

1009.3 Gages. Steam boilers shall be provided with a pressure gage and a water level glass. All water boilers shall be provided with a pressure gage and a temperature indicator.

1009.4 Stack Dampers. Stack dampers on boilers fired with oil or solid fuel shall not close off more than 80 percent of the stack area when closed, except on automatic boilers with prepurge, automatic draft control and interlock. Operative dampers shall not be placed within any stack, flue or vent of a gas-fired boiler, except on an automatic boiler with prepurge, automatic draft control and interlock.

1009.5 Welding. Welding on pressure vessels shall be done by approved welders in conformity with nationally recognized standards. Welding shall be subject to the approval of the building official.

SECTION 1010 — EXPANSION TANKS

1010.1 General. Hot-water-heating systems shall be provided with an air-expansion tank securely fastened to the structure. Supports shall be adequate to carry twice the weight of the tank filled with water without placing any strain on connecting piping.

Hot-water-heating systems incorporating hot-water tanks or fluid-relief columns shall be so installed as to prevent freezing under normal operating conditions.

1010.2 Systems with Open Expansion Tank. Systems equipped with an open expansion tank to satisfy thermal water expansion shall be provided with an indoor overflow from the upper portion of the expansion tank in addition to an open vent. The indoor overflow shall be carried within the building to a suitable plumbing fixture or to the basement.

1010.3 Closed-type Systems. Systems of the closed type shall have an airtight tank or other suitable air cushion that will be consistent with the volume and capacity of the system and shall be suitably designed for a hydrostatic test pressure of two and one-half times the allowable working pressure of the system. Expansion tanks for systems designed to operate at or above 30 psig be constructed in accordance with nationally recognized standards approved by the building official. Provisions shall be made for draining the tank without emptying the system, except for pressurized tanks.

1010.4 Minimum Capacity of Closed-type Tank. The minimum capacity of the closed-type expansion tank may be determined from Tables 10-A and 10-B or from the following formula:

$$V_t = \frac{(0.00041t - 0.0466)V_s}{(P_a/P_f) - (P_a/P_o)}$$

WHERE:

P_a = atmospheric pressure, feet H$_2$O absolute.

P_f = fill pressure, feet H$_2$O absolute.

P_o = maximum operating pressure, feet H$_2$O absolute.

t = average operating temperature, °F.

V_s = volume of system, not including expansion tank, gallons.

V_t = minimum volume of expansion tank, gallons.

SECTION 1011 — SAFETY OR RELIEF VALVE DISCHARGE

The discharge from relief valves shall be piped to within 18 inches (457 mm) of the floor or to an open receptacle, and when the operating temperature is in excess of 212°F (100°C), shall be equipped with a splash shield or centrifugal separator. When the discharge from safety valves would result in a hazardous discharge of steam inside the boiler room, such discharge shall be extended outside the boiler room. No valve of any description shall be placed between the safety or relief valve and the boiler, nor on the discharge pipe between the safety valve and the atmosphere.

SECTION 1012 — SHUTOFF VALVES

An approved manual shutoff valve shall be installed upstream of all control devices on the main burner of a gas-fired boiler. The takeoff point for the gas supply to the pilot shall be upstream of the gas shutoff valve of the main burner and shall be valved separately. A union or other approved means of disconnect shall be provided immediately downstream of these shutoff valves.

SECTION 1013 — GAS-PRESSURE REGULATORS

An approved gas-pressure regulator shall be installed on gas-fired boilers where the gas supply pressure is higher than that at which the main burner is designed to operate. A separate approved gas-pressure regulator shall be installed to regulate the gas pressure to the pilot or pilots. A separate regulator shall not be required for the pilot or pilots on manufacturer-assembled boiler-burner units which have been approved by the building official and on gas-fired boilers in Group R Occupancies of less than six units and in Group M Occupancies.

SECTION 1014 — LOW-WATER CUTOFF

Hot-water-heating boilers, other than manually fired, shall be equipped with a low-water cutoff except that a coil-type boiler or a water-tube boiler which requires forced circulation to prevent overheating of the coils or tubes shall have a flow-sensing device installed in the outlet piping in lieu of the low-water cutoff. The required low-water cutoff or flow switch, as applicable, shall be mounted so as to prevent damage to the boiler and to permit testing of the fuel-supply cutoff without draining the heating system, except that such boilers used in Group R Occupancies of less than six dwelling units and Group U Occupancies need not be equipped with the low-water cutoff or flow switch.

SECTION 1015 — COMBUSTION REGULATORS: SAFETY VALVES

The following requirements shall be retroactive:

1. A hot-water-heating boiler, other than manually fired, shall be equipped with two temperature combustion regulators in series. Every steam-heating boiler, other than manually fired, shall be equipped with a pressure combustion regulator and a low-water cutoff. (See Section 1014.)

2. Boilers and pressure vessels shall be provided with the required number, size and capacity of safety or relief valves to ensure positive relief of overpressure in accordance with nationally recognized standards, as applicable. Valves so employed shall be constructed, sealed and installed in accordance with nationally recognized standards, as applicable.

SECTION 1016 — AUTOMATIC BOILERS

1016.1 General. Automatic boilers shall be equipped with controls and limit devices as set forth in Table 10-C. Automatic boilers shall also be equipped with the following gauges, as applicable: oil temperature, oil suction pressure, high and low gas pressure, stack temperature and windbox pressure.

1016.2 Conformity with Nationally Recognized Standards. Except as otherwise specified, gas-fired boilers exceeding 400,000 Btu/h (117 kW) input shall conform to nationally recognized standards approved by the building official.

1016.3 Solid-fuel-fired Boilers. The building official may approve solid-fuel-fired boilers that can meet the safety requirements for automatic gas- or oil-fired boilers.

SECTION 1017 — CLEARANCE FOR ACCESS

1017.1 General. When boilers are installed or replaced, clearance shall be provided to allow access for inspection, maintenance and repair. Passageways around all sides of boilers shall have an unobstructed width of not less than 18 inches (457 mm). Clearance for repair and cleaning may be provided through a door or access panel into another area, provided the opening is of sufficient size.

> **EXCEPTION:** Subject to the approval of the building official, boilers may be installed with a side clearance of less than 18 inches (457 mm), provided that the lesser clearance does not inhibit inspection, maintenance or repair.

1017.2 Over 5,000 Pounds per Hour (2268 kg/h). Power boilers having a steam-generating capacity in excess of 5,000 pounds per hour (2268 kg/h) or having a heating surface in excess of 1,000 square feet (93 m^2) or input in excess of 5,000,000 Btu/h (1465 kW) shall have a minimum clearance of 7 feet (2134 mm) from the top of the boiler to the ceiling.

1017.3 Over Five Million Btu/h (1465 kW). Steam heating boilers and hot-water-heating boilers which exceed one of the following limits: 5,000,000 Btu/h input (1465 kW); 5,000-pound-steam-per-hour (2268 kg/h) capacity or 1,000-square-foot (93 m^2) heating surface; and power boilers which do not exceed one of the following limits: 5,000,000 Btu/h input (1465 kW); 5,000-pound-steam-per-hour (2268 kg/h) capacity or 1,000-square-foot (1465 kW) heating surface; and all boilers with manholes on top of the boiler, except those described in the second and fourth paragraphs, shall have a minimum clearance of 3 feet (914 mm) from the top of the boiler to the ceiling.

1017.4 Manholes not Required. Package boilers, steam-heating boilers and hot-water-heating boilers with no manhole on top of shell and not exceeding one of the above limits shall have a minimum clearance of 2 feet (610 mm) from the ceiling.

SECTION 1018 — BOILER ROOMS AND ENCLOSURES

Boiler rooms and enclosures and access thereto shall comply with Chapter 3 of this code and the Building Code.

SECTION 1019 — MOUNTING

Equipment shall be set or mounted on a level base capable of supporting and distributing the weight contained thereon.

Boilers, tanks and equipment shall be securely anchored to the structure.

Equipment requiring vibration isolation shall be installed as designed by a registered engineer to the satisfaction of the building official.

SECTION 1020 — FLOORS

Boilers shall be mounted on floors of noncombustible construction unless listed for mounting on combustible flooring.

SECTION 1021 — CHIMNEYS OR VENTS

Boilers shall be connected to a chimney or vent as provided for other fuel-burning equipment as provided for in Chapter 8 of this code.

SECTION 1022 — DRAINAGE

For heating or hot-water-supply boiler applications, the boiler room shall be equipped with a floor drain or other means suitable for disposing of the accumulation of liquid wastes incidental to cleaning, recharging and routine maintenance.

SECTION 1023 — FUEL PIPING

Fuel piping shall conform to Chapter 13 or the standard cited in the list of recognized standards for oil tanks, piping, etc.

SECTION 1024 — AIR FOR COMBUSTION AND VENTILATION

Air for combustion and ventilation shall be provided in accordance with Chapter 7 of this code.

SECTION 1025 — OPERATING ADJUSTMENTS AND INSTRUCTIONS

Upon completion, hot-water boiler installations shall have controls set, adjusted and tested by the installing contractor. A complete control diagram of a permanent legible type, together with complete boiler operating instructions, shall be furnished by the installer for each installation.

SECTION 1026 — INSPECTIONS AND TESTS

An installation for which a permit is required shall not be put into service until it has been inspected and approved by the building official.

It shall be the duty of the owner to notify the building official that the installation is ready for inspection and test. Also, it shall be the duty of the owner to post in a conspicuous position on the installation a notice in substantially the following form: "Warning! This installation has not been inspected and approved by the building official and shall not be covered or concealed until so inspected and approved," and it shall be unlawful for anyone other than the building official to remove such notice. Test data shall be submitted to show that the installation complies with the provisions of this code. Such tests shall be made by the owner in the presence of the building official.

> **EXCEPTION:** On installations designed and supervised by a registered professional engineer, the building official may permit inspection and testing by such engineer in lieu of the above requirements.

When the owner requests inspection of a boiler prior to its installation, the building official shall make such inspection.

SECTION 1027 — OPERATING PERMIT

It shall be unlawful to operate a boiler or pressure vessel without first obtaining a valid operating permit to do so from the building official. Such permit shall be displayed in a conspicuous place adjacent to the boiler or vessel. The operating permit shall not be issued until the equipment has been inspected and approved by the building official.

> **EXCEPTION:** The operation only of steam-heating boilers, low-pressure hot-water-heating boilers, hot-water-supply boilers and pressure vessels in Group R Occupancies of less than six dwelling units and in Group U Occupancies.

SECTION 1028 — MAINTENANCE INSPECTION

The building official shall inspect boilers and pressure vessels operated under permit at appropriate intervals but not less frequently than noted below:

1. Power boilers and miniature boilers shall be inspected externally annually. Where construction and operating conditions permit, they shall, in addition, be subject to inspection internally annually.

2. Steam-heating boilers and hot-water-heating boilers shall be inspected externally annually. Where construction and operating conditions permit, they shall, in addition, be subject to inspection internally annually.

3. Automatic steam-heating boilers shall be inspected externally biennially. Where construction and operating conditions permit, they shall, in addition, be subject to inspection internally biennially.

4. Unfired pressure vessels shall be inspected externally biennially. When subject to corrosion and construction permits, they shall, in addition, be subject to inspection internally biennially.

Inspection of boilers and pressure vessels covered by insurance may be made by employees of the insuring company holding commissions from the National Board of Boiler and Pressure Vessel Inspectors, subject to approval of the building official. Approved insuring company inspectors shall make reports on prescribed forms on inspections authorized by the building official. The reports shall be filed in the building official's office. Company inspectors shall notify the building official of suspension of insurance because of dangerous conditions, new insurance in effect, and discontinuance of insurance coverage.

SECTION 1029 — OPERATION AND MAINTENANCE OF BOILERS AND PRESSURE VESSELS

Boilers and pressure vessels shall be operated and maintained in conformity with requirements for adequate protection of the public established by the building official in accordance with nationally recognized standards.

The building official shall notify the owner or authorized representative of defects or deficiencies which shall be promptly and properly corrected. If such corrections are not made, or if the operation of the boiler or pressure vessel is deemed unsafe by the building official, the permit to operate the boiler or pressure vessel may be revoked. If the operation of a boiler or pressure vessel is deemed by the building official to constitute an immediate danger, the pressure on such boiler or pressure vessel may be relieved at the owner's cost and the boiler or pressure vessel shall not thereafter be operated without approval of the building official.

TABLE 10-A—EXPANSION TANK CAPACITIES FOR GRAVITY HOT-WATER SYSTEMS
Based on two-pipe system with average operating water temperature 170°F (77°C),
using cast-iron column radiation with heat emission rate 150 Btu per hour per square foot
(3.15 W/m^2) equivalent direct radiation.

INSTALLED EQUIVALENT DIRECT RADIATION[1] (square feet)	TANK CAPACITY (gallons)
× 0.0929 for m²	× 3.785 for L
Up to 350	18
Up to 450	21
Up to 650	24
Up to 900	30
Up to 1,100	35
Up to 1,400	40
Up to 1,600	2—30
Up to 1,800	2—30
Up to 2,000	2—35
Up to 2,400	2—40

[1]For systems with more than 2,400 square feet (223 m²) of installed equivalent direct water radiation, the required capacity of the cushion tank shall be increased on the basis of 1-gallon (3.785 L) tank capacity per 33 square feet (3.07 m²) of additional equivalent direct radiation.

TABLE 10-B—EXPANSION TANK CAPACITIES FOR FORCED HOT-WATER SYSTEMS
Based on average operating water temperature 195°F (90°C), a fill pressure
12 psig (82.7 kPa), and maximum operating pressure 30 psig (207 kPa).

SYSTEM VOLUME[1] (gallons)	TANK CAPACITY (gallons)
× 3.785 for L	
100	15
200	30
300	45
400	60
500	75
1,000	150
2,000	300

[1]Includes volume water in boiler, radiation and piping, not including expansion tank.

TABLE 10-C

1997 UNIFORM MECHANICAL CODE

TABLE 10-C—CONTROLS AND LIMIT DEVICES FOR AUTOMATIC BOILERS

BOILER GROUP	FUEL	FUEL INPUT RANGE[1] (Inclusive) (× 0.293071 for W)	TYPE OF PILOT[2]	Trial for Pilot	Direct Electric Ignition	Flame Pilot	Main Burner Flame Failure[3]	ASSURED FUEL SUPPLY CONTROL[4]	ASSURED AIR SUPPLY CONTROL[5]	LOW FIRE START UP CONTROL[6]	PRE-PURGING CONTROL[7]	HOT WATER TEMPERATURE AND LOW WATER LIMIT CONTROLS[8]	STEAM PRESSURE AND LOW WATER LIMIT CONTROLS[9]	APPROVED FUEL SHUTOFF[10]	CONTROL AND LIMIT DEVICE SYSTEM DESIGN[11]
A	Gas	0-400,000 Btu/h	Any type	90	Not required	90	90	Not required	Required	Not required	Not required	Required	Required	Not required	Required
B	Gas	400,001-2,500,000 Btu/h	Interrupted or intermittent	15	15	15	2-4	Not required	Required	Not required	Not required	Required	Required	Not required	Required
C	Gas	2,500,001-5,000,000 Btu/h	Interrupted or intermittent	15	15	15	2-4	Required	Required	Required	Required	Required	Required	Required	Required
D	Gas	Over 5,000,000 Btu/h	Interrupted	15	15	15	2-4	Required	Required	Required	Required	Required	Required	Required	Required
E	Oil	0-400,000 Btu/h	Any type	Not required	90	90	90	Not required	Required	Not required	Not required	Required	Required	Not required	Required
F	Oil	400,001-1,000,000 Btu/h	Interrupted	Not required	30	30	2-4	Required	Required	Not required	Not required	Required	Required	Not required	Required
G	Oil	1,000,001-3,000,000 Btu/h	Interrupted	Not required	15	15	2-4	Required	Required	Not required	Not required	Required	Required	Not required	Required
H	Oil	Over 3,000,000 Btu/h	Interrupted	15	15	60	2-4	Required	Required	Required	Required	Required	Required	Required	Required
K	Electric	All	Not required	Not required	Not required	Not required	Not required	Not required	Not required	Not required	Not required	Required	Required	Not required	Required

[1]Fuel input shall be determined by one of the following:

1.1 The maximum burner input as shown on the burner nameplate or as otherwise identified by the manufacturer.

1.2 The nominal boiler rating, as determined by the building official, plus 25 percent.

[2]Automatic boilers shall have one flame failure device on each burner which shall prove the presence of a suitable ignition source at the point where it will reliably ignite the main burner, except that boiler Groups A, B, E, F and G which are equipped with direct electric ignition shall monitor the main burner, and all boiler groups using interrupted pilots shall monitor only the main burner after the prescribed limited trial and ignition periods. Boiler Group A equipped with continuous pilot shall accomplish 100 percent shutoff within 90 seconds upon pilot flame failure. The use of intermittent pilots in boiler Group C is limited to approved burner units.

[3]In boiler Groups B, C and D, a 90-second main burner flame failure limit may apply if continuous pilots are provided on manufacturer-assembled boiler-burner units which have been approved by an approved testing agency as complying with nationally recognized standards approved by the building official. Boiler Groups F and G equipped to reenergize their ignition system within 0.8 second after main burner flame failure will be permitted 30 seconds for Group F or 15 seconds for Group G to reestablish its main burner flame.

[4]Boiler Groups C and D shall have controls interlocked to accomplish a nonrecycling fuel shutoff upon high or low gas pressure, and boiler Groups F, G and H using steam or air for fuel atomization shall have controls interlocked to accomplish a nonrecycling fuel shutoff upon low atomizing steam or air pressure. Boiler Groups F, G and H equipped with a preheated oil system shall have controls interlocked to provide fuel shutoff upon low oil temperature.

[5]Automatic boilers shall have controls interlocked to shut off the fuel supply in the event of draft failure if forced or induced draft fans are used or, in the event of low combustion airflow, if a gas power burner is used. Where a single motor directly driving both the fan and the oil pump is used, a separate control is not required.

[6]Boiler Groups C, D and H, when firing in excess of 400,000 Btu (117 kW) per combustion chamber, shall be provided with low fire start of its main burner system to permit smooth light-off. This will normally be a rate of approximately one third of its maximum firing rate.

[7]Boiler Groups C, D and H shall not permit pilot or main burner trial for ignition operation before a purging operation of sufficient duration to permit a minimum of four complete air changes through the furnace, including combustion chamber and the boiler passes. Where this is not readily determinable, five complete air changes of the furnace, including combustion chamber up to the first pass, will be considered equivalent. An atmospheric gas burner with no mechanical means of creating air movement or an oil burner which obtains two thirds or more of the air required for combustion without mechanical means of creating air movement shall not require purge by means of four air changes so long as its secondary air openings are not provided with means of closing. If such burners have means of closing secondary air openings, a time delay must be provided which puts these closures in a normally open position for four minutes before an attempt for ignition. An installation with a trapped combustion chamber shall in every case be provided with a mechanical means of creating air movement for purging.

[8]Every automatic hot-water-heating boiler, low-pressure hot-water-heating boiler, and power hot-water boiler shall be equipped with two high-temperature limit controls with a manual reset on the control with the higher setting interlocked to shut off the main fuel supply, except that manual reset on the high-temperature limit control shall not be required on any automatic package boiler not exceeding 400,000 Btu/h (117 kW) input and which has been approved by an approved testing agency. Every automatic hot-water heating, power boiler and package hot-water supply boiler shall be equipped with one low-water-level limit control with a manual reset interlocked to shut off the fuel supply so installed as to prevent damage to the boiler and to permit testing of the control without draining the heating system except on boilers used in Group R Occupancies of less than six units and in Group M Occupancies and further, except that the low-water-level limit control is not required on package hot-water-supply boilers approved by a nationally recognized testing agency. However, a low-water-flow limit control installed in the circulating water line may be used instead of the low-water-level limit control for the same purpose on coil-type boilers.

[9]Every automatic low-pressure steam-heating boiler, small power boiler and power steam boiler shall be equipped with two high-steam pressure limit controls interlocked to shut off the fuel supply to the main burner with manual reset on the control with the higher setting and two low-water-level limit controls, one of which shall be provided with a manual reset device and independent of the feed water controller. Coil-type flash steam boilers may use two high-temperature limit controls, one of which shall be manually reset in the hot-water coil section of the boiler instead of the low-water-level limit control.

[10]Boiler Groups C, D and H shall use an approved automatic reset safety shutoff valve for the main burner fuel shutoff, which shall be interlocked to the programming control devices required. On oil burners where the safety shutoff valve will be subjected to pressures in excess of 10 psi (69 kPa) when the burner is not firing, a second safety shutoff valve shall be provided in series with the first. Boiler Groups C and D, using gas in excess of 1-pound-per-square-inch (6.9 kPa) pressure or having a trapped combustion chamber or employing horizontal fire tubes, shall be equipped with two approved safety shutoff valves, one of which shall be an automatic-reset type, one of which may be used as an operating control, and both of which shall be interlocked to the limit-control devices required. Boiler Groups C and D using gas in excess of 1-pound-per-square-inch (6.9 kPa) pressure shall be provided with a permanent and ready means for making periodic tightness checks of the main fuel safety shutoff valves.

[11]Control and limit device systems shall be grounded with operating voltage not to exceed 150 volts, except that, on approval by the building official, existing control equipment to be reused in an altered boiler control system may use 220-volt single phase with one side grounded, provided such voltage is used for all controls. Control and limit devices shall interrupt the ungrounded side of the circuit. A readily accessible means of manually disconnecting the control circuit shall be provided with controls so arranged that when they are deenergized the burner shall be inoperative.

Chapter 11

REFRIGERATION

Part I—Mechanical Refrigeration Systems

SECTION 1101 — GENERAL

1101.1 Scope. Refrigeration systems, equipment and devices, including the replacement of parts, alterations and substitution of a different refrigerant, shall conform to the requirements of this chapter and other applicable provisions of this code.

Occupied spaces within refrigerated areas shall comply with this chapter and the applicable portions of the Building Code.

1101.2 Standards of Quality. The standards listed below labeled "UMC Standards" are also listed in Chapter 16, Part II, and are a part of this code.

1101.2.1 Standard test method for concentration limits of flammability of chemicals. UMC Standard 11-1, Standard Test Method for Concentration Limits of Flammability of Chemicals.

1101.2.2 Methods for system identification. UMC Standard 11-2, Methods for System Identification.

SECTION 1102 — REFRIGERANTS

The refrigerant used shall be of a type listed in Table 11-A.

> **EXCEPTION:** Lithium bromide absorption systems using water as the refrigerant.

Refrigerant shall be of a type for which the equipment was designed or to which the equipment was converted with approval.

1102.1 Safety Classification. Refrigerants shall be classified into groups according to toxicity and flammability in accordance with ANSI/ASHRAE Standard 34-1992 and addenda thereto. The classification shall consist of an uppercase letter followed by a number. The letter indicates the toxicity classification and the number denotes the flammability. Blends shall be assigned the group designation of the blend composition at the worst case of fractionation.

1102.2 Refrigerant Purity. New and reclaimed refrigerants are allowed to be used in refrigeration systems in accordance with this section. When requested, the installer shall furnish a declaration identifying the refrigerant by standard "R-" designation and stating that it meets the requirements of either Section 1102.2.1 or 1102.2.2.

> **EXCEPTION:** The refrigerant used shall meet the purity specifications set by the manufacturer of the equipment in which it is used when that specification is different from Section 1102.2.1 or 1102.2.2.

1102.2.1 New and reclaimed refrigerants. New and reclaimed refrigerants shall meet ARI Standard 700-93 in purity.

1102.2.2 Recovered refrigerants. Reuse of recovered refrigerant that shows no sign of contamination is allowed in equipment belonging to the same owner as the equipment from which it was removed, provided that it has been filtered and dried with a listed or approved recovery machine. Recovered refrigerants shall not be used in a different owner's equipment unless the refrigerant has been analyzed and found to meet the purity requirements of ARI 700.

1102.3 Toxicity Classification. Refrigerants shall be assigned to one of two classes, A or B, based on allowable exposures.

1. Class A signifies refrigerants with a low degree of toxicity as indicated by a Permissible Exposure Limit (PEL) or measurement consistent therewith of 400 ppm or greater.

2. Class B signifies refrigerants with a PEL or measurement consistent therewith of less than 400 ppm.

1102.4 Flammability Classification. Refrigerants shall be assigned to one of three classes, 1, 2 or 3, based on flammability. Tests shall be made in accordance with UMC Standard 11-1.

1. Class 1 indicates refrigerants that do not show flame propagation when tested in air at 70°F (18°C) and 14.7 psia (101 kPa).

2. Class 2 indicates refrigerants having a lower flammability limit (LFL) of more than 0.00625 pound per cubic foot (0.10 kg/m^3) at 70°F (18°C) and 14.7 psia (101 kPa).

3. Class 3 indicates refrigerants that are highly flammable, as defined by an LFL of less than or equal to 0.00625 pound per cubic foot (0.10 kg/m^3) at 70°F (18°C) and 14.7 psia (101 kPa).

SECTION 1103 — CLASSIFICATION OF REFRIGERATION SYSTEMS

1103.1 General. Refrigeration systems shall be classified according to the degree of probability that a leakage of refrigerant could enter a normally occupied area.

1103.1.1 High-probability system. Systems in which the basic design, or the location of components, is such that a leakage of refrigerant from a failed connection, seal or component could enter the occupied space described in Section 1104.2.

1103.1.2 Low-probability system. Systems that cannot be considered as a high-probability system are classified as low-probability systems. This class includes systems in which leakage from a failed connection, seal or component cannot enter the occupied space described in Section 1104.2.

SECTION 1104 — REQUIREMENTS FOR REFRIGERANT AND REFRIGERATION SYSTEM USE

1104.1 System Selection. Refrigeration systems shall be limited in application in accordance with Table 11-B and the requirements of this section.

1104.2 Volume of Occupied Space. The quantity of refrigerant in a single, independent circuit of a high-probability system shall not exceed the amounts shown in Table 11-A based on the volume of the normally occupied space. The volume of the smallest, enclosed, normally occupied space shall be used to determine the permissible quantity of refrigerant in a system which is located in, serves or passes through such space.

> **EXCEPTIONS:** 1. If the airflow to any enclosed spaced served by a portion of an air-duct system cannot be shut off or reduced below one quarter of its maximum, the cubical contents of the entire space served by that portion of the air-duct system shall be used to determine the permissible quantity of refrigerant in the system.
>
> 2. Refrigerated process or storage areas meeting the requirements of Section 1104.3.

1104.3 Refrigerated Process and Storage Areas. Refrigerant quantities exceeding Table 11-A amounts in evaporators and piping within rooms or spaces used exclusively for processing or storage of materials under refrigerated conditions shall not be limited provided that exiting is provided as in Chapter 10 of the Building Code for special hazards and that:

1. The refrigerated room or space is equipped with a refrigerant vapor detection and alarm system complying with Section 1120.

2. The refrigerated room or space is sealed from all other portions of the building by vapor-tight construction and tightfitting gasketed doors.

EXCEPTION: Adjoining refrigerated rooms.

SECTION 1105 — GENERAL REQUIREMENTS

1105.1 Human Comfort. Cooling systems used for human comfort shall comply with the return-air and outside-air provisions for furnaces in Sections 402, 403 and 404 of this code.

1105.2 Supports and Anchorage. Supports and anchorage for refrigeration equipment and piping shall be designed in accordance with Chapter 16 of the Building Code as Occupancy Category II hazardous facilities. Supports shall be noncombustible.

EXCEPTIONS: 1. Equipment containing Group A1 refrigerants may be supported by the same materials permitted for the building type.

2. The use of approved vibration isolators specifically designed for the normal, wind and seismic loads to which they may be subject shall be permitted.

1105.2.1 Support from ground. A compressor or portion of a condensing unit supported from the ground shall rest on a concrete or other approved base extending not less than 3 inches (76 mm) above the adjoining ground level.

1105.3 Access. An unobstructed readily accessible opening and passageway not less than 36 inches (915 mm) in width and 6 feet 8 inches (2032 mm) in height shall be provided and maintained to the compressor, valves required by this chapter or other portions of the system requiring routine maintenance.

EXCEPTIONS: 1. Refrigerant evaporators, suspended overhead, may use portable means of access.

2. Air filters, brine control or stop valves, fan motors or drives, and remotely deenergized electrical connections may be provided access by an unobstructed space not less than 30 inches (762 mm) in depth, width and height. When an access opening is immediately adjacent to these items and the equipment can be serviced, repaired and replaced from this opening, the dimensions may be reduced to 22 inches (559 mm) by 30 inches (762 mm) provided the largest piece of equipment can be removed through the opening.

3. Cooling equipment, using Group A1 refrigerants or brine, located in an attic or furred space may be provided access as for furnaces in Section 307.3 of this code.

4. Cooling or refrigeration equipment, using Group A1 or B1 refrigerants or brine, located on a roof or on an exterior wall of a building may be provided access as for furnaces in Section 307.5 of this code.

1105.4 Illumination and Service Receptacles. In addition to the requirements of Section 309.1, permanent lighting fixtures shall be installed for all equipment required by this code to be accessible or readily accessible. Such fixtures shall provide sufficient illumination to safely perform the required tasks for which access is provided. Control of the illumination source shall be provided at the access entrance.

EXCEPTIONS: 1. Lighting fixtures may be omitted when the fixed lighting of the building will provide the required illumination.

2. Equipment located on the roof or on the exterior walls of a building.

1105.5 Protection from Mechanical Damage. Refrigeration systems and portions thereof shall not be located in an elevator shaft, dumbwaiter shaft or a shaft having moving objects therein, nor in a location where it will be subject to mechanical damage.

1105.6 Electrical. Electrically energized components of refrigeration systems shall conform to the Electrical Code.

1105.7 Ventilation of Rooms Containing Condensing Units. Rooms or spaces other than a refrigeration machinery room complying with the requirements of this chapter in which any refrigerant-containing portion of a condensing unit is located shall be provided with one of the following means of ventilation:

1. Permanent gravity ventilation openings of not less than 2 square feet (0.19 m^2) net free area opening directly to the outside of the building or extending to the outside of the building by continuous ducts.

2. A mechanical exhaust system arranged to provide a complete change of air in such room or space at least every 20 minutes and to discharge to the outside of the building.

EXCEPTIONS: 1. A condensing unit in a room or space if the cubical content exceeds 1,000 cubic feet per horsepower (8.05 m^3/kW) of the unit.

2. A condensing unit in a room or space that has permanent gravity ventilation having an area of 2 square feet (0.19 m^2) or more to other rooms or openings exceeding 1,000 cubic feet per horsepower (8.05 m^3/kW).

1105.8 Prohibited Locations. Refrigeration systems or portions thereof shall not be located within a required exit enclosure. Refrigeration compressors exceeding 5 horsepower rating (17.6 kW) shall be located at least 10 feet (3048 mm) from an exit opening in a Group A; Group B; Group E; Group I; or Group R, Division 1 Occupancy unless separated by a one-hour fire-resistive occupancy separation.

1105.9 Condensation Control. Piping and fittings which convey brine, refrigerant or coolants which during normal operation could reach a surface temperature below the dew point of the surrounding air and which are located in spaces or areas where condensation could cause a hazard to the building occupants, damage to the structure, electrical or other equipment shall be protected to prevent such an occurrence.

1105.10 Condensate. Condensate from air-cooling coils shall be collected and drained to an approved location. Drain pans and coils shall be arranged to allow thorough drainage and access for cleaning. Where temperatures can drop below freezing, heat tracing and insulation of condensate drains shall be installed.

1105.11 Defrost. When defrost cycles are required for portions of the system, provisions shall be made for collection and disposal of the defrost liquid in a safe and sanitary manner.

1105.12 Overflows. Where condensate or defrost liquids are generated in an attic or furred space and damage may result from overflow, provision for disposal of overflow shall be provided. Overflow piping shall be of materials and slope as required by Section 309.3. The required overflow line shall be separate and uniquely identified for each piece of equipment served and shall be in piping separate from the required condensate drain. Sizing shall be as for the condensate drain itself required by this section. The point of discharge shall be at an approved location where it is readily observable.

1105.13 Condensate, Defrost and Overflow Disposal. Disposal of condensate, defrost or overflow discharges shall comply with Section 309.3. Condensate flows from coils shall be determined by:

$$\text{gpm} = 0.1198 \, (W_1 - W_2)(\text{cfm})/v \qquad (11\text{-}1)$$

For **SI:** $\qquad L_w/s = 14.36 \, [(W_1 - W_2)L_a/s \cdot v]$

WHERE:

cfm = cubic feet per minute.

gpm = gallons per minute of water.

L_a/s = liters per second of air.

L_w/s = liters per second of water.

v = specific volume of the air entering the coil, in ft.^{3}/pound (m^3/kg).

W_1 = humidity ratio of air entering the coil, in pounds (kg) of water per pound (kg) of dry air.

W_2 = humidity ratio of air leaving the coil, in pounds (kg) of water per pound (kg) of dry air.

Values for W and v may be obtained from any standard psychometric chart appropriate to the elevation at which the coil is installed.

For common comfort cooling applications serving cooling coils delivering air at 55°F (13°C), the pipe sizes shown in Table 11-E may be used.

SECTION 1106 — REFRIGERATION MACHINERY ROOMS

1106.1 When Required. Refrigeration systems shall be provided with a refrigeration machinery room when any of the following conditions exist:

1. The quantity of refrigerant in a single system exceeds Table 11-A amounts.

2. Direct-fired absorption equipment.

> **EXCEPTION:** Direct- and indirect-fired lithium bromide absorption systems using water as the refrigerant.

3. A Group A1 system having an aggregate compressor horsepower of 100 (351.6 kW) or more.

4. The system contains other than a Group A1 refrigerant.

> **EXCEPTIONS:** 1. Lithium bromide absorption systems using water as the refrigerant.
>
> 2. Ammonia-water absorption unit systems installed outdoors, provided that the quantity of refrigerant in a single system does not exceed Table 11-A amounts and the discharge is shielded and dispersed.
>
> 3. Systems containing less than 300 pounds (136 kg) of refrigerant R-123 and located in an approved exterior location.
>
> 4. Systems containing less than 35 pounds (16 kg) of refrigerant R-717 and located in an approved exterior location.

1106.1.1 Equipment in refrigeration machinery rooms. Refrigeration machinery rooms shall house all refrigerant-containing portions of the system other than the piping and evaporators permitted by Section 1104.3, discharge piping required by this chapter, and cooling towers regulated by Part II of this chapter and their essential piping.

1106.2 Dimensions. Refrigeration machinery rooms shall be of such dimensions that all system parts are readily accessible with adequate space for maintenance and operations. An unobstructed walking space at least 3 feet (914.4 mm) in width and 6 feet 8 inches (2032 mm) in height shall be maintained throughout allowing free access to at least two sides of all moving machinery and approaching each stop valve. Access to refrigeration machinery rooms shall be restricted to authorized personnel and posted with a permanent sign.

1106.3 Exits. Exits shall comply with Chapter 10 of the Building Code for special hazards.

1106.4 Refrigerant-vapor Alarms. Machinery rooms shall have approved refrigerant-vapor detectors, located in an area where refrigerant from a leak is likely to concentrate, and shall activate visual and audible alarms. Alarms shall be activated at a value not greater than one half the immediately dangerous to life or health (IDLH), or measurement consistent therewith; the PEL, or measurement consistent therewith; or 25 percent of the LFL, whichever is less.

1106.5 Separation. Refrigeration machinery rooms shall be separated from other portions of the building as required in the special hazards provisions of the Building Code. Penetrations shall be sealed to inhibit the passage of refrigerant vapor.

1106.6 Combustion Air and Return Air. Combustion air or return air shall not be taken from or through a refrigeration machinery room.

> **EXCEPTIONS:** 1. Refrigeration machinery rooms used exclusively for direct-fired absorption equipment.
>
> 2. Direct-vented combustion equipment.

1106.7 Special Requirements. Open flames or devices having an exposed surface exceeding 800°F (427°C) are prohibited in refrigeration machinery rooms.

> **EXCEPTIONS:** 1. Momentary temperature excursions such as electrical contacts in Groups A1 and B1 systems.
>
> 2. Refrigeration machinery rooms used exclusively for direct-fired absorption equipment.
>
> 3. Existing nonconforming installations may be allowed if approved by the building official when the combustion system is interlocked with the refrigerant detection system to shut off at the PEL and the risks to the equipment life arising from dissociation products are acknowledged in writing by the owner.

SECTION 1107 — REFRIGERATION MACHINERY ROOM VENTILATION

1107.1 General. Refrigeration machinery rooms shall be provided with a continuous source of outside air for ventilation and removal of rejected heat.

1107.2 Refrigeration Machinery Rooms. Refrigeration machinery rooms shall be provided with dedicated mechanical exhaust systems. The exhaust systems shall have the capacity to achieve each of the following:

1. Continuously maintain the refrigeration machinery room at 0.05-inch water gage (12.4 Pa) negative relative to adjacent spaces calculated by:

$$Q = 2,610 A_e \sqrt{\Delta p} \qquad (11\text{-}2)$$

For **SI:**
$$Q = 0.0839 A_e \sqrt{\Delta p}$$

> **EXCEPTION:** Refrigeration machinery rooms located in entirely detached structures and more than 20 feet (6.1 m) from property lines or openings into buildings.

2. Continuously provide 0.5 cubic foot per minute of airflow per gross square foot (m^2) (152 l/s·m^2) of floor area within the refrigeration machinery rooms as calculated by:

$$Q = 0.5 A_{gf} \qquad (11\text{-}3)$$

For **SI:**
$$Q = 0.0025 A_{gf}$$

3. Limit the temperature rise within the refrigeration machinery room to a maximum of 104°F (40°C) as calculated by:

$$Q = \Sigma q/1.08\Delta T \qquad (11\text{-}4)$$

For **SI:**
$$Q = \Sigma q/1.23\Delta T$$

4. Provide emergency purge of escaping refrigerant as calculated by:

$$Q = 100 \sqrt{G} \qquad (11\text{-}5)$$

For **SI:**
$$Q = 70 \sqrt{G}$$

WHERE:

A_e = equivalent leakage area, square feet (see Section 905 of the Building Code) (m²).

A_{gf} = gross floor area, square feet (m²).

G = refrigerant mass in largest system, lbs (kg).

Q = airflow rate, cubic feet per minute (m³/s).

q = Btu/h (kW) of all heat-producing equipment.

Δp = pressure difference, inches water gage (Pa).

ΔT = temperature difference between machinery room and supply air, °F (°C).

1107.3 Distribution of Ventilation. Exhaust inlets or permanent openings shall be located to provide ventilation throughout the entire refrigeration machinery room.

1107.4 Intermittent Control of the Ventilation Systems. Fans providing refrigeration machinery room temperature control or automatic response to refrigerant gas in order to maintain concentrations below the PEL may be automatically controlled to provide intermittent ventilation as conditions require.

1107.5 Emergency Control of the Ventilation Systems. Fans providing emergency purge ventilation for refrigerant escape shall have a clearly identified switch of the break-glass type providing on-only control immediately adjacent to and outside of each refrigerant machinery room exit. Purge fans shall also respond automatically to the refrigerant concentration detection system set to activate the ventilation system at no more than 25 percent of the LFL or 50 percent of the IDLH or a measure equivalent thereto, whichever is less. An emergency purge control shall be provided with a manual reset only.

1107.6 Central Control of Ventilation Systems. Mechanical ventilation systems shall have switches to control power to each fan. The switches shall be key operated or within a locked glass-covered enclosure at an approved location adjacent to and outside of the principal entrance to the machinery room. Necessary keys shall be located in a single approved location. Switches controlling fans providing continuous ventilation shall be of the two position, on-off type. Switches controlling fans providing intermittent or emergency ventilation shall be of the three position, automatic on-off type. Switches shall be labeled identifying both function and specific fan controlled. Two colored and labeled indicator lamps responding to the differential pressure created by airflow shall be provided for each switch. One lamp shall indicate flow, the other shall indicate no flow.

1107.7 Ventilation Discharge. Exhaust from mechanical ventilation systems shall be discharged at least 20 feet (6096 mm) from a property line or openings into buildings. Discharges capable of exceeding 25 percent of the LFL or 50 percent of the IDLH shall be equipped with approved treatment systems to reduce the discharge concentrations to these values or lower.

1107.8 Fans. Fans and associated equipment intended to operate the emergency purge of other than Group A1 or Group B1 refrigerants shall meet the requirements for a Class I, Division 1 hazardous location as specified in the Electrical Code.

1107.9 Ventilation Intake. Makeup-air intakes to replace the exhaust air shall be provided to the refrigeration machinery room directly from outside the building. Intakes shall be located as required by other sections of the code and fitted with backdraft dampers or similar approved flow-control means to prevent reverse flow. Distribution of makeup air shall be arranged to provide thorough mixing within the refrigeration machinery room to prevent short circuiting of the makeup air directly to the exhaust.

SECTION 1108 — REFRIGERATION MACHINERY ROOM EQUIPMENT AND CONTROLS

1108.1 General. Equipment, piping, ducts, vents or similar devices which are not essential for the refrigeration process, maintenance of the equipment or for the illumination, ventilation or fire protection of the room shall not be placed in or pass through a refrigeration machinery room.

Equipment essential to the refrigeration process often includes, but is not necessarily limited to, the following:

1. Refrigeration compressors.

2. Condensing units.

3. Pumps, associated piping and automatic control valves for refrigerant, condenser water, and brine or chilled water.

4. Refrigeration control devices and panels.

5. Machinery room ventilation equipment (see Section 1107).

6. Cooling towers or portions thereof (see Part II of this chapter).

7. Refrigerant receivers and accumulators.

8. Refrigerant vapor-detection and alarm systems (see Section 1106).

9. Machinery room fire sprinkler system exclusive of its shut-off valves.

10. Machinery room lighting and service receptacles.

11. Motor control centers and electrical panels for machinery room systems.

1108.2 Electrical. Electrical equipment and installations shall comply with the Electrical Code. The refrigeration machinery room shall not be required to be a hazardous (classified) location except as provided in Section 1107.8.

1108.3 Storage. Storage of materials in a refrigeration machinery room shall be as permitted in the Fire Code.

1108.4 Emergency Control. A clearly identified switch of the break-glass type providing off-only control of electrically energized equipment and devices within the refrigeration machinery room shall be provided immediately adjacent to and outside of each refrigeration machinery room exit. In addition, emergency shutoff shall also be automatically activated when the concentration of refrigerant vapor exceeds 25 percent of the LFL.

SECTION 1109 — REFRIGERANT PIPING, CONTAINERS AND VALVES

1109.1 General. Materials used in the construction and installation of refrigeration systems shall be suitable for the refrigerant, refrigerant oil or brine in the system. Material or equipment which will deteriorate due to the chemical action of the refrigerant or the oil, or combination of both, shall not be installed.

1109.2 Nonferrous Materials. Copper and brass refrigeration piping, valves, fittings and related parts used in the construction and installation of refrigeration systems shall be approved for the intended use.

1109.3 Ferrous Materials. Iron and steel refrigeration piping valves, fittings and related parts shall be approved for the intended use. Pipe more than 2 inches (51 mm) iron pipe size shall be electric-resistance welded or seamless pipe.

SECTION 1110 — ERECTION OF REFRIGERANT PIPING

1110.1 General. Piping and tubing shall be installed so as to prevent vibration and strains at joints and connections.

1110.2 Support. In addition to the requirements of Section 1105.1, piping and tubing shall be securely fastened to a permanent support within 6 feet (1.8 m) following the first bend in such tubing from the compressor and within 2 feet (610 mm) of each subsequent bend or angle. Piping and tubing shall be supported at points not more than 15 feet (4570 mm) apart.

1110.3 Protection from Damage. Refrigerant piping and tubing shall be installed so that it is not subject to damage from an external source. Soft annealed copper tubing shall not be larger than $1^3/_8$-inch (34.9 mm) nominal size. Mechanical joint shall not be made on tubing larger than $^3/_4$-inch (19 mm) nominal size. Soft annealed copper tubing conveying refrigerant shall be enclosed in iron or steel piping and fittings or in conduit, molding or raceway which will properly protect the tubing against mechanical injury from an exterior source.

> **EXCEPTIONS:** 1. Tubing entirely within or tubing within 5 feet (1524 mm) of a refrigerant compressor when so located that it is not subject to external injury.
>
> 2. Copper tubing serving a dwelling unit, when such tubing contains Group Al refrigerant and is placed in locations not subject to damage from an external source.

1110.4 Visual Inspection. Refrigerant piping and joints shall be exposed to view for visual inspection and acceptance by the building official prior to being covered or enclosed.

> **EXCEPTION:** Soft annealed copper tubing enclosed in iron or steel piping conduit, molding or raceway, provided there are no fittings or joints concealed therein.

1110.5 Prohibited Locations. Refrigerant piping shall not be located within a required exit.

1110.6 Underground Piping. Refrigerant piping placed underground shall be protected against corrosion.

1110.7 Joints. Iron or steel pipe joints shall be of approved threaded, flanged or welded types. Exposed threads shall be tinned or coated with an approved corrosion inhibitor. Copper or brass pipe joints of iron pipe size shall be of approved threaded, flanged or brazed types. Copper tubing joints and connections shall be approved flared, lapped, swaged or brazed joints.

1110.8 Identification. Piping shall be identified in accordance with UMC Standard 11-2. The type of refrigerant, function and pressure shall be indicated.

SECTION 1111 — REFRIGERANT CONTROL VALVES

1111.1 Location. Stop valves shall be installed in the refrigerant piping of a refrigeration system at the following locations:

1. At the inlet and outlet of a positive-displacement-type compressor, compressor unit or condensing unit.

2. At the refrigerant outlet from a liquid receiver.

3. At the refrigerant inlet of a pressure vessel containing liquid refrigerant and having an internal gross volume exceeding 3 cubic feet (85 L).

> **EXCEPTIONS:** 1. Systems with nonpositive-displacement compressors.
>
> 2. Systems having a pump-out receiver for storage of the charge.
>
> 3. Systems containing less than 110 pounds (50 kg) of Group A1 refrigerant.
>
> 4. Self-contained systems do not require a stop valve at the inlet of the receiver.

1111.2 Support. Stop valves installed in copper refrigerant lines of $^3/_4$ inch (19 mm) or less outside diameter shall be securely supported independently of the tubing or piping.

1111.3 Access. Stop valves required by this section shall be readily accessible from the refrigeration machinery room floor or a level platform.

1111.4 Identification. Stop valves shall be identified by tagging in accordance with UMC Standard 11-2. A valve chart shall be mounted under glass at an approved location near the principal entrance to a refrigeration machinery room.

SECTION 1112 — PRESSURE-LIMITING DEVICES

1112.1 When Required. Pressure-limiting devices shall be provided on all systems operating above atmospheric pressure.

> **EXCEPTION:** Factory-sealed systems containing less than 22 pounds (10 kg) of Group Al refrigerant listed by an approved agency.

1112.2 Setting. The maximum setting to which a pressure-limiting device may be set by use of the adjusting means provided shall not exceed the design pressure of the high side of a system not protected by a pressure-relief device or 90 percent of the pressure setting of the pressure-relief device installed on the high side of a system.

> **EXCEPTION:** In systems using other than positive-displacement compressors which are protected by a pressure-relief device, the setting may be the design pressure of the high side of the system provided the pressure-relief device is located in the low side, subject only to low-side pressure, and there is a permanent, unvalved relief path between the high side and the low side of the system.

1112.3 Connection. Pressure-limiting devices shall be connected between the pressure-imposing element and stop valve on the discharge side without intervening stop valves in the line leading to the pressure-limiting device.

1112.4 Operation. When the system is protected by a pressure-relief device, the pressure-limiting device shall stop the action of the pressure-imposing element at a pressure not more than 90 percent of the setting of the pressure-relief device.

SECTION 1113 — PRESSURE-RELIEF DEVICES

1113.1 General. Refrigeration systems shall be protected by a pressure-relief device or other means designed to safely relieve pressure due to fire or abnormal conditions.

1113.2 Positive-displacement Compressor. A positive-displacement compressor shall be equipped by the manufacturer with a pressure-relief device of adequate size and pressure setting to prevent rupture of the compressor or other component located between the compressor and the stop valve on the discharge side.

1113.3 Liquid-containing Portions of Systems. Liquid-containing portions of systems, including piping, which can be isolated from pressure-relief devices required elsewhere and which can develop pressures exceeding their working design pressures due to temperature rise, shall be protected by the installation of pressure-relief devices.

1113.4 Evaporators. Evaporators located within 18 inches (457 mm) of a heating element or coil shall be fitted with a pressure-relief device.

> **EXCEPTIONS:** 1. Self-contained equipment.
>
> 2. Factory-built coil assemblies specifically designed for installation on the discharge of forced-air heating units.
>
> 3. If the connected and unvalved volume of the low side of the system meets the following:

$$V_1 > [W_1 - (V_2 - V_1)/V_{gt}]V_{gc} \qquad (11\text{-}6)$$

WHERE:

V_1 = low-side volume, cubic feet (L).

V_2 = total volume of system, cubic feet (L).

V_{gc} = specific volume at critical temperature and pressure, cubic feet per pound (L/kg).

V_{gt} = specific volume of refrigerant vapor at 110°F (43°C), cubic feet per pound (L/kg).

W_1 = total weight of refrigerant in system, pounds (kg).

   4. Reheat coils using the refrigerant for heat recovery.

1113.5 Actuation. Pressure-relief devices shall be direct-pressure actuated. Each part of a refrigeration system that can be valved off and that contains one or more pressure vessels having internal diameters greater than 6 inches (152 mm) and containing liquid refrigerant shall be protected by a pressure-relief device.

1113.6 Stop Valves Prohibited. Stop valves shall not be located between a pressure-relief device and the portion of the system protected thereby.

1113.7 Location. Pressure-relief devices shall be connected as near as practical to the portion of the system protected thereby, above the liquid refrigerant level, and accessible for inspection and repair.

> **EXCEPTION:** Fusible plugs on the high side may be located above or below the liquid refrigerant level.

1113.8 Materials. Seats and discs of pressure-relief devices shall be constructed of suitable material to resist corrosion or other chemical action caused by the refrigerant. Seats or discs of cast iron are prohibited.

SECTION 1114 — PRESSURE-RELIEF DEVICE SETTINGS

1114.1 Pressure-relief Valve Setting. Pressure-relief valves shall actuate at a pressure not exceeding the design pressure of the parts of the system protected.

1114.2 Rupture Member Setting. Rupture members used in lieu of, or in series with, a relief valve shall have a nominal rated rupture pressure not exceeding the design pressure of the parts of the system protected. Rupture members installed ahead of relief valves need not be larger, but shall not be smaller, than the relief-valve inlet.

SECTION 1115 — MARKING OF PRESSURE-RELIEF DEVICES

1115.1 Pressure-relief Valves. Pressure-relief valves for refrigerant-containing components shall be set and sealed by the manufacturer or by an approved assembler. Pressure-relief valves shall be marked by the manufacturer with the data required to show compliance with this chapter.

> **EXCEPTION:** Relief valves for systems with design pressures of 15 psig (103 kPa) or less may be marked by the manufacturer with pressure-setting capacity.

1115.2 Rupture Members. Rupture members for refrigerant pressure vessels shall be marked with the data required to show compliance with this chapter.

1115.3 Fusible Plugs. Fusible plugs shall be marked with the melting temperatures in degrees Fahrenheit (Celsius) to show compliance with this chapter.

SECTION 1116 — OVER-PRESSURE PROTECTION

1116.1 General. Pressure vessels shall be provided with over-pressure protection as required by this section.

1116.2 Type of Protection. Pressure vessels with 3 cubic feet (85 L) internal gross volume or less may use a single pressure-relief device or a fusible plug. Pressure vessels over 3 cubic feet (85 L) but less than 10 cubic feet (283 L) internal gross volume may use a single pressure-relief device but not a fusible plug. Pressure vessels of 10 cubic feet (283 L) or more internal gross volume shall use a single rupture member or dual pressure-relief valve.

1116.3 Three-way Valve Required. When dual pressure-relief valves are used, they shall be installed with a three-way valve to allow testing or repair.

> **EXCEPTION:** A single relief valve of the required relieving capacity may be used on low-side pressure vessels of 10 cubic feet (283 L) or more when meeting the requirements of Section 1116.8, Exception 2.

1116.4 Parallel Pressure-relief Devices. Two or more pressure-relief devices in parallel to obtain the required capacity shall be considered as one pressure-relief device. The discharge capacity shall be the sum of the capacities required for each pressure vessel being protected.

1116.5 Discharge Capacity. The minimum required discharge capacity of pressure-relief devices for each pressure vessel shall be determined by the following:

$$C = fDL \qquad (11\text{-}7)$$

WHERE:

C = minimum required discharge capacity of the relief device in pounds of air per minute (kg/s).

D = outside diameter of vessel, feet (m).

f = factor dependent upon type of refrigerant from Table 11-C.

L = length of vessel, feet (m).

1116.6 Rating of Pressure-relief Valves. Pressure-relief valves shall be of approved types and capacities. The rated discharge capacity of a pressure-relief valve shall be expressed in pounds of air per minute. Pipe and fittings between the pressure-relief valve and the parts of the system it protects shall have at least the area of the pressure-relief valve inlet.

1116.7 Rating of Rupture Members and Fusible Plugs. The rated discharge capacity of a rupture member or fusible plug discharging to atmosphere under critical flow conditions in pounds of air per minute shall be determined by the following formulas:

$$C = 0.8\, P_1 d^2 \qquad (11\text{-}8)$$

For **SI:** $\qquad C = 1.36 \times 10^{-6}\, P_1 d^2$

$$d = 1.12\sqrt{C/P_1} \qquad (11\text{-}9)$$

For **SI:** $\qquad d = 857.5\sqrt{C/P_1}$

WHERE:

C = rated discharge capacity of air, pounds per minute (kg/s).

d = smallest internal diameter of the inlet pipe, retaining flanges, fusible plug, rupture member, inches (mm).

For rupture members:

$\qquad P_1$ = rated pressure psi gage × 1.10 + 14.7.　(11-10)

For **SI:**　P_1 = rated pressure kPa gage × 1.10 + 101.33.

For fusible plugs:

P_1 = absolute saturation pressure, corresponding to the stamped temperature melting point of the fusible plug or the critical pressure of the refrigerant used, whichever is smaller, psia (kPa absolute).

1116.8 Discharge Location. Pressure-relief devices shall discharge to the atmosphere unless otherwise prohibited by this chapter at a location at least 15 feet (4.6 m) above the adjoining grade level and at least 20 feet (6096 mm) from an opening into a building. The discharge termination shall be fitted with an approved diffuser directed to prevent spray of discharged refrigerant on personnel or entry of foreign material or water into the discharge piping. Discharge piping connected to the discharge side of a fusible plug or rupture member shall have provisions to prevent internal plugging of the pipe caused by the fusible plug or rupture-member function.

EXCEPTIONS: 1. Systems containing less than 110 pounds (50 kg) of a Group A1 refrigerant.

2. A pressure-relief valve may discharge into the low side of the system, if the pressure-relief valve is of a type not affected by back pressure, provided the low side is equipped with pressure-relief devices of equal relieving capacity. The low-side pressure-relief device shall be set and discharged as required by this section. Fusible plugs or rupture members shall not be used for pressure relief into the low side.

SECTION 1117 — DISCHARGE PIPING

1117.1 General. The area of the discharge pipe from the pressure-relief device or fusible plug shall be at least as large as the outlet area of the pressure-relief device or fusible plug. A discharge pipe accepting discharge from more than one relief device or fusible plug shall be sized and have a maximum length of the common discharge not less than that required by the sum of the rated capacities of all relief valves discharging into the header at the lowest pressure setting of any of the relief valves discharging into the header.

1117.1.1 Length. The maximum length of the discharge piping permitted to be installed on the outlet of a pressure-relief device shall be determined by:

$$L = 9P^2d^5/16C^2 \qquad (11\text{-}11)$$

For **SI:** $\qquad L = 7 \times 10^{-13} P^2d^5/36C_r^2$

WHERE:

C = minimum required discharge capacity in pounds of air per minute (kg/s).

d = internal diameter of pipe in inches (mm).

L = length of discharge pipe in feet (m).

1117.1.2 Valves and disks. For relief valves and rupture disks:

$$P = \text{rated pressure psi gage} \times 1.10 + 14.7. \qquad (11\text{-}12)$$

For **SI:** $\quad P = \text{rated pressure kPa gage} \times 1.10 + 101.33.$

1117.1.3 Fusible plugs. For fusible plugs:

P = absolute saturation pressure correspond- $\qquad$ (11-13)
ing to the stamped temperature melting point of the fusible plug or the critical pressure of the refrigerant used, whichever is smaller, psia (kPa).

SECTION 1118 — SPECIAL DISCHARGE REQUIREMENTS

1118.1 General. Systems containing other than Group A1 or B1 refrigerants shall discharge to atmosphere only through an approved flaring device. For treatment system requirements, see also the Fire Code.

EXCEPTIONS: 1. Ammonia systems complying with Section 1119.

2. Ammonia absorption systems serving a single dwelling unit.

3. When the building official determines upon review of a rational engineering analysis that significant fire, health or environmental hazard would not result from the proposed atmospheric release.

4. Lithium bromide absorption system using water as the refrigerant.

1118.2 Design Requirements. Flaring devices shall be designed to incinerate the entire discharge. The products of refrigerant incineration shall not pose health or environmental hazards. Incineration shall be automatic upon initiation of discharge, shall be designed to prevent blowback and shall not expose structures or materials to threat of fire. Standby fuel, such as LP-gas, and standby power shall have the capacity to operate for one and one half times the required time for complete incineration of the refrigerant in the system.

1118.3 Testing. Flaring systems shall be tested to demonstrate their safety and effectiveness. A report from an approved agency shall be submitted detailing the emission products from the system as installed.

SECTION 1119 — AMMONIA DISCHARGE

Ammonia systems shall be provided with an emergency discharge into a tank of water provided exclusively for ammonia absorption. At least 1 gallon (379 mL) of fresh water shall be provided for each pound (454 g) of ammonia in the system. The water used shall be prevented from freezing without the use of salt or chemicals. The tank shall be substantially constructed of not less than $1/8$-inch or No. 10 M.S.G. (2.51 mm) steel. The horizontal dimensions of the tank shall be equal to or less than one half of the height. The tank shall have a hinged cover or, if of the enclosed type, shall have a vent hole at the top. Pipe connections shall be through the top of the tank. The discharge pipe from the pressure-relief valves shall discharge ammonia in the center of the tank near the bottom but not more than 30 feet (9104 mm) below the surface of the water.

EXCEPTION: An emergency discharge is not required for ammonia-water absorption unit systems installed outdoors provided that the discharge is shielded and dispersed.

SECTION 1120 — DETECTION AND ALARM SYSTEMS

1120.1 General. When required by this chapter, approved refrigerant-vapor detection and alarm systems utilizing listed fire alarm signaling devices providing a sound pressure level of at least 15 dBA above the operating ambient sound pressure level of the space in which they are installed and providing an approved, distinctive audible and visual alarm. Refrigerant vapor alarms shall be activated whenever the refrigerant vapor Permissible Exposure Limit (PEL) is exceeded. In other than machinery rooms, such systems shall also automatically stop the flow of refrigerant to evaporators within the space and stop the flow of refrigerant in all supply lines leaving the machinery room whenever the refrigerant vapor concentration is detected at or above 50 percent of the IDLH or 25 percent of the lower explosive limit (LEL). Detection of refrigerant-vapor concentrations at or above 25 percent of the LEL shall automatically de-energize electrical power within the space which does not meet the requirements for a Class I, Division 1, Group D electrical installation.

1120.2 Power and Supervision. Detection and alarm systems shall be powered and supervised as required for fire alarm systems in accordance with UFC Standard 14-1.

1120.3 Annunciation. Detection and alarm systems shall be annunciated at an approved location in accordance with the Fire Code.

1120.4 Installation, Maintenance and Testing. Detection and alarm systems shall be installed, maintained and tested in accordance with the manufacturer's instructions and the Fire Code.

SECTION 1121 — EQUIPMENT IDENTIFICATION

In addition to labels required elsewhere in this code, a refrigeration system shall be provided with labels complying with the requirements of this section.

A condenser, receiver, absorber, accumulator and similar equipment having an internal volume of more than 3 cubic feet (85 L) and containing refrigerant shall be equipped with a permanent label setting forth the type of refrigerant in such vessel.

In a refrigeration machinery room and for a direct refrigerating system of more than 10 horsepower (35 kW), there shall be a permanent sign at an approved location giving the following information:

1. Name of contractor installing equipment.

2. Name and number designation of refrigerant in system.

3. Pounds of refrigerant in system.

SECTION 1122 — TESTING OF REFRIGERATION EQUIPMENT

1122.1 Factory Tests. Refrigerant-containing parts of units shall be tested and proved tight by the manufacturer at the design pressure for which it is rated. The test pressure applied to the high side of each factory-assembled refrigeration system shall be equal to the design pressure of the high side. The test pressure applied to the low side of each factory-assembled refrigeration system shall be equal to the design pressure of the low side.

> **EXCEPTION:** Units with a design pressure of 15 psig (103 kPa) or less shall be tested at a pressure not less than 1.33 times the design pressure.

1122.2 Field Tests. Refrigerant-containing parts of a system that is field erected shall be tested and proved tight to the satisfaction of the building official after complete installation and before operation. The high and low side of each system shall be tested and proved tight at not less than the lower of the pressure in Table 11-D or the setting of the pressure-relief device.

> **EXCEPTIONS:** 1. Compressors, condensers, evaporators, coded pressure vessels, safety devices, pressure gages, control mechanisms and systems that are factory tested.
>
> 2. Refrigeration systems containing R-22, not exceeding 5 tons of refrigeration (17.5 kW) capacity and field piped using approved, factory-charged line sets may be proved tight by observing retention of pressure on a set of charging gages and soaping connections while the system is operating.

See the Fire Code for additional tests of emergency devices and systems.

1122.3 Test Medium. Oxygen, flammable or combustible gases or gas mixtures shall not be used for leak testing. The means used to build up the test pressure shall have either a pressure-limiting device or a pressure-reducing device with a pressure-relief device and a gage on the outlet side. The pressure-relief device shall be set above the test pressure but low enough to prevent permanent deformation of system components.

1122.4 Declaration. A dated declaration of test shall be provided for systems containing 55 pounds (25 kg) or more of refrigerant. The declaration shall give the name and number designation of the refrigerant and the field test pressure applied to the high side and the low side of the system. The declaration of test shall be signed by the installer.

1122.5 Brine Systems. Brine-containing portions of a system shall be tested at one and one half times design pressure of the system using brine as the test fluid.

SECTION 1123 — MAINTENANCE AND OPERATION

Refrigeration systems shall be operated and maintained as required by the Fire Code.

SECTION 1124 — STORAGE OF REFRIGERANTS AND REFRIGERANT OILS

Refrigerants and refrigerant oils not charged within the refrigeration system shall be stored as required by the Fire Code.

Part II—Cooling Towers

SECTION 1125 — COOLING TOWERS, EVAPORATIVE CONDENSERS AND FLUID COOLERS

1125.1 General. Cooling towers, evaporative condensers and fluid coolers shall be readily accessible. When located on roofs, such equipment, having combustible exterior surfaces, shall be protected with an approved automatic fire-extinguishing system.

1125.2 Support and Anchorage. Cooling towers, evaporative condensers and fluid coolers shall be supported on noncombustible grillage designed in accordance with the Building Code, Part V. Seismic restraints shall be as required by Chapter 16 of the Building Code.

1125.3 Water Supply. Water supplies and backflow protection shall be as required by the Plumbing Code.

1125.4 Drainage. Drains, overflows and blow-down provisions shall have indirect connection to an approved disposal location. Discharge of chemical waste shall be as approved by the appropriate regulatory authority.

1125.5 Chemical Treatment Systems. Chemical treatment systems shall comply with the Fire Code. When chemicals used present a contact hazard to personnel, approved emergency eye-wash and shower facilities shall be installed.

1125.6 Location. Cooling towers, evaporative condensers and fluid coolers shall be located such that their plumes cannot enter occupied spaces. Plume discharges shall be at least 5 feet (1524 mm) above or 20 feet (6096 mm) away from any ventilation inlet to a building. Location on the property shall be as required for buildings by the Building Code.

1125.7 Electrical. Electrical systems shall be in accordance with the Electrical Code. Equipment shall be provided with a vibration switch to shut off fans operating with excessive vibration. In climates commonly subject to electrical storms, lightning protection shall be provided on roof-mounted equipment.

1125.8 Refrigerants and Hazardous Fluids. Equipment containing refrigerants as a part of a closed-cycle refrigeration system shall comply with Chapter 11 of this code. Equipment containing other fluids which are flammable, combustible or hazardous shall comply with the Fire Code.

TABLE 11-A—REFRIGERANT GROUPS[1], PROPERTIES[2] AND ALLOWABLE QUANTITIES[3]

REFRIGERANT	CHEMICAL FORMULA	CHEMICAL NAME[4] (Composition for Blends)	CHEMICAL ABSTRACT SERVICE NUMBER	SAFETY GROUP[1]	PEL[5] (ppm)	IDLH[6] (ppm)	LFL (% by Vol.)[7]	SPECIFIC GRAVITY (Air = 1)	POUNDS PER 1,000 CUBIC FEET OF SPACE[8] × 0.016 for kg/m³
R-11	CCl_3F	Trichlorofluoromethane	75-69-4	A1	1,000[9]	5,000[10]	N/A	4.74	1.60
R-12	CCl_2F_2	Dichlorodifluoromethane	75-71-8	A1	1,000	50,000	N/A	4.17	12.00
R-22	$CHClF_2$	Chlorodifluoromethane	75-45-6	A1	1,000[11]	50,000[12]	N/A	2.99	9.40
R-113	CCl_2FCClF_2	1,1,2-Trichloro-1,2,2-Trifluoroethane	76-13-1	A1	1,000	4,500	N/A	6.47	1.90
R-114	$CClF_2CClF_2$	1,2-Dichlorotetrafluoroethane	76-14-2	A1	1,000	50,000	N/A	5.90	9.40
R-123	$CHCl_2\text{-}CF_3$	1,1-Dichloro-2,2,2-Trifluoroethane	306-83-2	B1	30[11]	4,000[12]	N/A	5.28	0.40
R-134a	CH_2FCF_3	1,1,1,2-Tetrafluoroethane	811-97-2	A1	1,000[11]	50,000[12]	N/A	3.52	16.00
R-500 73.8% 26.2%	Azeotrope CCl_2F_2 CH_3CHF_2	R-12/152a(73.8/26.2) Dichlorodifluoromethane 1,1-Difluoroethane	75-71-8 75-37-6	A1	1,000[11]	50,000[12]	N/A	3.43	12.00
R-502 48.8% 51.2%	Azeotrope $CHClF_2$ $CClF_2CF_3$	R-22/115(48.8/51.2) Chlorodifluoromethane 1-Chloro-1,1,2,2,2-Pentafluoroethane	75-45-6 76-15-3	A1	1,000[11]	50,000[12]	N/A	3.85	19.00
R-717	NH_3	Ammonia	7664-41-7	B2	50[13]	500	15.5	0.59	0.022
R-744	CO_2	Carbon dioxide	124-38-9	A1	5,000	50,000	N/A	1.52	5.70

[1]Refrigerant group classification is in accordance with Section 1102.

[2]Refrigerant properties are those needed for this chapter.

[3]Allowable quantities are for high-probability systems under Section 1103 only.

[4]Chemical name shown is the preferred name.

[5]PEL is that designated in 29 C.F.R. 1910.1000 unless otherwise indicated.

[6]IDLH is that designated by NIOSH unless otherwise indicated.

[7]LFL is percentage refrigerant by volume in air at 68°F (20°C) and 29.92 in Hg; N/A—Not applicable (not flame limits).

[8]Pounds (kg) of refrigerant in a high-probability system per 1,000 cubic feet (28.3 m³) of occupied space. See Section 1104. This column does not apply to refrigerant machinery rooms or areas covered by Section 1106.

[9]The PEL value shown is the TLV-C recommended by the American Conference of Governmental Industrial Hygienists.

[10]The IDLH value shown is reduced from that designated by NIOSH in light of cardiac sensitization potential.

[11]A PEL has not yet been established; the value given was determined in a consistent manner.

[12]An IDLH has not yet been established, the value given was determined in a consistent manner.

[13]OSHA PEL is 50 ppm; ACGIH TLV-TWA is 25 ppm.

TABLE 11-B
TABLE 11-C

1997 UNIFORM MECHANICAL CODE

TABLE 11-B—PERMISSIBLE REFRIGERATION SYSTEMS[1] AND REFRIGERANTS

OCCUPANCY GROUP AND DIVISION	HIGH-PROBABILITY SYSTEM	LOW-PROBABILITY SYSTEM	MACHINERY ROOM
A-1	Group A1 only	Any	Any
A-2.1	Group A1 only	Any	Any
A-3	Group A1 only	Any	Any
A-4	Group A1 only	Any	Any
B	Group A1 only[2]	Any	Any
E-1	Group A1 only	Any	Any
E-2	Group A1 only	Any	Any
E-3	Group A1 only	Any	Any
F-1	Group A1 only[2]	Any	Any
F-2	Group A1 only[2]	Any	Any
H-1	Any	Any	Any
H-2	Any	Any	Any
H-3	Any	Any	Any
H-4	Group A1 only	Any	Any
H-5	Group A1 only	Any	Any
H-6	Group A1 only	Any	Any
H-7	Any	Any	Any
I-1.1	None	Any	Any
I-1.2	Group A1 only	Any	Any
I-2	Group A1 only	Any	Any
I-3	None	Any	Any
M	Group A1 only[2]	Any	Any
R-1	Group A1 only	Any	Any
R-2	Group A1 only	Any	Any
R-3	Group A1 only	Any	Any
S-1	Group A1 only[2]	Any	Any
S-2	Group A1 only[2]	Any	Any
S-3	Group A1 only	Any	Any
S-4	Group A1 only	Any	Any
S-5	Group A1 only	Any	Any
U-1	Any	Any	Any
U-2	N/A	N/A	N/A

[1]See Section 1104.

[2]Any refrigerant may be used within a high-probability system when the room or space complies with Section 1104.3.

N/A—Not applicable.

TABLE 11-C—VALUE OF f (f) FOR EQUATION 11-7

REFRIGERANT NUMBER	f	SI
11	1.0	(0.082)
12	1.6	(0.163)
22	1.6	(0.163)
113	1.0	(0.082)
114	1.6	(0.163)
115	2.5	(0.203)
123	1.0	(0.082)
134a	1.6	(0.163)
142b	1.0	(0.082)
152a	1.0	(0.082)
500	1.6	(0.163)
502	2.5	(0.203)
717	0.5	(0.041)
744	1.0	(0.082)

TABLE 11-D—FIELD LEAK TEST PRESSURES IN PSIG

REFRIGERANT NUMBER	HIGH SIDE WATER COOLED	HIGH SIDE AIR COOLED	LOW SIDE
	$kPa = (psig + 14.7) \times 6.894$		
11	15	35	15
12	140	220	140
22	230	360	230
113	15	15	15
114	40	80	40
115	275	340	275
123	15	30	15
134a	150	250	150
142b	70	125	70
152a	130	220	130
500	165	265	165
502	250	385	250
717	235	390	235
744*	N/A	N/A	N/A

*Special design required; test pressures typically exceed 1,000 psig (6995 kPa).
N/A—Not applicable.

TABLE 11-E—CONDENSATE WASTE SIZE

EQUIPMENT CAPACITY	MINIMUM CONDENSATE PIPE DIAMETER
Up to 20 tons (70.3 kW) of refrigeration	$^{3}/_{4}$ inch (19 mm)
Over 20 (70.3 kW) to 40 tons (141 kW) of refrigeration	1 inch (25 mm)
Over 40 (141 kW) to 90 tons (317 kW) of refrigeration	$1^{1}/_{4}$ inches (32 mm)
Over 90 (317 kW) to 125 tons (440 kW) of refrigeration	$1^{1}/_{2}$ inches (38 mm)
Over 125 (440 kW) to 250 tons (879 kW) of refrigeration	2 inches (51 mm)

Chapter 12
HYDRONICS

NOTE: The provisions of this chapter were moved from Appendix B.

Part I—Hydronic Piping

SECTION 1201 — STEAM AND WATER PIPING

1201.1 Requirements. Steam and water piping systems which are part of a heating or cooling system shall comply with the following requirements:

1. Those portions of piping systems in which the pressure exceeds 160 psig (1103 kPa) or the temperature exceeds 250°F (121°C) shall comply with nationally recognized standards approved by the building official and the requirements of Item 2.

2. Those portions of piping systems in which the pressure does not exceed 160 psig (1103 kPa) and the temperature does not exceed 250°F (121°C) shall comply with the following requirements:

1201.1.1 Materials and construction.

1201.1.1.1 Pipe. Pipe shall be brass, copper, cast iron, galvanized or black wrought iron, galvanized or black steel, or other approved materials.

1201.1.1.2 Tubing. Tubing shall be copper water tube.

1201.1.1.3 Valves. Valves up through 2 inches (51 mm) in size shall be brass, malleable iron, or steel bodies. Each gate valve shall be a full-way type with working parts of noncorrosive metal.

1201.1.1.4 Fittings.

1. Plain screwed fittings shall be brass, bronze, cast iron or galvanized or black malleable iron, or galvanized or black steel.

2. Fittings for copper tubing shall be wrought copper, wrought bronze or cast brass.

3. Welding fittings shall be black steel.

4. Fittings for asbestos-cement shall be cast iron.

1201.1.1.5 Pipe joint compound. Pipe joint compound shall be noncorrosive and insoluble in the material being carried in the pipe.

1201.1.1.6 Protective coatings. Protective coatings shall be watertight, durable, heat resistant, electrically nonconductive and tightly adherent to the pipe.

1201.1.1.7 Fluxes. Fluxes for solder, sweat, and brazed joints shall be a noncorrosive type and suitable for the use intended.

1201.1.1.8 Insulation. Coverings or insulation used on hot-water or steam pipes shall be of materials suitable for the operating temperature of the system. The insulation, jackets and lap-seal adhesives shall be tested as a composite product and shall have a flame spread of not more than 25 and a smoke-developed rating of not more than 50 when tested in accordance with UBC Standard 8-1.

1201.1.1.9 Flashing material. Flashings shall be lead, copper, galvanized iron or other approved materials.

1201.1.1.10 Gaskets. Flange gaskets shall be metal or asbestos or other approved materials.

1201.1.1.11 Hangers and anchors. Hangers and anchors shall be suitable for the use intended.

1201.1.1.12 Sleeves. Sleeves shall be of steel, cast-iron or wrought-iron pipe, or tile.

1201.1.1.13 Standards. All piping, tubing, valves, joints, fittings, devices and materials shall be free of defects and shall comply with nationally recognized standards approved by the building official.

1201.1.1.14 Marking. Materials and devices shall be suitably identified. In addition to the incised marking required in the standards, all hard-drawn copper tubing shall be marked by means of a continuous and indelible colored stripe, at least $1/4$ inch (6.4 mm) in width as follows:

> Type L—Blue
> Type K—Green
> Type M—Red

1201.1.1.15 Other materials. Other materials and construction may be installed as provided in this chapter or in their approval, provided that they are first acceptable to the building official and are equivalent, for the use intended, to those specified in this chapter.

1201.1.2 Fabrication of joints. Joints shall be made by use of fittings, except as otherwise permitted in this chapter.

1201.1.2.1 Screwed joints. Threads on iron pipe size (I.P.S. pipe) shall be standard taper pipe threads. All burrs shall be removed. Pipe ends shall be reamed or filed out to full size of bore and all chips shall be removed.

1201.1.2.2 Solder joints. Surfaces to be joined by soldering shall be cleaned bright by manual or mechanical means. The joints shall be properly fluxed. Tubing shall be reamed out to the full size of bore.

1201.1.2.3 Welded joints. Welding shall be performed in accordance with nationally recognized standards approved by the building official.

1201.1.2.4 Flanged joints. Flanged joints shall be tightened evenly and provided with suitable nuts, bolts and gaskets.

1201.1.2.5 Mechanical joints. Mechanical joints shall comply with nationally recognized standards.

1201.1.3 Connections.

1201.1.3.1 Brass and copper piping. Joints in brass and copper piping shall be threaded, brazed, welded, flanged or mechanical type.

1201.1.3.2 Cast-iron piping. Joints in cast-iron pipe shall be threaded, flanged or mechanical type.

1201.1.3.3 Steel piping. Joints in galvanized wrought-iron and galvanized steel piping shall be threaded, flanged or mechanical type.

1201.1.3.4 Black wrought-iron piping. Joints in black wrought-iron piping shall be threaded, brazed, welded, flanged or mechanical type except that joints built into or embedded in concrete or masonry shall be welded.

1201.1.3.5 Black steel piping. Joints in black steel piping shall be threaded, brazed, welded, flanged or mechanical type.

1201.1.3.6 Asbestos-cement piping. Joints in asbestos-cement piping shall be mechanical type and suitable for the service temperature intended.

1201.1.3.7 Copper water tubing. Joints in copper tubing shall be soldered, sweated or brazed; except that joints under a building and in or under any concrete slab resting on the ground, shall be silver brazed, or equal, and fittings shall be of wrought copper. All solder and sweat joints may be made with 95 percent tin—5 percent antimony solder; however, if the steam pressure does not exceed 15 psig (103 kPa) nor the water pressure exceed 30 psig (206 kPa), then 50 percent tin—50 percent lead solder may be used. Lead-based solders shall not be used in piping conveying potable water.

1201.1.3.8 Piping to tubing. Joints connecting piping to tubing shall be made with adapter fittings connected as required in Sections 1201.1.2.1 through 1201.1.3.7.

1201.1.4 Changes in direction. Changes in direction shall be made by the appropriate use of fittings, except that changes in direction in copper tubing may be made with bends having a radius not less than six diameters of the tubing, provided that such bends are made by the use of forming equipment which does not deform or reduce appreciably the cross-sectional area of the tubing.

1201.1.5 Changes in pipe sizes. Where different sizes of pipe or pipe and fittings are to be connected, the proper size increasers or reducer fittings shall be used between the two sizes. When the branch is at least two sizes smaller than the main, weldolets or threadolets may be used in lieu of welding tees. Bushings shall not be used. Eccentric reducing fittings shall be used wherever necessary to provide free drainage of lines.

1201.1.6 Hangers and supports. All piping and equipment shall be adequately supported to the satisfaction of the building official. Hot-water and steam piping shall be supported, anchored, provided with swing joints, expansion loops or joints, or other means to avoid excessive strain on piping, equipment, or the building structure to the satisfaction of the building official.

1201.1.6.1 Vertical piping—attachment. Vertical piping and tubing shall be secured at sufficiently close intervals to keep the pipe in alignment and carry the weight of the pipe and contents.

1201.1.6.2 Horizontal piping.

1. **Supports.** Horizontal piping and tubing shall be supported at sufficiently close intervals to keep it in alignment and prevent excessive sagging.

2. **In ground.** Piping and tubing in the ground shall be laid on a firm bed for its entire length, except where support which is adequate in the judgment of the building official is otherwise provided. Asbestos-cement piping shall be provided with adequate blocking.

1201.1.7 Installation.

1201.1.7.1 Same materials required. All piping materials used, except valves and similar devices, shall be of a like material except as otherwise acceptable to the building official.

1201.1.7.2 Wall thickness.

1. **Standard pipe.** Piping shall be at least standard weight brass or copper, Class 150 cast iron, standard weight wrought iron, ASTM Schedule 40 steel, or suitable asbestos-cement of adequate pressure rating.

2. **Tubing shall be at least.** Type K—for condensate return lines; Type L—for steam condenser cooling water lines, underground water lines, and aboveground water lines; Type M—for aboveground water lines not embedded in concrete or masonry.

1201.1.7.3 Piping embedded in structure. Piping shall not be built into or embedded in concrete or masonry; except, where used for radiant panel heating or cooling, black steel pipe, wrought-iron piping or Type L copper tubing may be so embedded.

1201.1.7.4 Cutting structure. Structural member shall not be seriously weakened or impaired by cutting or notching.

1201.1.7.5 Providing for expansion, contraction and settling. Piping shall be installed so that piping, connections and equipment shall not be subjected to excessive strains or stresses and provisions shall be made for expansion, contraction, shrinkage, and structural settlement.

1201.1.7.6 Circulation. Piping shall provide adequate circulation. Piping shall be graded so that all gases can move in the direction of the water flow to a vented section of the system. When sections of a piping system cannot be installed with the required grade, such sections shall be provided with automatic or manual air vents whose discharge is piped to an approved location. Steam traps shall be provided where required.

1201.1.7.7 Underground piping.

1. **Cinders and other corrosive material fills.** All piping passing through or under cinders or other corrosive fill materials shall be suitably protected from corrosion.

> **EXCEPTION:** Where a soil analysis by an acceptable testing laboratory shows the soil to be free of materials which may corrode the pipe to be installed, the requirements for protective coatings may be waived.

2. **Beneath buildings.** Piping installed within a building and in, or under, a concrete floor slab resting on the ground shall be installed as follows:

Ferrous piping. Ferrous piping shall be galvanized and covered with an approved protective coating.

Copper tubing. Copper tubing shall be installed without joints, where possible.

Asbestos-cement. Asbestos-cement pipe shall not be installed beneath any building.

3. **Outside of building—black wrought iron and black steel.** Black wrought-iron and black steel piping shall be protected against corrosion by an approved pipe wrapping.

4. **Asbestos-cement.** Asbestos-cement piping shall be installed in accordance with the manufacturer's recommendations, but shall not be installed within 2 feet (51 mm) of any building.

5. **Under walls or foundations.** Piping passing under walls or foundations shall be protected from breakage.

6. **Openings into buildings.** Voids around piping passing through concrete or masonry floors or walls shall be appropriately sealed at the opening into the building; sleeves shall be provided at such openings.

1201.1.7.8 Aboveground piping.

1. **Sleeves.** Sleeves shall be installed where piping passes through masonry or concrete, or through any fire separation.

2. **Insulation.** The temperature of surfaces within normal reach of building occupants shall not exceed 140°F (60°C) unless they are protected by suitable insulation. Where sleeves are installed, any insulation shall continue full-sized through them.

3. **Lining.** Combustible portions of unventilated spaces which contain piping or devices whose outside temperature, including

insulation, exceeds 140°F (60°C), shall be lined with No. 24 gage (0.021 inch) (0.53 mm) steel, or $^1/_4$-inch-thick (6.4 mm) insulating millboard.

4. **Clearance.** There shall be at least 1-inch (26 mm) clearance from structure around steam pipes.

5. **Exposed piping.** Exposed piping subject to excessive corrosion, erosion, or mechanical damage shall be suitably protected.

6. **Asbestos-cement piping.** Asbestos-cement piping shall not be installed within any building.

7. **Roof and wall openings.** Joints at the roof around pipes or appurtenances shall be made watertight by the use of approved flashings or flashing materials. Exterior wall openings shall be made watertight.

8. **Drainage.** Means shall be provided to drain all piping.

9. **Freezing.** Where required, piping outside of a building or in an exterior wall shall be protected from freezing.

1201.1.7.9 Trenches and tunnels.

1. **Protection of structure.** Trenches deeper than the footings of a building or structure and paralleling the same shall be at least 45 degrees therefrom, unless otherwise permitted by the building official.

2. **Mechanical equipment.** Use of mechanical excavating equipment is prohibited within 2 feet (610 mm) of existing piping or appurtenances.

3. **Tunneling and driving.** Tunnels shall, before backfilling, have a clear height of 2 feet (610 mm) above the pipe and shall be limited in length to one half the depth of the trench, with a maximum length of 8 feet (2438 mm). When pipes are driven, the drive pipe shall be at least one size larger than the pipe to be laid.

4. **Backfilling.** Excavations shall be completely backfilled as soon after inspection as practicable. Adequate precaution shall be taken to ensure proper compaction of backfill around piping without damage to such piping. Trenches shall be backfilled in thin layers to 12 inches (305 mm) above the top of the piping with clean earth which shall not contain stones, boulders, cinder-fill or other materials which would damage or break the piping or cause corrosive action. Mechanical devices such as bulldozers, graders, etc., may then be used to complete backfill to grade. Fill shall be properly compacted. Suitable precautions shall be taken to ensure permanent stability for pipe laid in filled or made ground.

1201.1.8 Pressure testing.

1201.1.8.1 Responsibility. The equipment, material and labor necessary for inspection or test shall be furnished by the person to whom the permit is issued or by whom inspection is requested.

1201.1.8.2 Media. The piping shall be tested with water.

1201.1.8.3 Pressure test. Piping shall be tested with a hydrostatic pressure of not less than 100 psig (689 kPa), but at least 50 psig (345 kPa) greater than operating pressure. This pressure shall be maintained for at least 30 minutes. Required tests shall be conducted by the owner or contractor in the presence of an authorized inspector. The piping being tested shall remain exposed to the inspector and shall not leak during the test.

1201.1.8.4 Moved structures. Piping systems of a building, and parts thereof, that are moved from one foundation to another shall be completely tested as prescribed elsewhere in this section for new work, except that walls or floors need not be removed during such test when equivalent means of inspection acceptable to the building official are provided.

1201.1.8.5 Test waived. No test or inspection shall be required where a system, or part thereof, is set up for exhibition purposes and has no connection with a water system.

1201.1.8.6 Exceptions. In cases where it would be impractical to provide the aforementioned tests, or for minor installations and repairs, the building official may make such inspection as deemed advisable in order to ensure that the work has been performed in accordance with the intent of this chapter.

SECTION 1202 — POLYBUTYLENE PIPE OR TUBING

1202.1 General. Those portions of the hot-water piping systems in which the continuous pressure-temperature relationship does not exceed the following may be constructed of polybutylene pipe or tubing of SDR-11 conforming to specification ASTM D 3309.

TEMPERATURE (°F)	PRESSURE (psi)
73 (23 °C)	200 (1379 kPa)
180 (82 °C)	100 (689 kPa)
200 (93 °C)	80 (552 kPa)

Polybutylene also may be used for applications requiring up to one year total exposure at conditions of 210°F (98.8°C), 150 psi (1027 kPa), typical conditions for temperature and pressure-relief valve discharge lines in heating systems.

1202.1.1 Materials and construction.

1202.1.1.1 PB pipe and tubing. Pipe shall be IPS or copper tube size polybutylene, both SDR-11 conforming to ASTM D 3309.

1202.1.1.2 Fittings. Fittings shall be of polybutylene or metal.

1202.1.1.3 Insulation. Coverings and insulation used on hot-water pipes shall be of materials suitable for the operating temperature of the system. The insulation, jackets and lap-seal adhesives shall be tested as a composite product and shall have a flame spread of not more than 25 and a smoke-developed rating of not more than 50 when tested in accordance with UBC Standard 8-1.

1202.1.1.4 Gaskets. Flanged PB systems may be installed without gaskets.

1202.1.1.5 Hangers, sleeves and anchors. Hangers, sleeves and anchors shall be suitable for the use intended as recommended by the manufacturer's installation instructions.

1202.1.1.6 Standards. All piping, tubing, valves, joints, fittings, devices and materials shall be free of defects and comply with nationally recognized standards approved by the building official.

1202.1.1.7 Marking. Materials and devices shall be suitably identified.

1202.1.2 Fabrication of joints. Joints shall be made by one or more of the following methods:

1202.1.2.1 Socket fusion. Polybutylene socket fittings may be heat fused to the pipe.

1202.1.2.2 Crimp/insert fittings. Insert fittings of metal with crimp rings of aluminum or copper may be used.

1202.1.2.3 Compression fittings. Metallic or polybutylene fittings utilizing compression seals are acceptable.

1202.1.2.4 Transition fittings. Connections to other piping materials shall be made by approved types of special transition fittings.

1202.1.3 Changes in direction. Changes in direction shall be made by the appropriate use of fittings or with pipe bends having a radius of not less than 10 diameters of the pipe. No forming equipment or heating is required.

1202.1.4 Hangers and supports. Piping and equipment shall be adequately supported to the satisfaction of the building official. Hot-water piping shall be supported, anchored and provided with swing joints, expansion loops or joints, or utilize the pipe's flexibility to avoid excessive strain on piping, equipment or the building structure to the satisfaction of the building official.

1202.1.5 Installation details.

1202.1.5.1 Piping embedded in structure. Piping shall not be built into or embedded in concrete or masonry, except where used for radiant panel heating or cooling. See Part II of this chapter.

1202.1.5.2 Cutting structure. Structural members shall not be seriously weakened or impaired by cutting or notching.

1202.1.5.3 Under walls or foundations. All piping passing under load-bearing foundations shall be protected by sleeving.

1202.1.5.4 Openings into buildings. Voids around piping passing through concrete or masonry floors or walls shall be appropriately sealed at the opening into the building; sleeves shall be provided at such openings.

1202.1.5.5 Aboveground piping.

1. **Sleeves.** Sleeves shall be installed where piping passes through masonry or concrete, or through any fire separation.

2. **Insulation.** The temperature of surfaces within normal reach of building occupants shall not exceed 140°F (60°C) unless they are protected by suitable insulation. Where sleeves are installed, any insulation shall continue full sized through them.

1202.1.5.6 Belowground piping.

1. **Protection of structure.** All trenches deeper than the footings of any building or structure and paralleling the same shall be at least 45 degrees therefrom, unless otherwise permitted by the building official.

2. **Mechanical equipment.** Use of mechanical excavating equipment is prohibited within 2 feet (610 mm) of existing piping or appurtenances.

3. **Boring and pulling.** Boring pipe shall be at least one size larger than the pipe to be laid. Pulling force shall not exceed the tensile yield strength of the pipe.

4. **Backfilling.** All excavations shall be completely backfilled as soon after inspection as practicable. Adequate precaution shall be taken to ensure proper compaction of the backfill around piping without damage to such piping. Trenches shall be backfilled in thin layers to 12 inches (305 mm) above the top of the piping with clean earth which shall not contain stones, boulders, cinderfill or other materials which would damage or break the piping. Mechanical devices such as bulldozers, graders, etc., may then be used to complete backfill to grade. Fill shall be properly compacted. Suitable precautions shall be taken to ensure permanent stability for pipe laid in filled or made ground.

5. **Pipe or tube under concrete.** Pipe or tubing installed beneath footings or slab shall be in continuous lengths or with fused joints.

1202.1.6 Pressure testing.

1202.1.6.1 Responsibility. The equipment, material and labor necessary for inspection or test shall be furnished by the person to whom the permit is issued or by whom inspection is requested.

1202.1.6.2 Media. The piping shall be tested with water.

1202.1.6.3 Pressure test. Piping shall be tested with a hydrostatic pressure of not less than 100 psig (689 kPa) or 1.5 times the system design operating pressure. The pressure shall be maintained for 30 minutes at which time the indicated pressure may have decreased due to the initial expansion of the pipe. After 30 minutes, adjust the system to the required pressure and visually inspect for leaks. Required tests shall be conducted by the owner or contractor in the presence of an authorized inspector. The piping being tested shall remain exposed to the inspector and shall not leak during the test.

Part II—Hydronic Panel Heating Systems

SECTION 1203 — GENERAL

1203.1 Purpose. The purpose of Part II is to establish and provide minimum standards for the protection of public health, welfare and property by regulating and controlling the design and installation of panel heating systems.

SECTION 1204 — INSTALLATION

1204.1 Design and Installation. Panel systems shall be designed and installed in accordance with the recognized standard incorporated in Chapter 16, Part III, Panel Heating, and the requirements of this code.

1204.2 Pressure Test. Piping to be embedded in concrete shall be pressure tested prior to pouring concrete. During pouring, the pipe shall be maintained at the proposed operating pressure.

SECTION 1205 — PIPING MATERIALS

1205.1 Panel. Piping for heating panel shall be standard-weight steel pipe, Type L copper tubing, polybutylene or other approved plastic pipe or tubing rated at 100 psi (690 kPa) at 180°F (82°C) in accordance with design stresses listed in Appendix C, or other materials suitable for this type of design approved by the building official.

1205.2 Hot-water Supply Lines. Piping for hot-water supply lines shall be installed according to requirements in Part I of this chapter.

SECTION 1206 — PIPING JOINTS

1206.1 General. Joints of pipe or tubing forming the panel that are embedded in a portion of the building, for example, concrete or plaster, shall be in accordance with the following:

1. Steel pipe welded with electrical arc or oxygen/acetylene method.

2. Copper tubing joined with solder or copper brazing rods having a melting point of 1,000°F (537°C).

3. Polybutylene pipe and tubing installed in continuous lengths or with heat-fused polybutylene fittings.

Joints of other piping in cavities or running exposed shall be joined by the use of normally accepted methods in accordance with manufacturer's recommendations and related sections of this code.

SECTION 1207 — HEAT SOURCES

1207.1 Hot Water. Heat sources for generating hot water for use in hydronic panel radiant heating systems shall include conventional fossil fuel, hot water boilers, electrical resistance heated boilers, air/water or water/water heat pumps.

Systems shall be protected by pressure-temperature relief valves as outlined in this code.

SECTION 1208 — TESTING

1208.1 Hydrostatic Test. Approved piping or tubing installed as a portion of a radiant panel system that will be embedded in the walls, floors or ceilings of the building it is designed to heat shall be tested for leaks by the hydrostatic test method by applying at least 100 psi (690 kPa) water pressure or one and one half times the operating pressure, whichever is the greater.

1208.2 Metal Pipe. For metal piping, a pressure gauge shall be connected to the piping, and after the pressure has been raised, the hydrostatic pressure connection shall be discontinued, and the systems under pressure shall remain at the test pressure for a sufficient period of time to determine whether any leaks exist in the system. Leaks shall be indicated by the pressure drop on the gauge. Minimum test period shall be 30 minutes.

1208.3 Plastic Pipe. For flexible plastic piping, the test pressure shall be applied for a period of 30 minutes. During this time, the system shall be maintained at the test pressure by the periodic addition of makeup water to compensate for the initial stretching of the pipe. The system shall then be visually inspected for tightness.

1208.4 Acceptance. Tests for tightness of radiant piping systems shall be witnessed by the building official.

Chapter 13
FUEL-GAS PIPING

NOTE: The provisions of this chapter were moved from Appendix B.

SECTION 1301 — GENERAL

1301.1 Scope. The regulations of this chapter shall govern the installation of fuel-gas piping in or in connection with a building or structure or within the property lines of premises, other than service pipe.

SECTION 1302 — PERMIT

A permit shall be obtained prior to installation, removal, alteration or repair of fuel-gas piping systems as required by the provisions of Chapter 1 of this code.

SECTION 1303 — PLANS REQUIRED

The building official may require submission of plans, specifications, drawings and such other information as deemed necessary prior to the commencement of and at any time during the progress of work regulated by this chapter.

SECTION 1304 — WORKMANSHIP

Gas piping shall not be strained or bent nor shall appliances be supported by or develop strain or stress on supply piping. Gas piping supplying appliances designed to be supported by the piping may be used to support appliances.

SECTION 1305 — INSPECTIONS

1305.1 General. Upon completion of installation, alteration or repair of gas piping, and prior to the use thereof, the building official shall be notified that gas piping is ready for inspection.

1305.2 Accessibility for Inspection. Excavations required for the installation of underground piping shall be kept open until such time as the piping has been inspected and approved. If piping is covered or concealed before approval, it shall be exposed upon the direction of the building official.

1305.3 Required Inspections. The building official shall make the following inspections and shall either approve that portion of the work as completed or shall notify the permit holder wherein the same fails to comply with this chapter.

1305.3.1 Rough piping inspection. This inspection shall be made after gas piping authorized by the permit has been installed and before such piping has been covered or concealed or a fixture or appliance has been attached thereto. This inspection shall include a determination that the gas piping size, material and installation meet the requirements of this chapter.

1305.3.2 Final piping inspection. This inspection shall be made after piping authorized by the permit has been installed and after all portions thereof which are to be covered or concealed are so concealed and before fixtures, appliances or shutoff valves have been attached thereto.

This inspection shall include an air, carbon dioxide or nitrogen pressure test, at which time the gas piping shall stand a pressure of not less than 10-pounds-per-square-inch (69 kPa) gage or, at the discretion of the building official, the piping and valves may be tested at a pressure of at least 6 inches mercury (20.3 kPa), measured with a manometer or slope gage. Test pressures shall be held for a length of time satisfactory to the building official but not less than 15 minutes, with no perceptible drop in pressure. For welded piping, and for piping carrying gas at pressures exceeding 14 inches water column (3.5 kPa) pressure, the test pressure shall be at least 60 pounds per square inch (414 kPa) and shall be continued for a length of time satisfactory to the building official but not less than 30 minutes. These tests shall be made using air, carbon dioxide or nitrogen pressure only and shall be made in the presence of the building official. Necessary apparatus for conducting tests shall be furnished by the permit holder.

1305.4 Other Inspections. In cases where the work authorized by the permit consists of a minor installation of additional piping to piping already connected to a gas meter, the foregoing inspections may be waived at the discretion of the building official. The building official shall make such inspections as are deemed advisable to ensure that the work has been performed in accordance with the intent of this chapter.

SECTION 1306 — CERTIFICATE OF INSPECTION

1306.1 Issuance of Certificate. If, upon final piping inspection, the installation is found to comply with the provisions of this chapter, a certificate of inspection may be issued by the building official.

1306.2 Copy to Utility. A copy of the certificate of final piping inspection shall be issued to the serving gas supplier supplying gas to the premises.

1306.3 Turn On. It shall be unlawful for a serving gas supplier, or person furnishing gas, to turn on, or cause to be turned on, fuel gas or gas meters, until the certificate of final inspection, as herein provided, has been issued.

SECTION 1307 — AUTHORITY TO RENDER GAS SERVICE

1307.1 Reconnection. It shall be unlawful for a person, firm or corporation, excepting an authorized agent or employee of a person, firm or corporation engaged in the business of furnishing or supplying gas and whose service pipes supply or connect with the particular premises, to turn on or reconnect gas service in or on a premises where and when gas service is, at the time, not being rendered.

1307.2 System Capped. It shall be unlawful to turn on or connect gas in or on a premises unless gas piping outlets are properly and securely connected to gas appliances or capped or plugged with threaded fittings.

SECTION 1308 — AUTHORITY TO DISCONNECT

1308.1 General. The building official or the serving gas supplier is authorized to disconnect any gas piping or appliance, or both, which is found not to conform to the requirements of this chapter or which is found defective and a danger to life or property.

1308.2 Disconnection Notice. A notice of disconnection shall be attached to defective piping and appliances stating why they have been disconnected.

1308.3 Closing Outlets. It shall be unlawful to remove or disconnect gas piping or a gas appliance without capping or plugging the outlet from which said pipe or appliance was removed with a threaded fitting. Outlets on a piping system which has been installed, altered or repaired to which gas appliances are not connected shall be left capped gastight.

> **EXCEPTION:** When an approved listed quick-disconnect device is installed.

SECTION 1309 — TEMPORARY USE OF GAS

The building official may allow temporary use of fuel gas from a gas piping system conforming to the requirements of this chapter. The period of temporary use shall be established by the building official.

SECTION 1310 — GAS METER LOCATIONS

1310.1 General. Gas meter locations shall be approved by the building official.

1310.2 Multiple Meters. When more than one meter is set on a premises, they shall all be set at one location, except when this is impractical. In multiple meter installations, each gas piping system shall be identified by the permittee in manner satisfactory to the building official and the serving gas supplier.

1310.3 Main Shutoff. Gas meters shall be preceded by a main supply shutoff valve and shall be so placed as to be readily accessible for inspection, reading, testing and shutting off the gas supply. Service piping and main supply shutoff valves shall be outside of the building and readily accessible.

1310.4 Inlet Location. The gas piping inlet shall be located adjacent to the approved meter location.

1310.5 Meter Access. Access to enclosed gas meters, except those located in an approved vault supplied by the serving gas supplier, shall be through an opening or door not less in size than 22 inches by 24 inches (559 mm by 610 mm).

1310.6 Meter Location. Gas meters shall not be located under a show window or under interior stairways or in engine, boiler, heater or electric meter rooms. Where not prohibited by other regulations, gas meters may be located in the open under exterior stairways.

SECTION 1311 — MATERIAL FOR GAS PIPING

1311.1 General. Pipe used for the installation, extension, alteration or repair of gas piping shall be standard weight wrought iron or steel (galvanized or black), yellow brass containing not more than 75 percent copper, or internally tinned or equivalently treated copper of iron pipe size. Corrugated stainless steel tubing may be permitted provided that it is part of a system listed by an approved agency as complying with the reference standard listed in Chapter 16, Part III. Approved PE pipe may be used in exterior buried piping systems.

1311.2 Reused Pipe. Gas pipe shall be new or shall have been used previously for no purpose other than conveying gas; it shall be in good condition, clean and free from internal obstructions. Burred ends shall be reamed to the full bore of the pipe.

1311.3 Fittings. Fittings used in connection with the piping shall be of malleable iron, yellow brass containing not more than 75 percent copper or approved plastic fittings.

1311.4 Valves and Appurtenances. Valves and appurtenances for gas piping shall be of a type designed and approved for use with fuel gas.

SECTION 1312 — INSTALLATION OF GAS PIPING

1312.1 Joints. Joints in the piping system, unless welded, shall be threaded joints having approved standard threads. The threaded joints shall be made with approved pipe joint material, insoluble in fuel gas and applied to the male threads only. Welded joints in a gas-supply system shall be made by an approved, qualified welder. See Section 218.

1312.2 Location. Gas piping shall not be installed in or on the ground under any building or structure and exposed gas piping shall be kept at least 6 inches (152 mm) above grade or structure. The term "building or structure" shall include structures such as porches and steps, whether covered or uncovered, breezeways, roofed porte-cocheres, roofed patios, carports, covered walks, covered driveways, and similar structures or appurtenances.

Concealed unprotected gas piping may be installed above grade in approved recesses or channels.

> **EXCEPTION:** When necessary due to structural conditions, approved-type gas piping may be installed in other locations when permission has first been obtained from the building official.

1312.3 Piping through Foundation Wall. Underground piping, where installed below grade through the outer foundation or basement wall of a building, shall be encased in a protective pipe. The annular space between the gas piping and the sleeve shall be sealed at the foundation or basement wall to prevent entry of gas or water.

1312.4 Aboveground Piping Outside. Piping installed aboveground shall be securely supported and located where it will be protected from physical damage. Where passing through an outside wall, the piping shall also be protected against corrosion by coating or wrapping with an inert material. Where piping is encased in a protective pipe sleeve, the annular space between the gas piping and the sleeve shall be sealed at the wall to prevent the entry of water, insects or rodents.

1312.5 Drip Pipes. When water vapor is present in the fuel gas served, accessible drip pipes shall be provided at points where condensation will collect.

1312.6 Corrosion and Covering Protection. Ferrous gas piping installed underground in exterior locations shall be protected from corrosion by approved coatings or wrapping materials applied in an approved manner. Horizontal metallic piping shall have at least 12 inches (305 mm) of earth cover or equivalent protection. Plastic gas piping shall have at least 18 inches (457 mm) of earth cover or equivalent protection. Risers, including prefabricated risers inserted with plastic pipe, shall be metallic and shall be protected in an approved manner to a point at least 6 inches above grade. When a riser connects to plastic pipe underground, the horizontal metallic portion underground shall be at least 30 inches (762 mm) in length before connecting to the plastic service pipe. An approved transition fitting or adaptor shall be used where the plastic joins the metallic riser.

> **EXCEPTION:** Listed one-piece 90-degree transition fittings or risers may have less than 30 inches (762 mm) of horizontal metallic piping.

1312.7 Electrical Isolation of Fuel Gas Piping. Underground ferrous gas piping shall be electrically isolated from the rest of the gas system with listed or approved isolation fittings installed a minimum of 6 inches (152 mm) above grade.

1312.8 Wrapping. Gas pipe protective coatings shall be approved types, machine applied, conforming to recognized standards. Field wrapping shall provide equivalent protection and is restricted to those fittings, short sections, and where the factory wrap has been damaged or necessarily stripped for threading or welding. Zinc coatings (galvanizing) shall not be deemed adequate protection for gas piping below ground. Ferrous metals exposed in exterior locations shall be protected from corrosion in a manner satisfactory to the building official.

1312.9 Support and Fill. Gas piping shall be adequately supported by metal straps or hooks at intervals not to exceed those shown in Table 13-A. Gas piping installed below grade shall be effectively supported at all points on undisturbed or well-compacted soil or sand.

1312.10 Building Shutoff. Gas piping supplying more than one building on a premises shall be equipped with separate shutoff valves to each building, so arranged that the gas supply can be turned on or off to an individual or separate building. The shutoff valve shall be located outside the building it supplies and shall be readily accessible. Buildings accessory to single-family residences are exempt from the requirements of this section.

1312.11 Unions. Where unions are necessary, right and left nipples and couplings shall be used. Ground-joint unions may be used at exposed fixture, appliance or equipment connections and in exposed exterior locations immediately on the discharge side of a building shutoff valve. Heavy-duty flanged-type unions may be used in special cases, when approved by the building official. Bushings shall not be in concealed locations.

1312.12 Interjections. When air, oxygen or other special supplementary gas under pressure is introduced with the regularly supplied gas, either directly into the gas piping system or at burners, a device approved by the building official shall be installed to prevent backflow of the supplemental gas into the gas piping system. The device shall be located between the source of the supplemental gas and meter and shall be on the gas line leading to the appliance using the special gas. This device may be either a spring-loaded or diaphragm-type check valve and shall be capable of withstanding the pressure imposed on it.

When liquefied petroleum or other standby gas is interconnected with the regular gas piping system, an approved three-way two-port valve or other adequate safeguard acceptable to the building official shall be installed to prevent backflow into either supply system.

1312.13 Valves. Valves used in connection with gas piping shall be approved types, and shall be accessible.

1312.14 Barbecue or Fireplace Outlets. Gas outlets in a barbecue or fireplace shall be controlled by an approved operating valve located in the same room and outside the fireplace but not more than 4 feet (1219 mm) from the outlets. If piping on the discharge side of the control valve is standard weight brass or galvanized steel, the piping may be embedded in or surrounded by not less than 2 inches (51 mm) of concrete or masonry.

1312.15 Shutoff Valve. An accessible shutoff valve of a type set forth in Section 1312.13 shall be installed in the fuel-supply piping outside of each appliance and ahead of the union connection thereto, and in addition to any valve on the appliance. Shutoff valves shall be within 3 feet (914 mm) of the appliance they serve, and in the same room or space where the appliance is located.

Shutoff valves may be located immediately adjacent to and inside or under an appliance when placed in an accessible and protected location and when such appliance may be removed without removal of the valve.

Shutoff valves may be accessibly located inside wall heaters and wall furnaces listed for recessed installation where necessary maintenance can be performed without removal of the shutoff valve.

1312.16 Tracer for Nonmetallic Buried Piping. An electrically continuous minimum No. 18 AWG [0.040-inch diameter (1 mm)] copper tracer wire with yellow insulation shall be installed with and attached to underground nonmetallic gas piping and shall terminate above grade at each end.

1312.17 Directional Changes. Changes in direction of gas piping shall be made by use of appropriate fittings, except that polyethylene gas piping and tubing may be bent to a radius not less than 20 times the nominal diameter of the pipe or tube.

SECTION 1313 — APPLIANCE FUEL CONNECTORS

Appliance connections shall have a diameter not less than that of the inlet connection to the appliance as provided by the manufacturer and each appliance shall be rigidly connected to the gas piping with materials as provided in Section 1311.1.

> **EXCEPTION:** A gas appliance may be connected with an approved listed metal appliance connector under the following conditions:
>
> 1. Listed metal appliance connectors shall have an overall length not to exceed 3 feet (914 mm), except range and domestic clothes dryer connectors, which may not exceed 6 feet (1829 mm).
>
> 2. Connectors shall not be concealed within or extended through a wall, floor or partition and shall not extend through an appliance housing or casing.
>
> 3. A listed appliance connector valve not less than the nominal size of the connector shall be accessible at the gas piping outlet immediately ahead of the connector.
>
> 4. Connectors shall be of adequate size to provide the total demand of the connected appliance based on Table 13-B-1 or 13-B-2 as applicable.
>
> 5. Aluminum alloy connectors may be used only in interior locations where they shall not be in contact with masonry, plaster or insulation or are not subject to repeated corrosive wettings.
>
> 6. The connection of an indoor appliance with any type of gas hose is prohibited, except when used for laboratory or shop equipment or equipment that requires mobility during operation. Such connections shall have the shutoff or stopcock installed at the connection to the building piping. When gas hose is used, it shall be of the minimum practical length, but not to exceed 6 feet (1829 mm), except for hand torches and special mobile equipment, and shall not extend from one room to another nor pass through walls, partitions, ceilings or floors. Gas hose shall not be concealed from view or used in a concealed location. Only listed gas hose shall be used in accordance with its listing. Gas hose shall not be used where it is likely to be subject to temperatures exceeding 125°F (52°C), nor shall it be used as a substitute for a standard appliance connector.
>
> 7. Outdoor portable appliances may be connected with an approved outdoor hose connector not to exceed 15 feet (4572 mm) in length, provided it connects outdoors to approved gas piping, including an approved valve at the inlet of the hose connector.
>
> 8. Appliances may be connected to fuel-gas piping with an approved listed quick-disconnect device.

SECTION 1314 — LIQUEFIED PETROLEUM GAS FACILITIES AND PIPING

1314.1 General. In addition to the requirements of this chapter for gas piping, the facilities and piping for use with liquefied petroleum gas shall meet the following requirements:

1. Liquefied petroleum gas facilities shall conform to approved standards. Liquefied petroleum gas facilities and their locations shall be approved by the building official and shall conform to state and local fire-prevention regulations.

2. When liquefied petroleum gas facilities serve more than one customer through separate piping systems, each system shall be identified in a manner satisfactory to the building official.

3. Liquefied petroleum gas facilities shall be so placed as to be readily accessible for inspection, reading, testing and shutting off the gas supply. Service piping and main supply shutoff valves shall be outside of the building. Main supply valves shall be of approved type and readily accessible.

4. Gas piping inlets shall be located with respect to the proposed liquefied petroleum gas facility location in accordance with the requirements of this section.

5. Liquefied petroleum gas facilities shall not be located in a pit or basement, under show windows or interior stairways, or in engine, boiler, heater or electric meter rooms. When not prohibited by another regulation, approved liquefied petroleum gas metering devices may be located in the open under exterior stairways.

6. Liquefied petroleum gas piping shall not serve appliances located in a pit or basement where heavier-than-air gas might collect to form a flammable mixture.

7. Pipe-joint compounds used on threaded connections shall be insoluble in liquefied petroleum gas.

8. Valves and appurtenances used in liquefied petroleum gas systems shall be designed and approved for use with liquefied petroleum gas.

9. Discharge from relief valves shall be into open air and shall be at least 5 feet (1524 mm) measured horizontally from an opening into a building which is below the discharge.

SECTION 1315 — LEAKS

1315.1 Locating Leaks. Leaks in gas piping shall be located by applying soapy water to the exterior of the piping.

1315.2 Prohibited Materials. Flame or acid shall not be used to locate or repair leaks, nor shall substances other than air, carbon dioxide or nitrogen be introduced into the gas piping.

1315.3 Replacements. Defective pipe or fitting shall be removed and replaced with sound material when found.

SECTION 1316 — INTERCONNECTIONS OF GAS PIPING SYSTEMS

1316.1 More than One System. It shall be unlawful to connect a gas appliance in such a manner that the appliance may receive gas from more than one system of gas piping.

1316.2 Prohibition. The installation, use or maintenance of a gas valve which makes it possible to turn on, control or otherwise direct the flow of gas from one system of gas piping to another, where the systems are supplied with gas from separate meters, is prohibited, and valves or other interconnection between separate systems of gas piping shall be removed upon order of the building official.

SECTION 1317 — REQUIRED GAS SUPPLY

1317.1 General. Natural gas regulations and tables are based on the use of gas having a specific gravity of 0.60 supplied at 6 to 8 inches water column (1.5 to 2.0 kPa) pressure at the outlet of the meter. For undiluted liquefied petroleum gas, gas piping may be sized for 2,500 Btu per cubic foot (93 148 kJ/m^3) at 11 inches water column (2.7 kPa) and specific gravity of 1.52.

When gas of a different specific gravity is to be delivered, the serving gas supplier should be contacted for conversion factors or revised capacity tables to use in sizing piping systems.

1317.2 Determining Volume. The hourly volume of gas required at each piping outlet shall be taken as not less than the maximum hourly rating as specified by the manufacturer of the appliance or appliances to be connected to each such outlet.

When gas appliances to be installed have not been definitely specified, Table 13-C may be used to estimate requirements of typical appliances.

To obtain the cubic feet per hour (L/s) of gas required, divide Btu per hour (W) input of appliances by the average Btu heating value per cubic foot (J/L) of the gas. The average Btu per cubic foot (J/L) of the gas in the area of the installation may be obtained from the serving gas supplier.

1317.3 Minimum Size. The size of the supply piping outlet for a gas appliance shall be at least $^1/_2$ inch (13 mm). The minimum size piping outlet for a mobile home shall be $^3/_4$ inch (19 mm).

SECTION 1318 — REQUIRED GAS PIPING SIZE

1318.1 General. When the maximum demand does not exceed 250 cubic feet per hour (1.97 L/s) and the maximum length of piping between the meter and the most distant outlet does not exceed 250 feet (76 200 mm), the size of each section and each outlet of any system of gas piping shall be determined by using Table 13-D. Other systems within the range of Table 13-D may be sized from that table or by the methods set forth in Section 1318.2.

To determine the size of each section of pipe in a system within the range of Table 13-D, proceed as follows:

1. Measure the length of the pipe from the gas meter location to the most remote outlet on the system.

2. In Table 13-D, select the column showing that distance, or the next longer distance, if the table does not give the exact length.

3. Starting at the most remote outlet, find in the vertical column just selected, the gas demand for that outlet. If the exact figure of demand is not shown, choose the next larger figure below in the column.

4. Opposite this demand figure, in the first column at the left in Table 13-D, the correct size of pipe will be found.

5. Using this same vertical column, proceed in a similar manner for each section of pipe serving this outlet. For each section of pipe, determine the total gas demand supplied by that section. Where gas piping sections serve both heating and cooling equipment and the installation prevents both units from operating simultaneously, only the larger of the two demand loads need be used in sizing these sections.

6. Size each section of branch piping not previously sized by measuring the distance from the gas meter location to the most remote outlet in that branch and follow the procedures of steps 2, 3, 4 and 5 above. **NOTE:** Size branch piping in the order of their distance from the meter location, beginning with the most distant outlet not previously sized.

1318.2 High Demands and Long Runs. For conditions other than those covered by Section 1318.1, such as longer runs or greater gas demands, the size of each gas piping system shall be determined by standard engineering methods acceptable to the building official and each system shall be so designed that the total pressure drop between the meter or other point of supply and any outlet when full demand is being supplied to all outlets will not exceed 0.5-inch water column pressure (124 Pa).

1318.3 Other Systems. When the gas pressure is higher than 14 inches or lower than 6 inches water column (< 3.5 kPa or > 1.5 kPa), or when diversity demand factors are used, the design, pipe, sizing, materials, location and use of such systems shall be approved by the building official. Piping systems designed for pressures higher than the serving gas supplier's standard delivery pressure shall have prior verification from the gas supplier of the availability of the design pressure. Systems using undiluted liquefied petroleum gas may be sized using Table 13-E for 11 inches water column and in accordance with the provisions of Sections 1318.1 and 1318.2.

SECTION 1319 — MEDIUM- AND HIGH-PRESSURE GAS PIPING

1319.1 General. Approval by the building official and verification from the serving gas supplier of the availability of the desired pressure shall be obtained before any medium- or high-pressure gas piping system is installed.

1319.2 Applicability. The following requirements shall apply to medium-pressure gas piping systems.

1319.3 Pressure Regulators. Approved regulators shall be installed on medium- and high-pressure gas piping systems, in approved locations, and shall be accessible for servicing. Each regulator shall have a separate vent to the outside.

> **EXCEPTION:** Pounds-to-inches water-column regulators equipped with limiting orifices capable of releasing not more than 5 cubic feet of gas per hour (2.36 L/s) when supplied with medium pressure need not be vented to an outside location when the regulators have been approved by the building official. These regulators shall:
>
> 1. Be connected to the same piping material used to pipe the structure. A listed gas connector may be used to attach the low-pressure piping downstream of the regulator to the appliance manifold.
>
> 2. Have an approved gas valve in the supply line upstream of the pounds-to-inches water-column regulator.
>
> 3. Be accessible.
>
> 4. Have the upstream pressure identified. Such identification shall be a metal tag permanently attached to the regulator and stating: Warning: $^1/_2$ pound to 5 pounds (3.4 to 34.4 kPa) natural gas pressure. DO NOT REMOVE.
>
> 5. Be installed in a location that communicates with a ventilated area.

An approved gas valve shall be installed immediately preceding each regulator. Regulators that may be subjected to mechanical damage shall be substantially protected to the satisfaction of the building official.

1319.4 Three or 5 psig (21 or 34 kPa). Tables 13-F and 13-G may be used to size a natural-gas piping system carrying 3 or 5 psig (21 or 34 kPa) gas. The procedure to determine the size of each section of the system is similar to that contained in Section 1318 using the pipe length from the meter to the most remote regulator on the medium-pressure system and sizing the downstream low-pressure piping from Table 13-D.

1319.5 Ten psig (69 kPa). Table 13-H may be used to size undiluted liquefied petroleum gas piping systems carrying 10 psig (69 kPa) gas. The procedure to determine the size of each section of the system is similar to Section 1318 using the pipe length from the first stage or tank regulator to the most remote regulator in the second-state system. Low-pressure piping shall be sized from Table 13-E.

1319.6 Corrosion and Cover Protection. Buried medium-pressure gas piping shall be protected from corrosion as required by Section 1312 and shall have a minimum earth cover of 18 inches (457 mm). Piping shall be covered with at least 6 inches

(152 mm) of hand-placed selected backfill devoid of rocks, building materials or other matter that may damage the pipe or wrapping.

SECTION 1320 — FUEL-GAS EQUIPMENT AND INSTALLATIONS IN MANUFACTURED OR MOBILE HOME OR RECREATIONAL VEHICLE PARKS

1320.1 General. Except as otherwise permitted or required by this section, fuel-gas equipment and installations in manufactured or mobile home or recreational vehicle parks shall comply with the provisions of this code. The provisions of this section do not apply to the manufactured or mobile home or recreational vehicle gas piping and equipment.

1320.2 Required Gas Supply. The minimum hourly volume of gas required at each manufactured or mobile home or recreational vehicle lot outlet or any section of the manufactured or mobile home or recreational vehicle park gas piping system shall be calculated as shown in Table 13-I.

Required gas supply for buildings or other fuel-gas-consuming appliances connected to the manufactured or mobile home or recreational vehicle park gas piping system shall be calculated as provided in this code.

1320.3 Installation. Gas piping installed below ground shall have a minimum earth cover of 18 inches (458 mm).

Gas piping shall not be installed above ground under a manufactured or mobile home, or recreational vehicle.

1320.4 Location. Gas piping shall not be installed underground beneath buildings or that portion of the manufactured or mobile home or recreational vehicle lots reserved for the location of manufactured or mobile homes or recreational vehicles, manufactured or mobile home or recreational vehicle accessory buildings or structures, concrete slabs or automobile parking, unless installed in a gastight conduit.

The conduit shall be of material approved for installation underground beneath buildings and not less than Schedule 40 pipe. The interior diameter of the conduit shall be at least $^1/_2$ inch (13 mm) larger than the outside diameter of the gas piping.

The conduit shall extend to a point at least 12 inches (305 mm) beyond any area where it is required, or the outside wall of a building, and the outer ends shall not be sealed. When the conduit terminates within a building, it shall be readily accessible and the space between the conduit and the gas piping shall be sealed to prevent leakage of gas into the building.

A gas piping lateral terminating in a manufactured or mobile home or recreational vehicle lot outlet riser surrounded by a concrete slab shall not be required to be installed in a conduit provided the concrete slab is entirely outside the wall line of the manufactured or mobile home or recreational vehicle, is not continuous with any other concrete slab and is used for stabilizing other utility connections.

1320.5 System Shutoff Valve. A readily accessible and identified approved shutoff valve controlling the flow of gas to the entire gas piping system shall be installed near the point of connection to the service piping or supply connection of the liquefied petroleum gas tank.

1320.6 Manufactured or Mobile Home or Recreational Vehicle Lot Shutoff Valve. Each manufactured or mobile home or recreational vehicle lot shall have an approved gas shutoff valve installed upstream of the manufactured or mobile home or recreational vehicle lot gas outlet and located on the outlet riser at a height at least 4 inches (102 mm) above grade. Such valve shall not be located under a manufactured or mobile home or recreational vehicle. When the manufactured or mobile home or recreational vehicle lot outlet is not in use, the outlet shall be equipped with an approved cap or plug to prevent accidental discharge of gas.

1320.7 Manufactured or Mobile Home or Recreational Vehicle Lot Gas Outlet. Each manufactured or mobile home or recreational vehicle lot piped for gas shall be provided with an individual outlet riser at the manufactured or mobile home or recreational vehicle lot.

The manufactured or mobile home or recreational vehicle lot gas outlet shall terminate with the service connection in the rear third section and within 4 feet (1219 mm) of the proposed location of the manufactured or mobile home or recreational vehicle on the lot.

1320.8 Manufactured or Mobile Home or Recreational Vehicle Connector. Each manufactured or mobile home or recreational vehicle shall be connected to the lot outlet by an approved or listed gas connector, a maximum of 6 feet (1829 mm) in length. Approved pipe fittings may be used between the flexible connector and the lot gas outlet when the distance between the manufactured or mobile home or recreational vehicle lot gas outlet and the manufactured or mobile home or recreational vehicle gas service connection exceeds that required to make a safe installation with only a manufactured or mobile home or recreational vehicle connector. Gas connectors shall be of a size to adequately supply the total demand of the connected manufactured or mobile home or recreational vehicle.

1320.9 Mechanical Protection. Gas outlet risers, regulators, meters, valves or other exposed equipment shall be protected from mechanical damage. Such protection may consist of posts, fencing or other permanent barriers.

Atmospherically controlled regulators shall be installed in such a manner that moisture cannot enter the regulator vent and accumulate above the diaphragm. When the regulator vent may be obstructed by snow or ice, shields, hoods or other suitable devices shall be provided to guard against obstruction of the vent opening.

1320.10 Gas Meters. Meters shall be installed in ventilated or accessible locations, not closer than 3 feet (914 mm) to sources of ignition.

When meters are installed, they shall not depend on the gas outlet riser for support, but shall be adequately supported by a post or bracket placed on a firm footing, or other approved means providing equivalent support.

1320.11 Gas Piping Size. The size of each section of natural gas or LP-gas piping systems shall be determined as specified in this chapter.

1320.12 Maintenance. The operator of the manufactured or mobile home or recreational vehicle park shall be responsible for maintaining gas piping installations and equipment in a safe working condition.

1320.13 Inspections and Tests. Inspections and tests shall be made in accordance with Section 1305.

TABLE 13-A—SUPPORT OF PIPING

SIZE OF PIPE (inches)	FEET
× 25.4 for mm	× 304.8 for mm
$^1/_2$	6
$^3/_4$ or 1	8
$1^1/_4$ or larger (horizontal)	10
$1^1/_4$ or larger (vertical)	Every floor level

TABLE 13-B-1—CAPACITIES OF LISTED METAL APPLIANCE CONNECTORS[1]
For use with gas pressure 8-inch or more water column (1990 Pa)

SEMIRIGID CONNECTOR O.D.[2] (inch)	FLEXIBLE CONNECTOR NOMINAL I.D.[3] (inch)	MAXIMUM CAPACITIES IN THOUSANDS Btu/h [Based on pressure drop of 0.4-inch water column (100 Pa)] Natural Gas[4] of 1,100 Btu/cu.ft. (41 030 kJ/m³)							
		× 0.293 for W							
		All Gas Appliances					Ranges and Domestic Clothes Dryers Only		
× 25.4 for mm		1-foot (305 mm)	$1^1/_2$-foot (457 mm)	2-foot (610 mm)	$2^1/_2$-foot (762 mm)	3-foot (914 mm)	4-foot (1219 mm)	5-foot (1524 mm)	6-foot (1829 mm)
$^3/_8$	$^1/_4$	40	33	29	27	25			
$^1/_2$	$^3/_8$	93	76	66	62	58			
$^5/_8$	$^1/_2$	189	155	134	125	116	101	90	80
	$^3/_4$	404	330	287	266	244			
	1	803	661	573	534	500			

[1]Gas connectors are certified by the approved agency as complete assemblies, including fittings and valves. Capacities shown are based on the use of fittings and valves supplied with the connector.

[2]Semirigid connector listings are based on outside diameter.

[3]Flexible connector listings are based on nominal diameter.

[4]For liquefied petroleum gas, use 1.6 times the natural gas capacities shown.

TABLE 13-B-2—CAPACITIES OF LISTED METAL APPLIANCE CONNECTORS[1]
For use with gas pressures less than 8-inch water column (1990 Pa)

SEMIRIGID CONNECTOR O.D.[2] (inch)	FLEXIBLE CONNECTOR NOMINAL I.D.[3] (inch)	MAXIMUM CAPACITIES IN THOUSANDS Btu/h [Based on pressure drop of 0.2-inch water column (50 Pa)] Natural Gas[4] of 1,100 Btu/cu.ft. (41 030 kJ/m³)							
		× 0.293 for W							
		All Gas Appliances					Ranges and Domestic Clothes Dryers Only		
× 25.4 for mm		1-foot (305 mm)	$1^1/_2$-foot (457 mm)	2-foot (610 mm)	$2^1/_2$-foot (762 mm)	3-foot (914 mm)	4-foot (1219 mm)	5-foot (1524 mm)	6-foot (1829 mm)
$^3/_8$	$^1/_4$	28	23	20	19	17			
$^1/_2$	$^3/_8$	66	54	47	44	41			
$^5/_8$	$^1/_2$	134	110	95	88	82	72	63	57
	$^3/_4$	285	233	202	188	174			
	1	567	467	405	378	353			

[1]Gas connectors are certified by the approved agency as complete assemblies, including fittings and valves. Capacities shown are based on the use of fittings and valves supplied with the connector.

[2]Semirigid connector listings are based on outside diameter.

[3]Flexible connector listings are based on nominal diameter.

[4]For liquefied petroleum gas, use 1.6 times the natural gas capacities shown.

TABLE 13-C—MINIMUM DEMAND OF TYPICAL GAS APPLIANCES
(Btu/h)   (× 0.293 for W)

APPLIANCE	DEMAND
Domestic gas range	65,000
Domestic recessed top burner section	40,000
Domestic recessed oven section	25,000
Storage water heater—up to 30-gal. (113.6 L) tank	30,000
Storage water heater—40- to 50-gal. (151 to 189 L) tank	50,000
Domestic clothes dryer	35,000
Fireplace log lighter (residential)	25,000
Fireplace log lighter (commercial)	50,000
Barbecue (residential)	50,000
Gas refrigerator	3,000
Bunsen burner	3,000
Mobile homes	1
Gas engines (per horsepower)	10,000
Steam boilers (per horsepower)	50,000

[1]See Table 13-I.

TABLE 13-D
TABLE 13-E

1997 UNIFORM MECHANICAL CODE

TABLE 13-D—SIZE OF GAS PIPING
Maximum Delivery Capacity in Cubic Feet of Gas Per Hour of I.P.S. Pipe Carrying Natural Gas of 0.60 Specific Gravity Based on 0.5-inch Water Column Pressure Drop (124.4 Pa)

PIPE SIZE (inches)	LENGTH (feet) × 304.8 for mm										
× 25.4 for mm	10'	20'	30'	40'	50'	60'	70'	80'	90'	100'	125'
	× 28.3 for L/s										
$1/2$	174	119	96	82	73	66	61	56	53	50	44
$3/4$	363	254	200	171	152	138	127	118	111	104	93
1	684	470	377	323	286	259	239	222	208	197	174
$1^1/4$	1,404	965	775	663	588	532	490	456	428	404	358
$1^1/2$	2,103	1,445	1,161	993	880	798	734	683	641	605	536
2	4,050	2,784	2,235	1,913	1,696	1,536	1,413	1,315	1,234	1,165	1,033
$2^1/2$	6,455	4,437	3,563	3,049	2,703	2,449	2,253	2,096	1,966	1,857	1,646
3	11,412	7,843	6,299	5,391	4,778	4,329	3,983	3,983	3,476	3,284	2,910
$3^1/2$	16,709	11,484	9,222	7,893	6,995	6,338	5,831	5,425	5,090	4,808	4,261
4	23,277	15,998	12,847	10,995	9,745	8,830	8,123	7,557	7,090	6,698	5,936

	150'	200'	250'	300'	350'	400'	450'	500'	550'	600'	
$1/2$	40	34	30	28	25	24	22	21	20	19	
$3/4$	84	72	64	58	53	49	46	44	42	40	
1	158	135	120	109	100	93	87	82	78	75	
$1^1/4$	324	278	246	223	205	191	179	169	161	153	
$1^1/2$	486	416	369	334	309	286	268	253	241	230	
2	936	801	710	643	592	551	517	488	463	442	
$2^1/2$	1,492	1,277	1,131	1,025	943	877	823	778	739	705	
3	2,637	2,257	2,000	1,812	1,667	1,551	1,455	1,375	1,306	1,246	
$3^1/2$	3,861	3,304	2,929	2,654	2,441	2,271	2,131	2,013	1,912	1,824	
4	5,378	4,603	4,080	3,697	3,401	3,164	2,968	2,804	2,663	2,541	

TABLE 13-E—MAXIMUM CAPACITY OF PIPE IN THOUSANDS OF Btu/h OF UNDILUTED LIQUEFIED PETROLEUM GASES
For Distribution Pressure of 11-inch Water Column (2737 Pa), Pressure Drop of 0.5-Inch Water Column (124.4 Pa)

NOMINAL IRON PIPE SIZE (inches)	LENGTH OF PIPE (feet) × 304.8 for mm												
× 25.4 for mm	10	20	30	40	50	60	70	80	90	100	125	150	200
	× 28.3 for L/s												
$1/2$	275	189	152	129	114	103	96	89	83	78	69	63	55
$3/4$	567	393	315	267	237	217	196	185	173	162	146	132	112
1	1,071	732	590	504	448	409	378	346	322	307	275	252	213
$1^1/4$	2,205	1,496	1,212	1,039	913	834	771	724	677	630	567	511	440
$1^1/2$	3,307	2,299	1,858	1,559	1,417	1,275	1,181	1,086	1,023	976	866	787	675
2	6,221	4,331	3,465	2,992	2,646	2,394	2,205	2,047	1,921	1,811	1,606	1,496	1,260

TABLE 13-F—MEDIUM-PRESSURE NATURAL GAS SYSTEM
For Sizing Gas Piping Systems Carrying Gas of 0.60 Specific Gravity Capacity of Pipes of Different Diameters and Lengths in Cubic Feet per Hour for Gas Pressure of 3.0 psi (21 kPa) with a Drop to 1.5 psi (10.3 kPa)

PIPE SIZE (inches)	LENGTH OF PIPE (feet) × 304.8 for mm											
× 25.4 for mm	50′	100′	150′	200′	250′	300′	350′	400′	450′	500′	550′	600′
							× 28.3 for L/s					
1/2	857	589	473	405	359	325	299	278	261	247	234	224
3/4	1,793	1,232	990	847	751	680	626	582	546	516	490	467
1	3,377	2,321	864	1,595	1,414	1,281	1,179	1,096	1,029	972	923	881
1 1/4	6,934	4,766	3,827	3,275	2,903	2,630	2,420	2,251	2,112	1,995	1,895	1,808
1 1/2	10,389	7,140	5,734	4,908	4,349	3,941	3,626	3,373	3,165	2,989	2,839	2,709
2	20,008	13,752	11,043	9,451	8,377	7,590	6,983	6,496	6,095	5,757	5,468	5,216
2 1/2	31,890	21,918	17,601	15,064	13,351	12,097	11,129	10,353	9,714	9,176	8,715	8,314
3	56,376	38,747	31,115	26,631	23,602	21,385	19,674	18,303	17,173	16,222	15,406	14,698
	650′	700′	750′	800′	850′	900′	950′	1,000′	1,100′	1,200′	1,300′	1,400′
1/2	214	206	198	191	185	180	174	170	161	154	147	141
3/4	448	430	414	400	387	375	365	355	337	321	308	296
1	843	810	780	754	729	707	687	668	634	605	580	557
1 1/4	1,731	1,663	1,602	1,547	1,497	1,452	1,410	1,371	1,302	1,242	1,190	1,143
1 1/2	2,594	2,492	2,401	2,318	2,243	2,175	2,112	2,055	1,951	1,862	1,783	1,713
2	4,995	4,799	4,623	4,465	4,321	4,189	4,068	3,957	3,758	3,585	3,433	3,298
2 1/2	7,962	7,649	7,369	7,116	6,886	6,677	6,484	6,307	5,990	5,714	5,472	5,257
3	14,075	13,522	13,027	12,580	12,174	11,803	11,463	11,149	10,589	10,102	9,674	9,294
4	28,709	27,581	26,570	25,658	24,831	24,074	23,380	22,741	21,598	20,605	19,731	18,956
	1,500′	1,600′	1,700′	1,800′	1,900′	2,000′	2,100′	2,200′	2,300′	2,400′	2,500′	2,600′
1/2	136	131	127	123	120	117	114	111	108	106	103	101
3/4	285	275	266	258	251	244	237	231	226	221	216	211
1	536	518	501	486	472	459	447	436	426	416	407	398
1 1/4	1,101	1,063	1,029	998	969	942	918	895	874	854	835	818
1 1/2	1,650	1,593	1,542	1,495	1,452	1,412	1,375	1,341	1,309	1,279	1,252	1,225
2	3,178	3,069	2,970	2,879	2,796	2,720	2,649	2,583	2,522	2,464	2,410	2,360
2 1/2	5,064	4,891	4,733	4,589	4,457	4,335	4,222	4,117	4,019	3,927	3,842	3,761
3	8,953	8,646	8,367	8,112	7,878	7,663	7,463	7,278	7,105	6,943	6,791	6,649
4	18,262	17,635	17,066	16,546	16,069	15,629	15,222	14,844	14,491	14,161	13,852	13,561
5	33,038	31,904	30,875	29,935	29,072	28,276	27,539	26,855	26,217	25,620	25,060	24,534
6	53,496	51,660	49,993	48,471	47,074	45,785	44,593	43,484	42,451	41,485	40,579	39,727

TABLE 13-G—MEDIUM-PRESSURE NATURAL GAS SYSTEM
For Sizing Gas Piping Systems Carrying Gas of 0.60 Specific Gravity Capacity of Pipes of Different Diameters and Lengths in Cubic Feet per Hour for Gas Pressure of 5.0 psi (34 kPa) with a Drop to 1.5 psi (10.3 kPa)

PIPE SIZE (inches)	LENGTH OF PIPE (feet) × 304.8 for mm											
× 25.4 for mm	50′	100′	150′	200′	250′	300′	350′	400′	450′	500′	550′	600′
							× 28.3 for L/s					
1/2	1,399	961	772	661	586	531	488	454	426	402	382	365
3/4	2,925	2,010	1,614	1,381	1,224	1,109	1,021	949	891	842	799	762
1	5,509	3,786	3,041	2,602	2,306	2,090	1,923	1,789	1,678	1,585	1,506	1,436
1 1/4	11,311	7,774	6,243	5,343	4,735	4,291	3,947	3,672	3,445	3,255	3,091	2,949
1 1/2	16,947	11,648	9,353	8,005	7,095	6,429	5,914	5,502	5,162	4,876	4,631	4,418
2	32,638	22,432	18,014	15,417	13,664	12,381	11,390	10,596	9,942	9,391	8,919	8,509
2 1/2	52,020	35,753	28,711	24,573	21,779	19,733	18,154	16,889	15,846	14,968	14,216	13,562
3	91,962	63,205	50,756	43,441	38,501	34,884	32,093	29,856	28,013	26,461	25,131	23,976
	650′	700′	750′	800′	850′	900′	950′	1,000′	1,100′	1,200′	1,300′	1,400′
1/2	349	335	323	312	302	293	284	277	263	251	240	231
3/4	730	701	676	653	632	612	595	578	549	524	502	482
1	1,375	1,321	1,273	1,229	1,190	1,153	1,120	1,089	1,035	987	945	908
1 1/4	2,824	2,713	2,614	2,524	2,442	2,368	2,300	2,237	2,124	2,027	1,941	1,865
1 1/2	4,231	4,065	3,916	3,781	3,659	3,548	3,446	3,351	3,183	3,037	2,908	2,794
2	8,149	7,828	7,542	7,283	7,048	6,833	6,636	6,455	6,130	5,848	5,600	5,380
2 1/2	12,988	12,477	12,020	11,608	11,233	10,891	10,577	10,288	9,771	9,321	8,926	8,575
3	22,960	22,057	21,249	20,520	19,858	19,253	18,698	18,187	17,273	16,478	15,780	15,160
4	46,830	44,990	43,342	41,855	40,504	39,271	38,139	37,095	35,231	33,611	32,186	30,921
	1,500′	1,600′	1,700′	1,800′	1,900′	2,000′	2,100′	2,200′	2,300′	2,400′	2,500′	2,600′
1/2	222	214	208	201	195	190	185	181	176	172	168	165
3/4	464	449	434	421	409	398	387	378	369	360	352	345
1	875	845	818	793	770	749	729	711	694	678	664	650
1 1/4	1,796	1,735	1,679	1,628	1,581	1,537	1,497	1,460	1,425	1,393	1,363	1,334
1 1/2	2,691	2,599	2,515	2,439	2,368	2,303	2,243	2,188	2,136	2,087	2,042	1,999
2	5,183	5,005	4,844	4,696	4,561	4,436	4,321	4,213	4,113	4,020	3,932	3,849
2 1/2	8,261	7,978	7,720	7,485	7,270	7,071	6,886	6,715	6,556	6,406	6,267	6,135
3	14,605	14,103	13,648	13,233	12,851	12,500	12,174	11,871	11,589	11,326	11,078	10,846
4	29,789	28,766	27,838	26,991	26,213	25,495	24,831	24,214	23,639	23,100	22,596	22,121
5	53,892	52,043	50,363	48,830	47,422	46,124	44,923	43,806	42,765	41,792	40,879	40,021
6	87,263	84,269	81,550	79,067	76,787	74,686	72,740	70,932	69,247	67,671	66,193	64,803

TABLE 13-H—FOR UNDILUTED LIQUEFIED PETROLEUM GAS PRESSURE OF 10.0 psi (69 kPa) WITH MAXIMUM PRESSURE DROP OF 3.0 psi (20.7 kPa)
Maximum Delivery Capacity in Cubic Feet of Gas per Hour of I.P.S. Pipe of Different Diameters and Lengths Carrying Undiluted Liquefied Petroleum Gas of 1.52 Specific Gravity

LENGTH OF PIPE (feet) — × 304.8 for mm — × 28.3 for L/s

PIPE SIZE (inches) × 25.4 for mm	50'	100'	150'	200'	250'	300'	350'	400'	450'	500'	550'	600'
1/2	1,000	690	550	470	420	380	350	325	300	285	272	260
3/4	2,070	1,423	1,142	978	867	785	722	672	631	596	566	540
1	3,899	2,680	2,152	1,842	1,632	1,479	1,361	1,266	1,188	1,122	1,066	1,017
1 1/4	8,005	5,502	4,418	3,782	3,351	3,037	2,794	2,599	2,439	2,303	2,188	2,087
1 1/2	11,994	8,244	6,620	5,666	5,022	4,550	4,186	3,894	3,654	3,451	3,278	3,127
2	23,100	15,877	12,750	10,912	9,671	8,763	8,062	7,500	7,037	6,647	6,313	6,023
2 1/2	36,818	25,305	20,321	17,392	15,414	13,966	12,849	11,953	11,215	10,594	10,062	9,599
3	65,088	44,734	35,923	30,746	27,249	24,690	22,714	21,131	19,827	18,728	17,787	16,969

PIPE SIZE (inches)	650'	700'	750'	800'	850'	900'	950'	1,000'	1,100'	1,200'	1,300'	1,400'
1/2	250	240	230	222	215	208	202	198	188	180	171	164
3/4	517	496	478	462	447	433	421	409	389	371	355	341
1	973	935	901	870	842	816	793	771	732	699	669	643
1 1/4	1,999	1,920	1,850	1,786	1,729	1,676	1,628	1,583	1,504	1,434	1,374	1,320
1 1/2	2,995	2,877	2,772	2,676	2,590	2,511	2,439	2,372	2,253	2,149	2,058	1,977
2	5,767	5,541	5,338	5,155	4,988	4,836	4,697	4,568	4,339	4,139	3,964	3,808
2 1/2	9,192	8,831	8,507	8,215	7,950	7,708	7,486	7,281	6,915	6,597	6,318	6,069
3	16,250	15,611	15,040	14,523	14,055	13,627	13,234	12,872	12,225	11,663	11,169	10,730
4	33,145	31,842	30,676	29,623	28,667	27,795	26,993	26,255	24,935	23,789	22,780	21,885

PIPE SIZE (inches)	1,500'	1,600'	1,700'	1,800'	1,900'	2,000'	2,100'	2,200'	2,300'	2,400'	2,500'	2,600'
1/2	158	152	148	143	139	136	133	130	127	124	121	118
3/4	329	317	307	298	289	281	274	267	261	255	249	244
1	619	598	579	561	545	530	516	503	491	480	470	460
1 1/4	1,271	1,228	1,138	1,152	1,119	1,088	1,060	1,033	1,009	986	964	944
1 1/2	1,905	1,839	1,780	1,726	1,676	1,630	1,588	1,548	1,512	1,477	1,445	1,415
2	3,669	3,543	3,428	3,324	3,228	3,140	3,058	2,982	2,911	2,845	2,783	2,724
2 1/2	5,847	5,646	5,464	5,298	5,145	5,004	4,874	4,753	4,640	4,534	4,435	4,342
3	10,337	9,982	9,660	9,366	9,096	8,847	8,616	8,402	8,203	8,016	7,841	7,676
4	21,083	20,360	19,705	19,103	18,552	18,045	17,575	17,138	16,731	16,350	15,993	15,657
5	38,143	36,834	35,645	34,560	33,564	32,645	31,795	31,005	30,268	29,579	28,933	28,325
6	61,762	59,643	57,718	55,961	54,348	52,860	51,483	50,204	49,011	47,895	46,849	45,865

TABLE 13-I—MINIMUM DEMAND FACTORS FOR CALCULATING GAS PIPING SYSTEMS IN MOBILE HOME PARKS

NUMBER OF MOBILE HOME LOTS	DEMAND FACTOR Btu/h PER MOBILE HOME LOT × 0.293 071 for W
1	250,000
2	234,000
3	208,000
4	198,000
5	184,000
6	174,000
7	166,000
8	162,000
9	158,000
10	154,000
11-20	132,000
21-30	124,000
31-40	118,000
41-60	112,000
Over 60	102,000

Chapter 14

SPECIAL PIPING AND STORAGE SYSTEMS

NOTE: The provisions of this chapter were moved from Appendix B.

SECTION 1401 — OIL-BURNING APPLIANCES

Tanks, piping and valves for appliances burning fuel oil shall be installed in accordance with the requirements of recognized standards listed in Part III of Chapter 16.

SECTION 1402 — PERMIT

It shall be unlawful to install, alter or repair or cause to be installed, altered or repaired any process material piping without first obtaining a permit.

Permits for process piping shall show the total number of outlets to be provided for on each system and such other information as may be required by the building official.

Fees for process piping permits are included in Table 1-A.

SECTION 1403 — PLANS REQUIRED

Plans, engineering calculations, diagrams and other data shall be submitted in one or more sets with each application for a permit. The building official may require plans, computations and specifications to be prepared and designed by an engineer licensed by the state to practice as such.

When plans or other data are submitted for review, a plan review fee shall be paid as provided in Section 115.3.

SECTION 1404 — WORKMANSHIP

Process piping shall not be strained or bent nor shall tanks, vessels, vats, appliances or cabinets be supported by or develop strain or stress on the piping.

SECTION 1405 — INSPECTIONS

1405.1 General. Upon completion of the installation, alteration or repair of process piping, and prior to the use thereof, the building official shall be notified that such piping is ready for inspection.

Excavations required for the installation of underground piping shall be kept open until such time as the piping has been inspected and approved. If any such piping is covered or concealed before such approval, it shall be exposed upon the direction of the building official.

1405.2 Required Inspections. The building official shall make the following inspections and shall either approve that portion of the work as completed, or shall notify the permit holder wherein the same fails to comply with this code.

1. **Rough piping inspection.** This inspection shall be made after all proces piping authorized by the permit has been installed, and before any such piping has been covered or concealed. This inspection shall include a determination that the piping size, material and installation meet the requirements of this code.

2. **Final piping inspection.** This inspection shall be made after all piping authorized by the permit has been installed and after all portions thereof which are to be covered or concealed are so con-

cealed. This inspection shall include a pressure test, at which time the piping shall stand a pressure of not less than two and one-half times the maximum designed operating pressure but in no case less than 100 psig (690 kPa). Test pressures shall be held for a length of time satisfactory to the building official, but in no case for less than 30 minutes with no perceptible drop in pressure. HPM drain, waste, and vent piping shall be tested in accordance with the Plumbing Code. Tests shall be made in the presence of the building official. Necessary apparatus for conducting tests shall be furnished by the permit holder.

1405.3 Other Inspections. In addition to the inspections required by this section, the building official may require a special inspector, as specified in Section 1701 of the Building Code, during installation of piping systems. In cases where the work authorized was installed in accordance with plans and specifications prepared by an engineer, the building official may require a final signed report stating that the work was installed in accordance with the approved plans and specifications and the applicable provisions of this chapter.

SECTION 1406 — PIPING AND TUBING

1406.1 General. Process piping and tubing shall comply with this section and shall be installed in accordance with nationally recognized standards. Piping and tubing systems shall be metallic unless the material being transported is incompatible with such system.

1406.2 Hazardous Process Piping (HPP).

1406.2.1 General. Hazardous process piping, supply piping or tubing in service corridors shall be exposed to view. Hazardous process piping shall be identified in accordance with nationally recognized standards to indicate the material being transported. All liquid HPP piping shall have an approved means for directing any spilled materials to an approved containment or drainage system.

All liquid HPP waste or drainage systems shall be installed in accordance with the Plumbing Code.

1406.2.2 Installation in exit corridors and above other occupancies. Hazardous process shall not be located within exit corridors or above areas not classified as Group H, Division 6 or 7 Occupancies except as permitted by this section.

Hazardous production material piping and tubing may be installed within the space defined by the walls of exit corridors and the floor or roof above or in concealed spaces above other occupancies under the following conditions:

1. Automatic sprinklers shall be installed within the space unless the space is less than 6 inches (152 mm) in least dimension.

2. Ventilation at not less than six air changes per hour shall be provided. The space shall not be used to convey air from any other area.

3. When the piping or tubing is used to transport HPP liquids, a receptor shall be installed below such piping or tubing. The receptor shall be designed to collect any discharge or leakage and drain it to an approved location. The one-hour enclosure shall not be used as part of the receptor.

4. All HPP supply piping and tubing and HPP nonmetallic waste lines shall be separated from the exit corridor and from any occupancy other than Group H, Division 6 by construction as required for walls or partitions that have a fire-protection rating of not less than one hour. When gypsum wallboard is used, joints on the piping side of the enclosure need not be taped, provided the joints occur over framing members. Access openings into the enclosure shall be protected by approved fire assemblies.

5. Readily accessible manual or automatic remotely activated fail-safe emergency shutoff valves shall be installed on piping and tubing other than waste lines at the following locations:

5.1 At branch connections into the fabrication area.

5.2 At entries into exit corridors.

6. Excess flow valves shall be installed as required by the Fire Code.

7. Electrical wiring and equipment located in the piping space shall be approved for Class I, Division 2 hazardous locations.

> **EXCEPTION:** Occasional transverse crossing of the corridors by supply piping which is enclosed within a ferrous pipe or tube for the width of the corridor need not comply with Items 1 through 7.

1406.3 Special Requirements for HPP Gases.

1406.3.1 General. In addition to other requirements of this section, HPP gases shall comply with this section and the Fire Code.

1406.3.2 Special provisions.

1406.3.2.1 Excess flow control. Where HPP supply gas is carried in pressurized piping, a fail-safe system shall shut off flow due to a rupture in the piping. Where the piping originates from outside the building, the valve shall be located outside the building as close to the bulk source as practical.

1406.3.2.2 Piping and tubing installation. Piping and tubing shall be installed in accordance with approved standards. Supply piping for hazardous production materials having a health hazard ranking of 3 or 4 shall have welded connections throughout unless an exhausted enclosure is provided.

> **EXCEPTION:** Material which is incompatible with ferrous piping may be installed in nonmetallic piping with approved connections.

1406.3.2.3 Gas-detection system. When hazardous production material gas is used or dispensed and the physiological warning properties for the gas are at a higher level than the accepted permissible exposure limit for the gas, a continuous gas-monitoring system shall be provided to detect the presence of a short-term hazard condition. When dispensing occurs and flammable gases or vapors may be present in quantities in excess of 20 percent of the lower explosive limit, a continuous gas-monitoring system shall be provided. The monitoring system shall be connected to the emergency control station.

Chapter 15
SOLAR SYSTEMS

No provisions. See Appendix B, Chapter 15.

Chapter 16
UNIFORM BUILDING CODE, UNIFORM MECHANICAL CODE AND UNIFORM FIRE CODE STANDARDS

Part I—Full Text Standards

SECTION 1601 — STANDARDS

Uniform Building Code, Uniform Mechanical Code and Uniform Fire Code standards referred to in various parts of this code, which are also listed in Part II of this chapter, are hereby declared to be part of this code and are referred to in this code as "UBC, UMC and UFC standards."

SECTION 1602 — STANDARD OF DUTY

The standard of duty established for the recognized standards listed in Part III of this chapter is that the design, construction, quality of materials, and the installation of mechanical equipment shall be reasonably safe for life, limb, health, property and public welfare.

SECTION 1603 — RECOGNIZED STANDARDS

The standards in Part III of this chapter are recognized standards. Compliance with these recognized standards shall be prima facie evidence of compliance with the standard of duty set forth in Section 1602.

Part II—Listings of UBC, UMC and UFC Standards

**UBC STD.
AND SEC.**   **TITLE AND SOURCE**

CHAPTER 2

2-1; 201.2.2
    Noncombustible material—Tests.

8-1; 201.2.3, 301.2.2, 601.2.1.3
    Test Method for Surface-burning Characteristics of Building Materials.

**UMC STD.
AND SEC.**   **TITLE AND SOURCE**

CHAPTER 2

2-2; 209, 602
    Galvanized Sheet Metals based on Specification A 525-87 of the American Society for Testing and Materials.

2-3; 201.2.5, 204
    Flash Point by Pensky-Martens Closed Tester Method D 93-75 of the American Society for Testing and Materials.

CHAPTER 4

4-1; 402.3
    UMC Standard 4-1, Test Performance of Air Filter Units, is UL® Standard 900, 1993.

CHAPTER 6

6-1; 601.1
    Standard for Metal Ducts based on First Edition, 1985, HVAC Duct Construction Standards, Metal and Flexible, published by the Sheet Metal and Air Conditioning Contractors National Association.

6-2, 601.1
    Test Method for Fire and Smoke Characteristics of Electrical Cable based on Standard 910, 1982, of Underwriters Laboratories Inc.

6-3; 601.4
    Standard for Installation of Factory-made Air Duct based on the 1989 Fibrous Glass Duct Construction Standards published by the Thermal Insulation Manufacturers Association and the Guidelines for Installing Flexible Ducts published by the Air Diffusion Council.

CHAPTER 11

11-1; 1102.4
    Standard Test Method for Concentration Limits of Flammability of Chemicals based on Designation E 681-85 of the American Society for Testing and Materials.

11-2; 1104.1
    Methods for System Identification based on ASME/ANSI Standard A13.1-1981.

**UFC STD.
AND SEC.**   **TITLE AND SOURCE**

CHAPTER 6

10-2; 601.2.1.6
    Testing Procedures for Local, Auxiliary, Remote Station and Proprietary Protective Signaling Systems.

Part III—Recognized Standards

NOTE: The titles and dates of recognized standards have been corrected and revised through 1996.

A

AIR-CONDITIONING APPLIANCES, GAS-FIRED ABSORPTION SUMMER, ANSI Z21.40.1-1981
Addenda Z21.40.1a-1982

AUTOMATIC GAS IGNITION SYSTEMS AND COMPONENTS, ANSI Z21.20-1993

AUTOMATIC INTERMITTENT PILOT IGNITION SYSTEMS FOR FIELD INSTALLATION, ANSI Z21.71-1993

B

BOILERS, GAS-FIRED LOW-PRESSURE STEAM AND HOT-WATER, ANSI Z21.13-1991
Addenda Z21.13a-1993
Addenda Z21.13b-1994

BOILERS, LOW-PRESSURE CAST-IRON HEATING, I-B-R Testing and Rating Code, The Institute of Boiler and Radiator Manufacturers, Seventh Edition, January, 1966

BOILERS, STEEL, SBI Testing and Rating Code, the Steel Boiler Institute, Tenth Edition, September, 1965

C

CEILING DAMPERS, UL 555C, 1992

CENTRAL COOLING AIR CONDITIONERS, UL 465,1982 with 1984 revision

CENTRAL FURNACES, GAS-FIRED, ANSI Z21.47-1993

CHIMNEYS, FACTORY-BUILT, MEDIUM-HEAT APPLIANCE, UL 959,1976 with 1982 revision

CHIMNEYS, FACTORY-BUILT, RESIDENTIAL TYPE AND BUILDING HEATING APPLIANCE, UL 103, 1983

CLIMATIC CONDITIONS
1989 *ASHRAE Handbook—Fundamentals,* Chapter 24, Table 1, Column 6

CLOSURE SYSTEMS FOR FLEXIBLE AIR DUCTS AND AIR CONNECTORS, UL 181B-1995

CLOSURE SYSTEMS FOR RIGID AIR DUCTS, UL 181A-1994

CLOTHES DRYERS, GAS
Volume I, Type 1—Clothes Dryers, ANSI Z21.5.1-1992
Volume II, Type 2—Clothes Dryers, ANSI Z21.5.2-1987
Addenda Z21.5.2a-1990
Addenda Z21.5.2b-1992

CODE OF FEDERAL REGULATIONS, Title 28, Section 1910.1000

COMMERCIAL ELECTRIC DISHWASHERS, UL 921,1978 with 1983 revisions

COMMERCIAL REFRIGERATORS AND FREEZERS, UL 471,1978 with 1983 revisions

COMPRESSED NATURAL GAS (CNG) VEHICULAR FUEL SYSTEMS, UFC Standard 52-1

CONNECTORS, METAL, FOR GAS APPLIANCES, ANSI Z21.24-1993
Addenda Z21.24a-1993

CONNECTORS FOR MOVABLE GAS APPLIANCES, ANSI Z21.69-1992

CONVERSION BURNERS, DOMESTIC GAS, ANSI Z21.17-1991
Addenda Z21.17a-1993
Addenda Z21.17b-1993

CONVERSION BURNERS, DOMESTIC GAS, INSTALLATION OF, ANSI Z21.8-1994

CORRUGATED STAINLESS STEEL TUBING, INTERIOR FUEL GAS PIPING SYSTEMS USING, ANSI/AGA LC1-1991
Addenda ANSI/AGA LC1a-1993
Addenda ANSI/AGA LC1b-1994

COUNTER APPLIANCES, FOOD SERVICE EQUIPMENT, GAS, ANSI Z83.14-1989
Addenda Z83.14a-1990
Addendx Z83.14b-1991

D

DECORATIVE GAS APPLIANCES, VENTED, ANSI Z21.50-1982
Addenda Z21.50a-1982

DECORATIVE GAS APPLIANCES FOR INSTALLATION IN SOLID-FUEL BURNING FIREPLACE, ANSI Z21.60-1991

DEEP FAT FRYERS, FOOD SERVICE EQUIPMENT, GAS, ANSI Z83.13-1989
Addenda Z83.13a-1991

DIRECT GAS-FIRED INDUSTRIAL AIR HEATERS, ANSI Z83.18-1990
Addenda Z83.18a-1991
Addenda Z83.18b-1992

DIRECT GAS-FIRED MAKE-UP AIR HEATERS, ANSI Z83.4-1991
Addenda Z83.4a-1992

DRAFT EQUIPMENT, UL 378,1973

DRAFT HOODS, ANSI Z21.12-1990
Addenda Z21.12a-1993
Addenda Z21.12b-1994

DUCT FURNACES, GAS-FIRED, ANSI Z83.9-1990
Addenda Z83.9a-1992

E

EARTHQUAKE ACTUATED AUTOMATIC GAS SHUTOFF SYSTEMS, ANSI Z21.70-1981

ELECTRIC CENTRAL AIR-HEATING EQUIPMENT, UL 1096, 1981 with 1983 revision

ELECTRIC COIN-OPERATED CLOTHES DRYING EQUIPMENT, UL 1556, 1982

ELECTRIC COMMERCIAL CLOTHES-DRYING EQUIPMENT, UL 1240, 1979

ELECTRIC COMMERCIAL CLOTHES-WASHING EQUIPMENT, UL 1206,1979

EXHAUST HOODS FOR COMMERCIAL COOKING EQUIPMENT, UL 710, December 21, 1990

F

FACTORY-MADE AIR DUCTS AND CONNECTORS, UL 181-1994

FAN COIL UNITS AND ROOM FAN HEATER UNITS, UL 883, 1980 with 1983 revisions

FIRECLAY REFRACTORIES, ASTM C27-60

FIRE DAMPERS, UL 555, 1990

FIREPLACE ACCESSORIES, proposed standard, UL 907, 1982

FIREPLACE STOVES, UL 737, 1982

FIREPLACES, FACTORY-BUILT, UL 127, 1981 with 1983 revisions

FLAME ARRESTORS FOR USE ON VENTS OF STORAGE TANKS FOR PETROLEUM OIL AND GASOLINE, ANSI/UL 525,1979 with 1982 revision

FLEXIBLE CONNECTORS OF OTHER THAN ALL-METAL CONSTRUCTION FOR GAS APPLIANCES, ANSI Z21.45-1992
Addenda Z21.45a-1983

FLOOR FURNACE, GAS-FIRED GRAVITY AND FAN TYPE, ANSI Z21.48-1992

FOOD SERVICE EQUIPMENT-BAKING AND ROASTING OVENS, GAS, ANSI Z83 12k-1989
Addenda Z83.12a-1990
Addenda Z83.12b-1991

FURNACES, SOLID-FUEL AND COMBINATION-FUEL CENTRAL AND SUPPLEMENTARY, UL 391, 1981 with 1983 revision

G

GAGES AND INDICATORS, LIQUID LEVEL, FOR ANHYDROUS AMMONIA AND LP GAS, UL 565-1973

GAGES AND INDICATORS, LIQUID LEVEL, FOR PETROLEUM PRODUCTS, UL 180, 1980

GAGES INDICATING PRESSURE FOR COMPRESSED GAS SERVICE, UL 404, 1979

GAS HOSE CONNECTORS FOR PORTABLE INDOOR GAS-FIRED APPLIANCES, ANSI Z21.2-1992

GAS HOSE CONNECTORS FOR PORTABLE OUTDOOR GAS-FIRED APPLIANCES, ANSI Z21.54-1987
Addenda Z21.54a-1992

GAS UTILIZATION EQUIPMENT IN LARGE BOILERS, ANZI Z83.3-1971
Addenda Z83.3a-1972
Addenda Z83.3b-1976 (Reaffirmed 1983, 1989)

GAS-FIRED CONSTRUCTION HEATERS, ANSI Z83.7-1990
Addenda Z83.7a-1991
Addenda Z83.7b-1993

GAS-FIRED HEATING EQUIPMENT, COMMERCIAL INDUSTRIAL (Inputs over 400,000 Btu per hour), UL 795, 1973 with 1982 revision

GREASE FILTERS FOR EXHAUST DUCTS, UL 1046, 1979

H

HEAT PUMPS, UL 559, 1975 with 1984 revisions

HEAT RESPONSIVE LINKS FOR FIRE PROTECTION SYSTEMS, UL 33, 1987

HEATING, WATER SUPPLY, AND POWER BOILERS, ELECTRIC, UL 834, 1980 with 1983 revisions

HERMETIC REFRIGERANT MOTOR COMPRESSORS, UL 984, 1984

HOSE, FLEXIBLE METALLIC, UL 536, 1976 with 1984 revision

HOSE, LP GAS, UL 21, 1980 with 1984 revision

HOT PLATES AND LAUNDRY STOVES, DOMESTIC, GAS, ANSI Z21.9-1979

HOUSEHOLD COOKING GAS APPLIANCES, ANSI Z21.1-1993
Addenda Z21.1a-1993

I

ILLUMINATING APPLIANCES, GAS-FIRED, ANSI Z21.42-1971
Addenda Z21.42a-1973
Addenda Z21.42b-1981

INCINERATORS, RESIDENTIAL, UL 791, 1973 with 1981 revision

INFRARED HEATERS, GAS-FIRED, ANSI Z83.6-1990
Addenda Z83.6a-1992
Addenda Z83.6b-1993

K

KETTLES, STEAM COOKERS AND STEAM GENERATORS, FOOD SERVICE EQUIPMENT, GAS, ANSI Z83.15-1989
Addenda Z83.15a-1990
Addenda Z83.15b-1991

L

LABORATORY METHODS OF TESTING FANS FOR RATINGS, ASHRAE 51-1985 (AMCA 210-85)

LEAKAGE RATED DAMPERS FOR USE IN SMOKE CONTROL SYSTEMS, UL 555S, 1983

LIMIT CONTROLS, UL 353, 1993

N

NATIONAL ELECTRICAL CODE, ANSI/NFPA 70

NUMBER DESIGNATION AND SAFETY CLASSIFICATION OF REFRIGERANTS, ANSI/ASHRAE 34-1992 and Addenda ANSI/ASHRAE 34a-34o; 34q-34x.

O

OIL BURNERS, SAFETY STANDARD FOR, ANSI/UL 296, 1980 with 1983 revisions

OIL BURNING STOVES, UL 896, 1973 with 1974 revisions

OIL-FIRED AIR HEATERS AND DIRECT-FIRED HEATERS, UL 733, 1975 with 1983 revisions

OIL-FIRED BOILER ASSEMBLIES, ANSI/UL 726, 1975 with 1982 revisions

OIL-FIRED CENTRAL FURNACES, ANSI/UL 727, 1980 with 1983 revisions

OIL-FIRED FLOOR FURNACES, ANSI/UL 729, 1976 with 1980 revisions

OIL-FIRED UNIT HEATERS, ANSI/UL 731, 1975 with 1980 revisions

OIL-FIRED WALL FURNACES, ANSI/UL 730, 1974 with 1980 revisions

OUTDOOR COOKING GAS APPLIANCES, ANSI Z21.58-1993

P

PANEL HEATING, ASHRAE HVAC Systems and Equipment Volume 1992, Chapter 6

PILOT GAS FILTERS, GAS, FILTERS ON APPLIANCES, ANSI Z21.35-1989
Addenda Z21.35a-1993

PIPE THREADS, ANSI B2.1-1968 and B2.2-1968 Dryseal

PRESSURE-REGULATING VALVES FOR LP GAS, ANSI/UL 144, 1978

PRESSURE REGULATORS, GAS APPLIANCE, ANSI Z21.18-1983

PUMPS FOR OIL-BURNING APPLIANCES, UL 343, 1982

PUMPS, POWER OPERATED FOR ANHYDROUS
AMMONIA AND LP GAS, UL 51, 1980

Q

QUICK-DISCONNECT DEVICES FOR USE WITH GAS
FUEL, ANSI Z21.41-1989
Addenda Z21.41a-1990
Addenda Z21.41b-1992

R

RANGES AND UNIT BROILERS, FOOD SERVICE
EQUIPMENT, GAS, ANSI Z83.11-1989
Addenda Z83.11a-1990
Addenda Z83.11b-1991

REFRIGERANT-CONTAINING COMPONENTS AND
ACCESSORIES, NONELECTRICAL, UL 207, 1982

REFRIGERATION AND AIR CONDITIONING
CONDENSING AND COMPRESSOR UNITS, UL 303,
1980 with 1983 revisions

REFRIGERATION PIPING, including valves, fittings and
welding, ANSI B31.5-1974

REFRIGERATORS USING GAS FUEL, ANSI Z21.19-1983

REGULATORS FOR COMPRESSED GAS, UL 252, 1979

ROOM HEATER, SOLID-FUEL TYPE, UL 1482, 1983

ROOM HEATERS, GAS-FIRED
Volume I, Vented Room Heaters, ANSI Z21.11.1-1991

S

SMOKE DAMPERS see LEAKAGE RATED DAMPERS

SPECIFICATION FOR CHROMIUM-NICKEL STAINLESS
AND HEAT RESISTING STEEL SPRING WIRE, ASTM A
313-87

SPECIFICATIONS FOR FLUOROCARBONS AND OTHER
REFRIGERANTS, ARI 700-93

STANDARD FOR GASKETS AND SEALS, UL 157

STANDARD FOR INSULATION COORDINATION
INCLUDING CLEARANCES AND CREEPAGE
DISTANCES FOR ELECTRICAL EQUIPMENT, UL 840

STANDARD METHOD FOR LABORATORY AIR FLOW
MEASUREMENT, ASHRAE 41.2-1987

STANDARD METHOD FOR MEASUREMENT OF FLOW
OF GAS—ASHRAE 41.7-1991

STANDARD METHOD FOR TEMPERATURE
MEASUREMENT, AHSRAE 41.1-1991

STANDARDS FOR ORGANIC COATINGS AND FOR
STEEL ENCLOSURES FOR OUTDOOR USE
ELECTRICAL EQUIPMENT, UL 1332

SWIMMING POOL HEATERS, GAS-FIRED, ANSI
Z21.56-1991
Addenda Z21.56a-1993
Addenda Z21.56b-1994

T

TANK, PIPING AND VALVES FOR OIL-BURNING
APPLIANCES, CHAPTERS 2 AND 3 OF NFPA 31-1978,
Standard for the Installation of Oil-burning Equipment

TEST METHOD FOR LOUVERS, DAMPERS AND
SHUTTERS—AMCA 500-89

THERMOPLASTIC PIPE AND FITTINGS COMPOUNDS,
RECOMMENDED HYDROSTATIC STRENGTHS AND
DESIGN STRESSES, PPI Technical Report TR-4, August,
1978

THERMOSTATS, GAS APPLIANCE, ANSI Z21.23-1989
Addenda Z21.23a-1991
Addenda Z21.23b-1993

TOILETS, GAS-FIRED, ANSI Z21.61-1983 (Reaffirmed
1989)

U

UNDERWRITERS LABORATORIES Standard 900, 1993

UNIT COOLERS, REFRIGERATION, UL 412, 1980 with
1982 revisions

UNIT HEATERS, GAS, ANSI Z83.8-1990
Addenda Z83.8a-1990
Addenda Z83.8b-1992

V

VALVES, AUTOMATIC FOR GAS APPLIANCES, ANSI
Z21.21-1993

VALVES, CONSTANT-LEVEL OIL, UL 352, 1982

VALVES, ELECTRICALLY OPERATED, UL 429, 1982 with
1983 revision

VALVES FOR ANHYDROUS AMMONIA AND LP GAS, UL
125, 1980

VALVES FOR APPLIANCES, APPLIANCES CONNECTOR
VALUES AND HOSE VALUES, MANUALLY OPERATED
GAS, ANSI Z21.15-1992
Addenda Z21.15a-1981

VALVES FOR FLAMMABLE LIQUIDS AND FUEL GASES,
UL 842,1980

VALVES, RELIEF AND AUTOMATIC GAS SHUTOFF
DEVICES FOR HOT WATER SUPPLY SYSTEMS, ANSI
Z21.22-1986
Addenda Z21.22a-1990

VALVES, SAFETY RELIEF FOR ANHYDROUS AMMONIA
AND LP GAS, UL 132, 1973

VENT DAMPER DEVICES, FOR USE WITH GAS-FIRED
APPLIANCES, AUTOMATIC, ANSI Z21.66-1994

VENT OR CHIMNEY CONNECTOR DAMPERS FOR OIL
FIRED APPLIANCES, UL 17,1982 with 1983 revisions

VENTING SYSTEMS, TYPE L, LOW TEMPERATURE,
ANSI, UL 641, 1976

VENTS, GAS, ANSI, UL 441, 1979 with 1983 revision

W

WALL FURNACES, GAS-FIRED GRAVITY AND
FAN-TYPE DIRECT-VENT, ANSI Z21.44-1991
Addenda Z21.44a-1992

WALL FURNACES, GAS-FIRED GRAVITY AND
FAN-TYPE VENTED, ANSI Z21.49-1992

WATER HEATERS, GAS
Volume I, Storage Water Heaters with Input Ratings of
75,000 Btu per Hour or Less, ANSI Z21.10.1-1993
Addenda Z21.101a-1994
Volume III, Storage with Input Ratings Above 75,000 Btu per
Hour, Circulating and Instantaneous Water Heaters, ANSI
Z21.10.3-1993
Addenda Z21.10.3a-1994

AMCA—Air Movement and Control Association, Inc., 30 West University Drive, Arlington Heights, IL 60004-1893

ANSI—American National Standard approved by the American National Standards Institute, Inc., 1430 Broadway, New York, New York 10018.

ARI—Air-Conditioning and Refrigeration Institute, 4301 North Fairfax Drive, Suite 425, Arlington, VA 22203.

ASHRAE—The American Society of Heating, Refrigerating, and Air-Conditioning Engineers, Inc., 1791 Tullie Circle, NE, Atlanta, GA 30329.

ASTM—American Society for Testing and Materials, 1916 Race Street, Philadelphia, PA 19103

I-B-R—The Institute of Boiler and Radiator Manufacturers, 393 Seventh Avenue, New York, New York 10001.

PPI—Plastics Pipe Institute, 355 Lexington Avenue, New York, New York 10017.

R—Reaffirmed as up-to-date.

SBI—Steel Boiler Institute, 393 Seventh Avenue, New York, New York 10001.

UL—Underwriters Laboratories Inc., Standards Issued by Underwriters Laboratories Inc., 333 Pfingsten Road, Northbrook, Illinois 60062.

APPENDIX

APPENDIX A

UNIFORM MECHANICAL CODE STANDARD 2-2
GALVANIZED SHEET METALS

**Based on Standard Specification A525-87T
of the American Society for Testing and Materials**

See Sections 209 and 602, *Uniform Mechanical Code*

SECTION 2.201 — SCOPE

This standard covers the coating requirements for sheets in coils and cut lengths, zinc coated (galvanized) by the hot-dip method to a coating mass of not less than coating class G-90. This material is intended to be used for duct construction. Galvanized sheet in coils and cut lengths is produced to decimal thickness only and thickness tolerances apply. The thickness of the sheet includes both the base steel and the coating.

SECTION 2.202 — BASE METAL MANUFACTURE

The base metal shall be of approved composition made by the open-hearth, basic oxygen or electric furnace process.

SECTION 2.203 — MASS OF COATING

2.203.1 General. The coating shall have a total mass, on both sides of a sheet, of not less than 0.90 ounce per square foot (90 g/m^2) of sheet when determined by the triple-spot check limit and not less than 0.80 ounce per square foot (75 g/m^2) of sheet when determined by the single-spot check limit. Material split after leaving the producer's works shall be subject to the single-spot test only.

2.203.2 Coating Test. The minimum check limit by the triple-spot test shall consist of the average of determinations from the test sheet as provided in Section 2.205.

The check limit by the single-spot test shall be that one of the three specimens of the triple-spot test bearing the lightest coating, or the building official may select a single specimen from any part of a sheet or coil as provided by Section 2.206.2.

The testing method shall determine to the nearest 0.01 ounce per square foot (0.003 kg/m^2) if the weight of coating in grams on a square sample 2.25 inches ± 0.01 inch (57.7 mm ± 0.1 mm) on a side or a circular sample 2.54 inches ± 01 inch (65.1 mm ± 0.1 mm) in diameter is numerically equal to the weight of coating in ounces per square foot of sheet (g/m^2).

SECTION 2.204 — BEND TEST

The bend test specimen specified in Section 2.207 shall stand being bent at room temperature through 180 degrees in any direction without flaking of the coating on the outside surface of the bend only. Flaking of the coating within $1/4$ inch (6 mm) of the edge of the test specimen shall be disregarded.

SECTION 2.205 — SPECIMENS FOR TRIPLE-SPOT TEST

2.205.1 General. Test specimens for coils and cut lengths coated in coils shall be taken from a sample piece approximately 1 foot (305 mm) in length by the as-coated width. For the triple-spot test, one specimen shall be cut from the middle of the width and one from each side not closer than 2 inches (25 mm) from the side edge.

2.205.2 Method. The triple-spot test shall be made in accordance with the procedure of ASTM Test Method A 90. The result shall consist of the average of determinations from the three specimens cut from the test sheet or sample piece as provided in Section 2.205.1.

SECTION 2.206 — SPECIMENS FOR SINGLE-SPOT TEST

2.206.1 Material Split from Wider Stock. Material 18 inches (457 mm) and under is normally produced by slitting from wider width coils and therefore is subject to the single-spot test only. Material slit after leaving the producer's works is subject to the single-spot test only.

2.206.2 Criteria. The minimum check limit by the single-spot test shall be that one of the triple-spot test bearing the lightest coating, or the building official may select a single specimen taken from any part of the test sheet, provided it is taken within the boundaries outlined in Section 2.205.1. For material narrower than 2.25 inches (57.15 mm), the test specimen length shall be chosen to give an area of 5.06 square inches (3265 mm^2).

SECTION 2.207 — SPECIMENS FOR BASE METAL BEND TEST

Bend test specimens shall be 2 inches to 4 inches (51 mm to 102 mm) in width and may be cut from any sheet or coil. The bend test specimen shall not be taken closer than 2 inches (51 mm) from the sides nor 4 inches (102 mm) from the ends. Specimens for base metal bend tests shall be as free of burrs as possible. Filing or machining to remove burrs is permitted. If any specimen develops a flaw, it shall be discarded and a new specimen substituted. Cracks of the base metal developing at the edge of the specimen or coarse grain developing at the line of the bend shall be disregarded.

SECTION 2.208 — SPECIMENS FOR COATING BEND TEST

Coated sheet shall be capable of being bent through 180 degrees in any direction without flaking of the coating on the outside of the bend only. The coating bend test inside diameter shall have a relation to the thickness of the specimen as prescribed in Table A2-2-B. Flaking of coating within $^1/_4$ inch (6 mm) of the edge of the bend specimen shall not be cause for rejection.

SECTION 2.209 — DIMENSIONAL REQUIREMENTS

The thickness shall not be less than shown in Table A2-2-A. The thickness indicated in Table A2-2-A includes both the base steel and the coating.

SECTION 2.210 — DEFECTS

Material which is damaged or which contains injurious defect such as blisters, flux or uncoated spots shall not be used.

SECTION 2.211 — REJECTION

If the building official ascertains that the material fails to conform to the requirements of this standard, its use may be rejected.

TABLE A2-2-A—GALVANIZED SHEET GAGE NUMBERS AND THICKNESS[1]

GALVANIZED SHEET GAGE NO.	THICKNESS EQUIVALENT FOR GALVANIZED SHEET GAGE NO. (inches)
	× 25.4 for mm
10	0.1382
12	0.1084
13	0.0934
14	0.0785
15	0.0710
16	0.0635
17	0.0575
18	0.0516
19	0.0456
20	0.0396
21	0.0366
22	0.0336
23	0.0306
24	0.0276
25	0.0247
26	0.0217
27	0.0202
28	0.0187
29	0.0172
30	0.0157

[1]This table is provided for information only. The product is ordered to decimal inch thickness only.

TABLE A2-2-B—COATING BEND TEST REQUIREMENTS

COATING DESIGNATION	RATIO OF BEND DIAMETER TO THICKNESS OF SPECIMEN (Any Direction)		
	Galvanized Sheet Thickness		
	0.1382 to 0.0748	0.0747 to 0.0382	0.0381 to 0.0157
G-90	1	0	0

UNIFORM MECHANICAL CODE STANDARD 2-3
FLASH POINT BY PENSKY-MARTENS CLOSED TESTER

**Based on Standard Test Method D 93-75 of the
American Society for Testing and Materials**

See Sections 201.2.5 and 204, *Uniform Mechanical Code*

NOTE: This standard was formerly Uniform Fire Code Standard 2-2.

SECTION 2.301 — SCOPE

This standard is the test procedure for determining the flash point by the Pensky-Martens Closed-Cup Tester of liquids with a viscosity of 5.82 centistokes (5.82×10^{-6} m^2/s) or more at 100°F (38°C), a flash point of 200°F (93°C) or higher, suspensions of solids and liquids that tend to form a surface film under test conditions.

SECTION 2.302 — APPARATUS

Apparatus used for this test shall be an approved Pensky-Martens Closed-Cup Flash Tester. Support the tester on a level, steady table.

SECTION 2.303 — SAMPLE

Samples should not be stored in plastic (such as polyethylene or polypropylene) bottles, since volatile material may diffuse through the walls of the bottle.

Samples of very viscous materials may be warmed until they are reasonably fluid before they are tested. However, no sample should be heated more than is absolutely necessary. It shall never be heated above a temperature of 30°F (17°C) below its expected flash point.

Samples containing dissolved or free water may be dehydrated with calcium chloride or by filtering through a qualitative filter paper or a loose plug of dry absorbent cotton. Warming the sample is permitted, but it shall not be heated for prolonged periods or above a temperature of 30°F (17°C) below its expected flash point.

SECTION 2.304 — PROCEDURE

2.304.1 Basic Procedure. Fill the cup with the sample to be tested to the level indicated by the filling mark. Place the lid on the cup and set the test cup in the stove. Insert the thermometer. Light the test flame and adjust it to $^5/_{32}$ inch in diameter. Supply the heat at such a rate that the temperature as indicated by the thermometer increases 9°F to 11°F per minute (5°C to 6°C per minute). Turn the stirrer 90 to 120 revolutions per minute (rpm), stirring in a downward direction.

If the sample is know to have a flash point of 230°F (110°C) or below, apply the test flame when the temperature of the sample is from 30°F to 50°F (17°C to 28°C) below the expected flash point and thereafter at a temperature reading that is multiple of 2°F (1°C). Apply the test flame by operating the mechanism on the cover which controls the shutter and test flame burner so that the flame is lowered into the vapor space of the cup in 0.5 second, left in its lowered position for 1 second and quickly raised to its high position. Do not stir the sample while applying the test flame.

If the sample is known to have a flash point above 230°F (110°C), apply the test flame in the manner just described at each temperature that is a multiple of 5°F (2.8°C), beginning at a temperature of 30°F to 50°F (17°C to 28°C) below the expected flash point.

When the test flame application causes a distinct flash in the interior of the cup, observe and record the temperature of the sample as the flash point. Occasionally, particularly near the actual flash point, the application of the test flame will cause a halo or an enlarged flame; this is not a flash and should be ignored.

Observe and record the ambient barometric pressure at the time of the test.

2.304.2 Procedure for Suspensions of Solids and Highly Viscous Materials. Bring the material to be tested and the tester to a temperature of 60°F ± 10°F (15.5°C ± 5°C) or 20°F (11°C) lower than the estimated flash point, whichever is lower. Turn the stirrer 250 rpm ± 10 rpm, stirring in a downward direction. Raise the temperature throughout the duration of the test at a rate of not less than 2°F (1°C) nor more than 3°F (1.6°C) per minute. With the exception of these requirements for rates of stirring and heating, proceed as prescribed in Section 2.304.1.

SECTION 2.305 — FLASH POINT

The flash point shall be the temperature read on the thermometer to the nearest 1°F (0.5°C) at the time the test flame application causes a distinct flash in the interior of the cup. The recorded flash point shall be corrected when the pressure differs from 760 mm Hg as follows:

Corrected flash point = $F + 0.06 (760 - P)$

For **SI:** Corrected flash point = $C + 0.06 (101.3 - P)$

WHERE:

F = observed flash point, °F (°C).

P = ambient barometric pressure, mm Hg (kPa).

UNIFORM MECHANICAL CODE STANDARD 6-1
STANDARD FOR METAL DUCTS

**Based on the First Edition, 1985 HVAC Duct Construction Standards, Metal and Flexible,
Published by the Sheet Metal and Air-Conditioning Contractors National Association**

See Section 601.1, *Uniform Mechanical Code*

SECTION 6.101 — SCOPE

The performance criteria and requirements herein contemplate a duct that is a structural assembly having the capacity to support occupant health and safety while minimizing its own contribution to property damage under emergency conditions. Ducts can supply fresh or treated air in support of life and health, can convey products of combustion away from a fire zone, can maintain a pressure differential that facilitates evacuation and reduces the spread of fire and smoke and can facilitate firefighter access to a fire source.

SECTION 6.102 — DEFINITIONS

CLOSURE is the joining components on duct surfaces that are subjected to a pressure differential across the duct wall, including mechanical locks and metallic and nonmetallic materials used as fillers or sealers whether on straight sections of ducts or fittings or used in connection of duct or fitting to other apparatus. Closure shall also pertain to penetrations of duct walls (such as by screws, rivets, pipes, electrical conduits, etc.).

CLOSURE FAILURE is any structural failure at a closure and also any loss of adhesive bond, creep, displacement or other deterioration of closure materials and methods that results in an increase in air leakage above an allowable level and any behavior contributing to accelerated aging of the closure systems.

DUCT ASSEMBLY is the completed composite connected assembly of straight sections, fittings and accessories attached to or occurring in the perimeter of an air passageway that is used for supply air, exhaust air or recirculated air mode. The passageway need not be continuous.

NOTE: Where apparatus, ceiling plenums, room boundaries, shafts, air terminals, etc., form a part of the passageways, such are not subject to the performance requirements in this standard but are not prohibited from being made subject to similar requirements.

METAL DUCT is a duct constructed of galvanized steel, uncoated steel, stainless steel or aluminum material of commercial grade. Accessories and reinforcements are not required by this standard to be of the same material as the duct wall but they must be electrolytically compatible and shall not reduce the performance levels for strength and tight closure of ducts.

STRUCTURAL FAILURE is any visible and measurable rupture, collapse, buckling or other permanent deformation or separation of the elements in the duct assembly.

SECTION 6.103 — PERFORMANCE REQUIREMENTS FOR DUCTS

6.103.1 Pressure. Structural failure or closure failure of duct assembly shall not occur at 150 percent of the designed operating pressure classification when supported at the maximum recommended support spacing.

6.103.2 Support Spacing. Structural failure or closure failure of duct assembly shall not occur when supported at twice the maximum recommended support spacing and atmospheric pressure is maintained inside the ducts.

6.103.3 Deflection, Longitudinal. The maximum allowable deflection of rectangular duct walls at design pressure classification shall not exceed the following:

DUCT DIMENSION	DEFLECTION
12″ (305 mm) down	$1/_2$″ (13 mm)
13″ to 18″ (330 to 457 mm)	$5/_8$″ (16 mm)
19″ to 24″ (483 to 610 mm)	$3/_4$″ (19 mm)
over 24″ (610 mm)	1″ (25 mm)

The deflection reference plane is that passing through two adjacent corners of the duct. For cross-broken ducts, the measurement point shall be on the centerline of the duct at a point one eighth of the duct width or reinforcement interval or joint spacing if unreinforced, whichever is greater, from the intersection of the cross breaks. For cross-broken ducts, the allowable wall deflection shall be increased by 50 percent of the deflection "set" measured at atmospheric pressure level in the duct.

6.103.4 Deflection, Transverse. The maximum allowable deflection for rectangular duct transverse joint systems and intermediate reinforcements shall be $1/_4$ inch (6.4 mm) for duct widths of 100 inches (2540 mm) or less and shall be 0.3 percent of the span for greater widths. In any case, the allowable deflection shall not be construed as permitting such members to exceed 60 percent of their yield stress.

6.103.5 Allowable Stress. Loads imposed by fabricated duct weight designed pressure differential across the duct wall, bending moment created by supports and $1/_2$ pound per square foot (2.4 kg/m^2) of insulation weight shall not exceed 60 percent of the yield stress of the metals in the duct and its connections. Other internal and external loads are not accounted for by this standard.

6.103.6 Cyclical Loading Resistance. Duct assemblies shall be capable of withstanding a daily on-off cycle of operation without structural failure.

6.103.7 Airtightness. Closures for ducts shall be substantially airtight.

SECTION 6.104 — SUPPORT REQUIREMENTS FOR DUCTS

6.104.1 Method and Interval. The support spacing interval and method of contact with the duct assembly shall be selected to avoid structural failure or closure failure in the duct.

6.104.2 Allowable Stress in Supports. Supports shall not be subjected to more than 60 percent of their yield stress.

6.104.3 Safety Factor. The upper attachment of a duct suspension (hanging) system to a building structure shall have a safety factor of at least 4 based on ultimate failure (pullout) load.

6.104.4 Loading. Supports shall account for loads identified in Section 6.103.1.

6.104.5 Fastening Loads. The location and arrangement of all fastenings in the support system shall be selected to avoid failure in tensile, compressive, shear and flexure modes.

6.104.6 Corrosion Control. The support system shall not cause corrosion by galvanic (electrolytic) action at points of contact with the duct.

6.104.7 Character of Support System. The support system shall not penetrate enclosures containing fluids or electrical wiring in such a manner as to create a hazard nor shall they penetrate a load-bearing member in such a manner as to cause excessive loading on the member.

SECTION 6.105 — COMPLYING SYSTEMS

Tables A6-1-A through A6-1-Q typify duct construction conforming with this standard. Throughout the tables in this standard, the minimum thickness in inches for galvanized sheet gage numbers is used.

TABLE A6-1-A—RECTANGULAR DUCT HANGERS, MINIMUM SIZE

MAXIMUM HALF OF DUCT PERIMETER	PAIR AT 10 FT. SPACING		PAIR AT 8 FT. SPACING		PAIR AT 5 FT. SPACING		PAIR AT 4 FT. SPACING	
	Strap	Wire/Rod	Strap	Wire/Rod	Strap	Wire/Rod	Strap	Wire/Rod
	× 25.4 for mm							
$\frac{P}{2}$ = 30″	1″ × 0.030 (1″ × 22 ga.)	10 ga. (0.135″)	1″ × 0.030 (1″ × 22 ga.)	10 ga. (0.135″)	1″ × 0.030 (1″ × 22 ga.)	12 ga. (0.106″)	1″ × 0.030 (1″ × 22 ga.)	12 ga. (0.106″)
$\frac{P}{2}$ = 72″	1″ × 0.047 (1″ × 18 ga.)	$3/8$″	1″ × 0.036 (1″ × 20 ga.)	$1/4$″	1″ × 0.030 (1″ × 22 ga.)	$1/4$″	1″ × 0.030 (1″ × 22 ga.)	$1/4$″
$\frac{P}{2}$ = 96″	1″ × 0.058 (1″ × 16 ga.)	$3/8$″	1″ × 0.047 (1″ × 18 ga.)	$3/8$″	1″ × 0.036 (1″ × 20 ga.)	$3/8$″	1″ × 0.030 (1″ × 22 ga.)	$1/4$″
$\frac{P}{2}$ = 120″	$1\frac{1}{2}$″ × 0.058 ($1\frac{1}{2}$″ × 16 ga.)	$1/2$″	1″ × 0.058 (1″ × 16 ga.)	$3/8$″	1″ × 0.047 (1″ × 18 ga.)	$3/8$″	1″ × 0.036 (1″ × 20 ga.)	$1/4$″
$\frac{P}{2}$ = 168″	$1\frac{1}{2}$″ × 0.058 ($1\frac{1}{2}$″ × 16 ga.)	$1/2$″	1″ × 0.058 ($1\frac{1}{2}$″ × 16 ga.)	$1/2$″	1″ × 0.058 (1″ × 16 ga.)	$3/8$″	1″ × 0.047 (1″ × 18 ga.)	$3/8$″
$\frac{P}{2}$ = 192″	—	$1/2$″	$1\frac{1}{2}$″ × 0.058 ($1\frac{1}{2}$″ × 16 ga.)	$1/2$″	1″ × 0.058 (1″ × 16 ga.)	$3/8$″	1″ × 0.058 (1″ × 16 ga.)	$3/8$″
$\frac{P}{2}$ = 193″ up	Special analysis required							

WHEN STRAPS ARE LAP JOINED USE THESE MINIMUM FASTENERS	SINGLE HANGER MAXIMUM ALLOWABLE LOAD	
	Strap	Wire or Rod (diameter)
× 25.4 for mm	(× 25.4 for mm) (× 0.453 for kg)	
1″ × 0.047″, 0.036″, 0.030″—two No. 10 or one $1/4$″ bolt 1″ × 0.058″—two $1/4$″ dia. $1\frac{1}{2}$″ × 0.058″—two $3/8$″ dia. Place fasteners in series, not side by side.	1″ × 0.030″ - 260 lbs. 1″ × 0.036″ - 320 lbs. 1″ × 0.047″ - 420 lbs. 1″ × 0.058″ - 700 lbs. $1\frac{1}{2}$″ × 0.058″ - 1,100 lbs.	0.106″ - 80 lbs. 0.135″ - 120 lbs. 0.162″ - 160 lbs. $1/4$″ - 270 lbs. $3/8$″ - 680 lbs. $1/2$″ - 1,250 lbs. $5/8$″ - 2,000 lbs. $3/4$″ - 3,000 lbs.

NOTES:
1. Dimensions other than gage are in inches.
2. Tables allow for duct weight 1 pound per square foot (4.8 kg/m^2) insulation weight normal reinforcement and trapeze weight, but no external loads.
3. Straps are galvanized steel; other materials are uncoated steel.
4. Allowable loads for $P/2$ assume that ducts are 0.058 (16 gage) (1.47 mm) maximum, except that when maximum duct dimension (w) is over 60 inches (1524 mm), then $P/2$ maximum is 1.25 w.
5. For trapeze sizes, see Table A6-1-B.
6. Twelve [0.081 in. (2.05 mm)], 10 [0.102 in. (2.59 mm)] or 8 gage [0.128 in. (3.25 mm)] wire is steel of black-annealed, bright basic or galvanized type.

TABLE A6-1-B—ALLOWABLE LOADS (Pounds) (kg) FOR TRAPEZE ANGLES (For Rectangular Ducts)

LENGTH (inches)	1 × 1 × 0.058″ (16 ga.)	1 × 1 × 1/8″	1 1/2 × 1 1/2 × 0.058″ (16 ga.)	1 1/2 × 1 1/2 × 1/8″	1 1/2 × 1 1/2 × 3/16″	1 1/2 × 1 1/2 × 1/4″ or 2 × 2 × 1/8″	2 × 2 × 3/16″	2 × 2 × 1/4″	2 1/2 × 2 1/2 × 3/16″	2 1/2 × 2 1/2 × 1/4″
					× 25.4 for mm × 0.453 for kg					
18	80	150	180	350	510	650	940	1,230	1,500	1,960
24	75	150	180	350	510	650	940	1,230	1,500	1,960
30	70	150	180	350	510	650	940	1,230	1,500	1,960
36	60	130	160	340	500	620	920	1,200	1,480	1,940
42	40	110	140	320	480	610	900	1,190	1,470	1,930
48	—	80	110	290	450	580	870	1,160	1,440	1,900
54	—	40	70	250	400	540	840	1,120	1,400	1,860
60	—	—	—	190	350	490	780	1,060	1,340	1,800
66	—	—	—	100	270	400	700	980	1,260	1,720
72	—	—	—	—	190	320	620	900	1,180	1,640
78	—	—	—	—	80	210	500	790	1,070	1,530
84	—	—	—	—	—	80	380	660	940	1,400
96	—	—	—	—	—	—	—	320	600	1,060
108	—	—	—	—	—	—	—	—	150	610

Loads above assume that a hanger rod is 6-inch (152 mm) maximum distance from duct side.

TABLE A6-1-C—ROUND DUCT HANGERS

DUCT DIAMETER (inches)	MAXIMUM SPACING (feet)	WIRE DIAMETER	ROD (inch)	STRAP
× 25.4 for mm	× 304.8 for mm		× 25.4 for mm	
10 dn	12	One 12 ga.	1/4	1″ × 0.030 (22 ga.)
11-18	12	Two 12 ga. or one 8 ga.	1/4	1″ × 0.030 (22 ga.)
19-24	12	Two 10 ga.	1/4	1″ × 0.030 (22 ga.)
25-36	12	Two 8 ga.	3/8	1″ × 0.036 (20 ga.)
37-50	12	→	Two 3/8	Two 1″ × 0.036 (20 ga.)
51-80	12	→	Two 3/8	Two 1″ × 0.047 (18 ga.)
81-94	12	→	Two 3/8	Two 1″ × 0.058 (16 ga.)

TABLE A6-1-D—FLAT OVAL DUCT CONSTRUCTION

DUCT WIDTH (inches)	INCHES (gage)		
	Spiral Lock Seam Duct	Longitudinal Seam Duct	Fittings
	× 25.4 for mm		
To 24	0.024 (24)	0.036 (20)	0.036 (20)
25 to 36	0.030 (22)	0.036 (20)	0.036 (20)
37 to 48	0.030 (22)	0.047 (18)	0.047 (18)
49 to 60	0.036 (20)	0.047 (18)	0.047 (18)
61 to 70	0.036 (20)	0.058 (16)	0.058 (16)
71 and up	0.047 (18)	0.058 (16)	0.058 (16)

TABLE A6-1-E—ROUND DUCT GAGE SELECTION FOR GALVANIZED STEEL

DUCT DIAMETER (inches)	MAXIMUM 2-INCH W.G. (498 Pa) STATIC POSITIVE		MAXIMUM 10-INCH W.G. (2.5 kPa) STATIC POSITIVE		MAXIMUM 2-INCH W.G. (498 Pa) STATIC NEGATIVE	
	Spiral Seam inch (gage)	Longitudinal Seam inch (gage)	Spiral Seam inch (gage)	Longitudinal Seam inch (gage)	Spiral Seam inch (gage)	Longitudinal Seam inch (gage)
	× 25.4 for mm					
3 through 8	0.016 (28)	0.016 (28)	0.019 (26)	0.024 (24)	0.016 (28)	0.024 (24)
9 through 14	0.016 (28)	0.019 (26)	0.019 (26)	0.024 (24)	0.019 (26)	0.024 (24)
15 through 26	0.019 (26)	0.024 (24)	0.024 (24)	0.030 (22)	0.024 (24)	0.030 (22)
27 through 36	0.024 (24)	0.030 (22)	0.030 (22)	0.036 (20)	0.030 (22)	0.036 (20)
37 through 50	0.030 (22)	0.036 (20)	0.036 (20)	0.036 (20)	0.036 (20)	0.047 (18)
51 through 60	0.036 (20)	0.047 (18)	0.047 (18)	0.047 (18)	0.047 (18)	0.058 (16)
61 through 84	0.047 (18)	0.058 (16)	0.047 (18)	0.058 (16)	0.058 (16)	0.070 (14)

(Continued)

TABLE A6-1-E—ROUND DUCT GAGE SELECTION FOR GALVANIZED STEEL—(Continued)

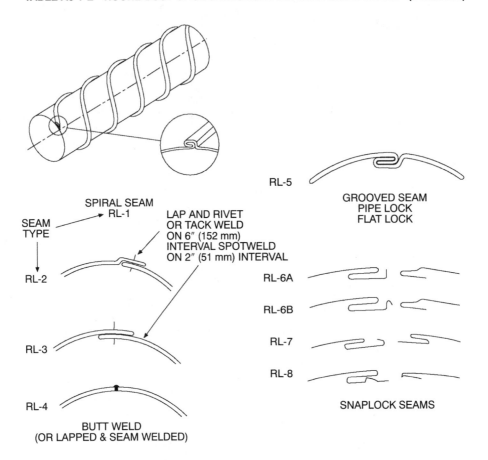

RL-5 — GROOVED SEAM PIPE LOCK FLAT LOCK

SPIRAL SEAM RL-1

SEAM TYPE

RL-2 — LAP AND RIVET OR TACK WELD ON 6″ (152 mm) INTERVAL SPOTWELD ON 2″ (51 mm) INTERVAL

RL-3

RL-4 — BUTT WELD (OR LAPPED & SEAM WELDED)

RL-6A

RL-6B

RL-7

RL-8

SNAPLOCK SEAMS

PRESSURE CLASS	SEAM TYPE PERMITTED
Positive	
To +10″ w.g. (2488 Pa)	RL-1, 4, 5 (2*, 3*) (51mm, 76 mm)
To + 3″ w.g. (746 Pa)	RL-1,2, 3, 4, 5
To + 2″ w.g. (498 Pa)	ALL
Negative	
To –2″ w.g. (498 Pa)	RL-1, 2, 3, 4, 5
To –1″ w.g. (249 Pa)	ALL

*Acceptable if spot welded on 1″ (25.4 mm) intervals.

TABLE A6-1-E—ROUND DUCT GAGE SELECTION FOR GALVANIZED STEEL—(Continued)

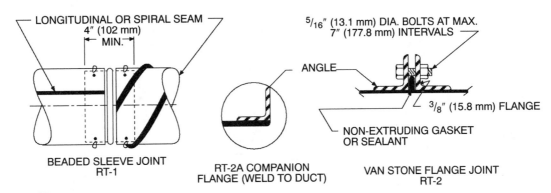

SLEEVE TO BE AT LEAST
DUCT GAGE

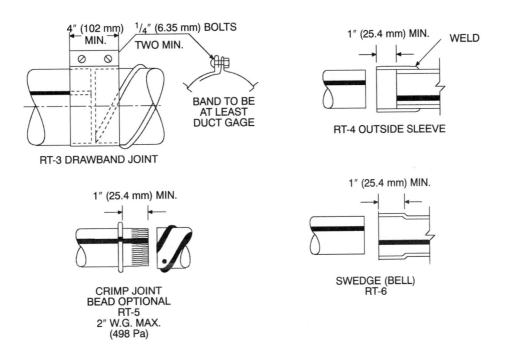

ON JOINTS RT-1, 3, 4 AND 6 SCREWS MUST
BE USED AT UNIFORM INTERVALS 15″ (381 mm) MAXIMUM ALONG THE
CIRCUMFERENCE; THREE SCREWS MINIMUM ON 14″ (356 mm) OR LESS DIAMETER.

MIN. FLANGE SIZES FOR RT-2 AND 2A
1″ × 1″ × 10 GA. ON 14″ (356 mm) MAX. DIA.
1½″ × 1½″ × ⅛″ (38 mm × 38 mm × 3.18 mm)
DIA. OVER 14″ (356 mm)

LONGITUDINAL OR SPIRAL SEAM DUCT IS
ACCEPTABLE FOR ALL JOINTS EXCEPT RT-4 AND 6 (FOR LONGITUDINAL ONLY)

TABLE A6-1-F—RECTANGULAR DUCT TRANSVERSE REINFORCEMENT
FOR DUCT MATERIAL THICKNESSES FROM 0.030″ (22 ga.) (0.76 mm) TO 0.019″ (26 ga.) (0.48 mm)

Pressure Class (water gage) → ×248.8 for Pa

Duct Thickness inches (gage) → ×25.4 for mm

Duct Dimensions	1/2″	1/2″	1″	1″	2″	2″	1/2″	1/2″	1″	1″	2″	2″	1/2″	1/2″	1″	1″	2″	2″
	0.030″ (22)	0.030″ (22)	0.030″ (22)	0.030″ (22)	0.030″ (22)	0.030″ (22)	0.024″ (24)	0.024″ (24)	0.024″ (24)	0.024″ (24)	0.024″ (24)	0.024″ (24)	0.019″ (26)	0.019″ (26)	0.019″ (26)	0.019″ (26)	0.019″ (26)	0.019″ (26)
7″ dn.																		
8-10″																		
11, 12″																		
13, 14″																	A/5[D]	A/8[D]
15, 16″					A/10[D]	A/8[D]			A/10[D]	A/8[D]	A/5[D]	A/8[D]			A/5[D]	A/8[D]	A/5[D]	A/4[D]
17, 18″					A/10[D]	A/8[D]			A/10[D]	A/8[D]	A/5[D]	A/8[D]			A/5[D]	A/8[D]	A/5[D]	A/4[D]
19, 20″			A/10[D]	A/8[D]	A/5[D]	B/8			A/10[D]	A/8[D]	A/5[D]	A/4[D]	A/10[D]	A/8[D]	A/5[D]	A/8[D]	A/5[D]	A/4[D]
21, 22″			A/10	A/8	A/5	B/8	A/10	A/8	A/10	A/8	A/5	A/4	A/10	A/8	A/5	A/4	A/5	A/4
23, 24″			B/10	B/8	B/5	C/8	A/10	A/8	B/10	B/8	B/5	B/4	A/10	A/8	A/5	A/4	A/5	A/4
25, 26″	A/10	A/8	B/10	B/8	B/5	C/8	A/10	A/8	A/5	B/8	B/5	B/4	A/10	A/8	A/5	A/4	B/5	B/4
27, 28″	B/10	B/8	C/10	C/8	C/5	B/4	B/10	B/8	B/5	C/8	C/5	B/4	B/5	B/8	B/5	B/4	B/2-1/2	B/4
29, 30″	B/10	B/8	C/10	C/8	C/5	C/4	B/10	B/8	B/5	C/8	C/5	C/4	B/5	B/8	B/5	B/4	C/2-1/2	C/4
31-36″	C/10	C/8	C/5	D/8	D/5	D/4	C/5	C/8	C/5	C/4	D/2-1/2	D/4	C/5	C/4	C/5	C/4		
37-42″	D/5	D/8	D/5	D/4	E/5	E/4	D/5	D/8	D/5	D/4	E/2-1/2	E/4	D/5	C/4	D/2-1/2	D/4		
43-48″	D/5	D/8	E/5	D/4	E/2-1/2	E/4	D/5	D/4	E/5	D/4	E/2-1/2	E/2	D/5	D/4	D/2-1/2	D/4		
49-54″	D/5	D/4	E/5	E/4	F/2-1/2	F/2	D/5	D/4	E/2-1/2	E/4	F/2-1/2	F/2	D/5	D/4				
55-60″	E/5	E/4	F/5	F/4	G/2-1/2	G/2	E/5	E/4	F/2-1/2	F/4			E/2-1/2	E/4				
61-72″	F/5	F/4	G/2-1/2	G/4	H/2-1/2	H/2	F/2-1/2	F/4										
73-84″	H/5	G/4					G/2-1/2	G/4										
85-96″	H/2-1/2	H/4																
97″ up																		

Standing reinforcement is not required on duct sizes above this heavy line. Flat slips and drives or other choice may be used. Flat slips and drives must not be less than one gage below duct gage and not less than 24 gage. — NOT REQUIRED — — — NOT ALLOWED (lower right of 24 ga. region)

Flat slips and drives may be backed with stiffeners from Table A6-1-I and thereby qualified for this table. Where the superscript D occurs, the flat drive is accepted as Class A. See Table A6-1-K.

THIS NUMBER IS THE SPACING INTERVAL BETWEEN REINFORCEMENTS, IN FEET (mm)

THIS LETTER DENOTES TYPE OF REINFORCEMENT TO BE SELECTED FROM JOINT TABLE A6-1-H, A6-1-I OR A6-1-J

TABLE A6-1-G—RECTANGULAR DUCT TRANSVERSE REINFORCEMENT
FOR DUCT MATERIAL THICKNESSES FROM 0.058″ (16 ga.) TO 0.036″ (20 ga.)

Pressure Class (water gage) → ×248.8 for Pa

Duct Thickness inches (gage) → ×25.4 for mm

Duct Dimensions	1/2″	1/2″	1″	1″	2″	2″	1/2″	1/2″	1″	1″	2″	2″	1/2″	1/2″	1″	1″	2″	2″
	0.058″ (16)	0.058″ (16)	0.058″ (16)	0.058″ (16)	0.058″ (16)	0.058″ (16)	0.047″ (18)	0.047″ (18)	0.047″ (18)	0.047″ (18)	0.047″ (18)	0.047″ (18)	0.036″ (20)	0.036″ (20)	0.036″ (20)	0.036″ (20)	0.036″ (20)	0.036″ (20)
7″ dn.																		
8-10″																		
11, 12″																		
13, 14″																		
15, 16″																		
17, 18″																		
19, 20″																	B/10	B/8
21, 22″											B/10	B/8	A/10	A/8			B/10	B/8
23, 24″											C/10	C/8			B/10	B/8	C/10	C/8
25, 26″					C/10	C/8					C/10	C/8			B/10	B/8	C/10	C/8
27, 28″					C/10	C/8			C/10	C/8	C/10	C/8	B/10	B/8	C/10	C/8	C/5	C/8
29, 30″					D/10	D/8			C/10	C/8	D/10	D/8	B/10	B/8	C/10	C/8	C/5	D/8
31-36″			D/10	D/8	E/10	E/8	C/10	C/8	D/10	D/8	D/5	E/8	C/10	C/8	D/10	D/8	D/5	D/4
37-42″	D/10	D/8	E/10	E/8	E/5	E/8	D/10	D/8	E/10	D/8	E/5	E/4	D/10	D/8	D/5	D/8	E/5	E/4
43-48″	E/10	D/8	F/10	F/8	F/5	G/8	E/10	D/8	E/5	E/8	F/5	E/4	E/10	D/8	E/5	D/4	E/5	E/4
49-54″	E/10	E/8	G/10	F/8	G/5	F/4	E/10	E/8	E/5	F/8	G/5	F/4	D/5	E/8	E/5	E/4	F/2-1/2	F/4
55-60″	F/10	F/8	F/5	G/8	H/5	G/4	F/10	F/8	F/5	G/8	H/5	G/4	E/5	F/8	F/5	F/4	G/2-1/2	G/2
61-72″	H/10	G/8	H/5	G/4	I/5	H/4	F/5	G/8	H/5	G/4	H/2-1/2	H/4	F/5	F/4	G/2-1/2	G/4	H/2-1/2	H/2
73-84″	H/5	H/8	I/5	H/4	I/2-1/2	J/4	H/5	G/4	I/5	H/4	I/2-1/2	J/4	H/5	G/4	H/2-1/2	H/4	I/2-1/2	I/2
85-96″	H/5	I/8	J/5	I/4	J/2-1/2	K/4	H/5	H/4	I/2-1/2	I/4	J/2-1/2	J/2	H/5	H/4	I/2-1/2	I/2	J/2-1/2	J/2
97″ up	H/5	H/4	J/2-1/2	J/2	K/2-1/2	K/2	H/5	H/4	J/2-1/2	J/2	K/2-1/2	K/2						

Standing reinforcement is not required on duct sizes above this heavy line. Flat slips and drives or other choice may be used. Flat slips and drives must not be less than one gage below duct gage and not less than 24 gage. — NOT REQUIRED —

Flat slips and drives may be backed with stiffeners from Table A6-1-I and thereby qualified for this table.

THIS NUMBER IS THE SPACING INTERVAL BETWEEN REINFORCEMENTS, IN FEET

THIS LETTER DENOTES TYPE OF REINFORCEMENT TO BE SELECTED FROM JOINT TABLE A6-1-H, A6-1-I OR A6-1-J

TABLE A6-1-H—TRANSVERSE JOINT REINFORCEMENT
FOR TABLES A6-1-F AND A6-1-G

MINIMUM RIGIDITY CLASS	EI	T-2 STANDING DRIVE SLIP — H × T ($\times$ 25.4 for mm)	WT/LF ($\times$ 1.488 for kg/m)	T-10 STANDING S — H × T ($\times$ 25.4 for mm)	WT/LF ($\times$ 1.488 for kg/m)	T-11 STANDING S — H × T ($\times$ 25.4 for mm)	WT/LF ($\times$ 1.488 for kg/m)	T-12 STANDING S — H × T ($\times$ 25.4 for mm)	WT/LF ($\times$ 1.488 for kg/m)	T-13 / T-14 STANDING S — H × T + HR ($\times$ 25.4 for mm)	WT/LF ($\times$ 1.488 for kg/m)
A	0.5					$1/2 \times 0.019''$ ($1/2 \times 26$ ga.)	0.5				
B	1.0	$1^1/8 \times 0.019''$ ($1^1/8 \times 26$ ga.)	0.5			$1/2 \times 0.030''$ ($1/2 \times 22$ ga.)	0.7				
C	2.5	$1^1/8 \times 0.030''$ ($1^1/8 \times 22$ ga.)	0.8	$1 \times 0.019''$ (1×26 ga.)	0.6	$1 \times 0.019''$ (1×26 ga.)	0.6				
D	5			$1 \times 0.024''$ (1×24 ga.)	0.7	$1 \times 0.024''$ (1×24 ga.)	0.7	$1^1/8 \times 0.019''$ ($1^1/8 \times 26$ ga.)	0.7		
E	10	Not given		$1^1/8 \times 0.036''$ ($1^1/8 \times 20$ ga.) w = $^3/16''$	0.9	Not given		$1^1/8 \times 0.047''$ ($1^1/8 \times 18$ ga.)	1.4		
F	15			$1^5/8 \times 0.030''$ ($1^5/8 \times 22$ ga.) w = $^3/16''$	1.0			$1^1/2 \times 0.024''$ ($1^1/2 \times 24$ ga.)	1.0	$1^1/2 \times 0.024''$ ($1^1/2 \times 24$ ga.) $1^1/2 \times ^1/8$ Bar	1.5
G	25			$1^5/8 \times 0.047''$ ($1^5/8 \times 18$ ga.) w = $^3/16''$	1.5			$1^1/2 \times 0.047''$ ($1^1/2 \times 18$ ga.)	1.7	$1^1/2 \times 0.030''$ ($1^1/2 \times 22$ ga.) $1^1/2 \times ^1/8$ Bar	1.6
H	50	Not given		Not given		Not given		Not given		$1^1/2 \times 0.036''$ ($1^1/2 \times 20$ ga.) ($1^1/2 \times 1^1/2 \times ^3/16$)	2.9
I	75									$2 \times 0.036''$ (2×20 ga.) $2 \times 2 \times ^1/8$	2.9
J	100									$2 \times 0.036''$ (2×20 ga.) $2 \times 2 \times ^3/16$	3.7
K	150									Not given	
L	200										

(Continued)

TABLE A6-1-H—TRANSVERSE JOINT REINFORCEMENT FOR TABLES A6-1-F AND A6-1-G—(Continued)

MINIMUM RIGIDITY CLASS	EI	H	LOCK T, DUCT T, HR (× 25.4 for mm)	WT/LF (× 1.488 for kg/m)	T-20 CAPPED FLANGE H × T (× 25.4 for mm)	U	WT/LF (× 1.488 for kg/m)	T-22 COMPANION ANGLES H × T (× 25.4 for mm)	WT/LF (× 1.488 for kg/m)	T-23 FLANGED H × T (× 25.4 for mm)	WT/LF (× 1.488 for kg/m)
A	0.5										
B	1.0				$3/4 \times 0.019''$ (26 ga.)	0.024" (24 ga.)	0.4				
C	2.5	T-17 1"	0.019" (26 ga.) lock on 0.019" (26 ga.)	0.6	$1 \times 0.024''$ (24 ga.)	0.024" (24 ga.)	0.5			$1 \times 0.024''$ (24 ga.)	1.0
D	5	T-17 1"	0.024" (24 ga.) lock on 0.024" (24 ga.)	0.7	$1 \times 0.030''$ (22 ga.)	0.030" (22 ga.)	0.6			$1 \times 0.030''$ (22 ga.)	1.0
E	10	T-18 1"	0.030" (22 ga.) lock $1 \times 1/8$ bar	1.4	$1^1/_2 \times 0.024''$ (24 ga.)	0.030" (22 ga.)	0.8	Two $1 \times 1/8$	1.7	$1 \times 0.058''$ (16 ga.) $1^1/_2 \times 0.024''$ (24 ga.)	1.0
F	15	T-17 $1^1/_2$"	0.030" (22 ga.) lock	1.0	$1^1/_2 \times 0.036''$ (20 ga.)	0.036" (20 ga.)	1.0			$1^1/_2 \times 0.030''$ (22 ga.) $1^1/_2 \times 0.036''$ (20 ga.)	1.0 1.0
G	25	T-18 $1^1/_2$"	0.030" (22 ga.) lock $1^1/_2 \times 1/8$ bar	1.6				Two $1^1/_4 \times 1/8$	2.1	$1^1/_2 \times 0.047''$ (18 ga.)	1.5
H	50	T-19 $1^1/_2$"	0.036" (20 ga.) lock $1^1/_2 \times 3/16$ angle	2.9	$2 \times 0.058''$ (16 ga.)	0.036" (20 ga.)	1.5	Two $1^1/_2 \times 1/8$	2.6	$2 \times 0.047''$ (18 ga.)	1.5
I	75	T-19 $1^1/_2$"	0.036" (20 ga.) lock $2 \times 1/8$ angle	2.8	$2 \times 0.058''$ (16 ga.) **			Two* $1^1/_2 \times 3/16$	3.7	$2 \times 0.058''$ (16 ga.)	2.0
J	100	T-19 $1^1/_2$"	0.036" (20 ga.) lock $2 \times 3/16$ angle	3.5				Two* $1^1/_2 \times 1/4$	4.7	$2 \times 0.047''$ (18 ga.)	
K	150	T-19 $1^1/_2$"	0.036" (20 ga.) lock $2^1/_2 \times 3/16$ angle	4.2				Two* $2 \times 3/16$	4.9	**WITH TIE RODS**	
L	200		Not given					Two* $2 \times 1/4$	6.5		

Nominal EI equals number listed times 10^5.

*Tie rod option also: Use Class H plus one tie rod.

(Continued)

TABLE A6-1-H—TRANSVERSE JOINT REINFORCEMENT FOR
TABLES A6-1-F AND A6-1-G—(Continued)

DUCT THICKNESS	Inches (Gage)	0.019″ to 0.030″ (26 to 22)	0.036″ (20)	0.047″ (18)	0.058″ (16)
		× 25.4 for mm			
Minimum Flat Slip and Drive Gage		0.024″ (24)	0.030″ (22)	0.036″ (20)	0.047″ (18)

By themselves flat-type slip connections and lap joints do not qualify as reinforcements. When backed by a stiffener from Table A6-1-I, the reinforcement is graded by the stiffener. See an exception for joint T-1 in Table A6-1-K. T-5, T-6 and T-7 are restricted to 2″ w.g. (498 Pa) maximum service pressure.

T-1—DRIVE SLIP
T-3—REINFORCED

H_R

LAP
T-4

PLAIN "S" SLIP
T-5

3″ (76 mm) MAX.

MAX.

T-6 HEMMED "S" SLIP
(T-6a REINFORCED)

0.047″ (1.19 mm) (18 GA.) OR
0.058″ (1.47 mm) (16 GA.)

1″ (25.4 mm)

REINFORCED "S" SLIP
T-7

T-8 DOUBLE "S" SLIP
(T-8a REINFORCED)

1″   1″ (25.4 mm)

INSIDE SLIP JOINT
T-9

For pressure classes over 2″ (498 Pa) water gage, double S slips of 30″ (762 mm) length or less shall be 0.024″ (0.61 mm) (No. 24 gage) minimum; lengths over 30″ (762 mm) shall be 0.030″ (0.76 mm) (No. 22 gage) minimum.

TABLE A6-1-I—INTERMEDIATE REINFORCEMENT

MINIMUM RIGIDITY CLASS	EI	ANGLE H × T (MIN.) ×25.4 for mm	WT/LF ×1.488 for kg/m	ZEE H × B × T (MIN.) ×25.4 for mm	WT/LF ×1.488 for kg/m	HAT SECTION H × B × D × T (MIN.) ×25.4 for mm	WT/LF ×1.488 for kg/m	CHANNEL H × B × T (MIN.) ×25.4 for mm	WT/LF ×1.488 for kg/m
A	0.05								
B	1.0			$3/4 \times 1/2 \times 0.036''$ (20 ga.)	0.28				
C	2.5	$1 \times 0.047''$ (18 ga.) $1 \times 0.058''$ (16 ga.) $3/4 \times 1/8$	0.34 0.44 0.59	$3/4 \times 1/2 \times 0.047''$ (18 ga.)	0.36			$3/4 \times 3 \times 0.047''$ (18 ga.)	0.81
D	5	$1 1/4 \times 0.047''$ (18 ga.) $1 \times 1/8$	0.45 0.80	$1 \times 3/4 \times 0.036''$ (20 ga.)	0.35			$1 1/8 \times 3 1/4 \times 0.047''$ (18 ga.) $1 \times 3 \times 0.047''$ (18 ga.)	1.0
E	10	$1 1/4 \times 0.090$ $1 1/2 \times 0.058''$ (16 ga.)	0.80 0.66	$1 \times 3/4 \times 0.090$ $1 1/2 \times 3/4 \times 0.036''$ (20 ga.)	0.78 0.41		0.7	$1 \times 2 \times 1/8$	1.6
F	15	$1 1/2 \times 1/8$*	1.23	$1 \times 3/4 \times 1/8$ $1 1/2 \times 3/4 \times 0.047''$ (18 ga.)	1.03 0.54	$1 1/2 \times 3/4 \times 5/8 \times 0.036''$ (20 ga.) $1 1/2 \times 1 1/2 \times 3/4\ 0.036''$ (20 ga.)	0.7 1.1	$1 1/4 \times 3 1/2 \times 0.058''$ (16 ga.) $1 1/8 \times 3 \times 1/8$	1.32 2.1
G	25	$1 1/2 \times 3/16$	0.96	$1 1/2 \times 3/4 \times 1/8$ $2 \times 1 1/8 \times 0.036''$ (20 ga.)	1.23 0.6	$1 1/2 \times 3/4 \times 5/8 \times 0.058''$ (16 ga.) $1 1/2 \times 1 1/2 \times 3/4 \times 0.047''$ (18 ga.) $2 \times 1 \times 3/4 \times 0.036''$ (20 ga.)	0.82 1.1 0.90		

MINIMUM RIGIDITY CLASS	EI	ANGLE H × T (MIN.) ×25.4 for mm	WT/LF ×1.488 for kg/m	ZEE H × B × T (MIN.) ×25.4 for mm	WT/LF ×1.488 for kg/m	CHANNEL H × B × D × T (MIN.) ×25.4 for mm	WT/LF ×1.488 for kg/m	HAT SECTION H × B × T (MIN.) ×25.4 for mm	WT/LF ×1.488 for kg/m
H	50	$2 \times 1/8$	1.65	$2 \times 1 1/8 \times 0.058''$ (16 ga.)	0.94	$1 1/2 \times 3/4 \times 5/8 \times 1/8$ $1 1/2 \times 1 1/2 \times 3/4 \times 0.090$ $2 \times 1 \times 3/4 \times 0.036''$ (20 ga.)	2.1 1.9 1.2	1.4×3	4.1
I	75	$2 \times 3/16$	2.44	$2 \times 1 1/8 \times 0.090$	1.33	$2 \times 1 \times 3/4 \times 0.090$ $2 1/2 \times 2 \times 3/4 \times 0.058''$ (16 ga.)	2.03 1.88	$2 \times 2 \times 1/8$ 1.5×3	2.4 5.0
J	100	$2 \times 1/4$ $2 1/2 \times 1/8$	3.2 2.1	$2 \times 1 1/8 \times 1/8$ $3 \times 1 1/8 \times 0.058''$ (16 ga.)	1.74 1.2	$2 \times 1 \times 3/4 \times 1/8$ $2 1/2 \times 2 \times 3/4 \times 0.090$	2.63 2.67	1.6×4	5.4
K	150	$2 1/2 \times 3/16$	3.1	$3 \times 1 1/8 \times 0.090$	1.64	$2 1/2 \times 2 \times 3/4 \times 1/8$ $3 \times 1 1/2 \times 3/4 \times 0.058''$ (16 ga.)	3.57 2.0	Not given	
L	200	$2 1/2 \times 1/4$	4.1	$3 \times 1 1/8 \times 1/8$	2.15	$3 \times 1 1/2 \times 3/4 \times 0.090$	2.82		

Nominal EI is number listed times 10^5.
*See tie rod options.

TABLE A6-1-J—TRANSVERSE JOINT REINFORCEMENT FOR TABLE A6-1-F, A6-1-G, A6-1-L, A6-1-N OR A6-1-O

For SI: H-3.2 mm

MINIMUM RIGIDITY CLASS	EI	T-15 STANDING SEAM $H_S \times T$ (× 25.4 for mm)	WT/LF (× 1.488 for kg/m)	STANDING SEAM OR WELDED FLANGE REINFORCED — 26 to 22 Ga. Duct H_S	$H \times H \times T$ (× 25.4 for mm)	WT/LF (× 1.488 for kg/m)	20 to 16 Ga. Duct H_S	$H \times H \times T$ (× 25.4 for mm)	WT/LF (× 1.488 for kg/m)	T-21 WELDED FLANGE $H_S \times T$ (× 25.4 for mm)	WT/LF (× 1.488 for kg/m)
A	0.5	$1/2 \times 0.024''$ (24 ga.)	0.2							$1/2 \times 0.030''$ (22 ga.)	0.1
B	1.0	$3/4 \times 0.024''$ (24 ga.)	0.3							$1/2 \times 0.058''$ (16 ga.) $3/4 \times 0.030''$ (22 ga.)	0.2 0.2
C	2.5	$1 \times 0.024''$ (24 ga.)	0.5							$3/4 \times 0.047''$ (18 ga.) $1 \times 0.030''$ (22 ga.)	0.3
D	5	$3/4 \times 0.058''$ (16 ga.) $1 \times 0.036''$ (20 ga.)	0.3 0.5	$1''$	$1 \times 1 \times 0.058''$ (16 ga.)	1.0				$1 \times 0.047''$ (18 ga.) $1^1/_4 \times 0.030''$ (22 ga.)	0.4 0.3
E	10	$1 \times 0.058''$ (16 ga.) $1^1/_2 \times 0.024''$ (24 ga.)	0.7 0.7	$1''$	$1 \times 1 \times 1/8$	1.4	$1''$	$1 \times 1 \times 0.058''$ (16 ga.)	1.0	$1^1/_4 \times 0.047''$ (18 ga.) $1^1/_2 \times 0.030''$ (22 ga.)	0.5 0.4
F	15	$1^1/_2 \times 0.036''$ (20 ga.)	0.7	$1^1/_2''$	$1^1/_2 \times 1^1/_2 \times 0.058''$ (16 ga.)	1.8	$1^1/_4''$	$1^1/_4 \times 1^1/_4 \times 0.058''$ (16 ga.)	1.7	$1^1/_4 \times 0.058''$ (16 ga.) $1^1/_2 \times 0.036''$ (20 ga.)	0.6 0.4
G	25	$1^1/_2 \times 0.047''$ (18 ga.)	0.8	$1^1/_2''$ $1^1/_2''$	$1^1/_2 \times 1^1/_2 \times 1/8$ $2 \times 2 \times 0.058''$ (16 ga.)	2.0	$1^1/_2''$	$1^1/_2 \times 1^1/_2 \times 1/8$	2.4	$1^1/_2 \times 0.058''$ (16 ga.)	0.7
H	50	See T-16 and tie rod options		$1^1/_2''$	$2 \times 2 \times 1/8*$	2.7	$1^1/_2''$ $1^1/_2''$	$1^1/_2 \times 1^1/_2 \times 3/16$ $2 \times 2 \times 0.058''$ (16 ga.)	2.8 2.0	See T-21A and tie rod options Table A6-1-Q	
I	75						$1^1/_2''$	$2 \times 2 \times 1/8*$	2.7		
J	100			$1^1/_2''$	$2 \times 2 \times 3/16*$	3.5	$1^1/_2''$	$2 \times 2 \times 3/16*$	3.5		
K	150			$1^1/_2''$	$2^1/_2 \times 2^1/_2 \times 3/16*$	4.1					
L	200			$1^1/_2''$	$2^1/_2 \times 2^1/_2 \times 1/4$	5.3	$1^1/_2''$	$2^1/_2 \times 2^1/_2 \times 3/16*$	4.1		

Nominal EI is number listed times 10^5.
*See tie rod option.

TABLE A6-1-K—JOINT T-1 FLAT DRIVE AS CLASS A REINFORCEMENT

STATIC PRESSURE (× 249 for Pa)	MAXIMUM ALLOWABLE DUCT WIDTH DIMENSION (inches) (× 25.4 for mm)	MAXIMUM REINFORCEMENT SPACING INTERVAL (feet) (× 304.8 for mm)
$1/2''$ w.g.	20	10
$1''$ w.g.	20	8
	14	10
$2''$ w.g.	20	5
	18	8
$3''$ w.g.	18	8
$4''$ w.g.	16	5
	12	8
$6''$ w.g.	12	5

NOTE: Where Tables A6-1-F, A6-1-G, A6-1-L, A6-1-M and A6-1-N require Class A reinforcement, joint T-1 is acceptable as Class A within these parameters and without supplemental reinforcement from Table A6-1-I.

TABLE A6-1-L—RECTANGULAR DUCT REINFORCEMENT

3" w.g. (757 Pa) STATIC POS. OR NEG.	NO REINFORCEMENT DUCT GAGE	MINIMUM RIGIDITY CLASS ON MINIMUM GAGE DUCT			
		Reinforcement Spacing			
	0.058" (16 gage)	0.047" (18 gage)	0.036" (20 gage)	0.030" (22 gage)	0.024" (24 gage)
× 25.4 for mm	× 304.8 for mm				
Duct Dimension	Minimum Class	Maximum Spacing			
10" down	Not required	Not required	Not required	Not required	Not required
11" to 12"					A @ 8'
13" to 14"				A @ 8'	A @ 5'
15" to 16"			A @ 8'	A @ 8'	A @ 5'
17" to 18"			A @ 8'	A @ 8'	A @ 5'
19" to 20"		B @ 10'	B @ 8'	A @ 5'	A @ 5'
21" to 22"		C @ 10'	B @ 8'	B @ 5'	B @ 5'
23" to 24"		C @ 10'	B @ 5'	B @ 5'	B @ 5'
25" to 26"	D @ 10'	D @ 10'	C @ 5'	C @ 5'	C @ 5'
27" to 28"	D @ 10'	D @ 10'	C @ 5'	C @ 5'	C @ 4'
29" to 30"	D @ 10'	D @ 8'	C @ 5'	C @ 5'	C @ 4'
31" to 36"	E @ 8'	E @ 5'	E @ 5'	D @ 4'	D @ 4'
37" to 42"	E @ 5'	E @ 5'	E @ 5'	E @ 4'	E @ 3'
43" to 48"	G @ 5'	G @ 5'	F @ 4'	E @ 3'	E @ 2½'
49" to 54"	H @ 5'	H @ 5'	G @ 3'	G @ 3'	E @ 2½'
55" to 60"	H @ 5'	H @ 4'	G @ 3'	G @ 2½'	G @ 2½'
61" to 72"	I @ 4'	H @ 3'	H @ 3'	H @ 2½'	F @ 2'*
73" to 84"	J @ 3'	J @ 3'	J @ 2½'	I @ 2'	
85" to 96"	L @ 3'	K @ 2½'	J @ 2'	G @ 2½'*	
Over 96"		H @ 2½'*			

NOTES:

1. Reinforcement class refers to transverse joint or intermediate members having stiffness and other characteristics indicated in tables.
2. Joint spacing is unrestricted.
3. Reinforcement is evaluated for each duct side separately. When required on four sides, corners shall be tied. When required on two sides, they shall be tied with rods or angles at the ends on 4-inch w.g. (995 Pa), 6-inch w.g. (1433 Pa) and 10-inch w.g. (2488 Pa) pressure classes.
4. The same gage of metal shall be used on all four sides of a cross section.

*Plus tie rods at 48 inches (1219 mm) maximum along joints and intermediates. Tie rod sizes: $^1/_4$-inch (6.4 mm) diameter for 36-inch (914 mm) length or less, $^3/_8$-inch (9.5 mm) diameter over 36 inches (914 mm). Space at even divisions of duct width.

TABLE A6-1-M—RECTANGULAR DUCT REINFORCEMENT

4″ w.g. (996 Pa) STATIC POSITIVE	NO REINFORCEMENT DUCT GAGE	MINIMUM RIGIDITY CLASS ON MINIMUM GAGE DUCT			
		Reinforcement Spacing			
	0.058″ (16 gage)	0.047″ (18 gage)	0.036″ (20 gage)	0.030″ (22 gage)	0.024″ (24 gage)
× 25.4 for mm	× 304.8 for mm				
Duct Dimension	Minimum Class	Maximum Spacing			
8″ down	Not required	Not required	Not required	Not required	Not required
9″ to 10″					A @ 5′
11″ to 12″				A @ 10′	A @ 5′
13″ to 14″			A @ 10′	A @ 8′	A @ 5′
15″ to 16″			A @ 10′	A @ 5′	A @ 5′
17″ to 18″		B @ 10′	B @ 8′	A @ 5′	A @ 5′
19″ to 20″	C @ 10′	C @ 10′	B @ 8′	B @ 5′	B @ 5′
21″ to 22″	C @ 10′	C @ 10′	B @ 5′	B @ 5′	B @ 4′
23″ to 24″	D @ 10′	D @ 10′	C @ 5′	C @ 5′	C @ 4′
25″ to 26″	D @ 10′	D @ 10′	C @ 5′	C @ 5′	C @ 4′
27″ to 28″	E @ 10′	E @ 8′	D @ 5′	D @ 5′	D @ 4′
29″ to 30″	E @ 10′	E @ 8′	D @ 5′	D @ 5′	D @ 4′
31″ to 36″	E @ 5′	E @ 5′	E @ 5′	E @ 4′	D @ 3′
37″ to 42″	F @ 5′	F @ 5′	F @ 4′	E @ 3′	E @ 2$^1/_2$′
43″ to 48″	G @ 5′	G @ 5′	F @ 3′	F @ 3′	E @ 2′
49″ to 54″	H @ 5′	H @ 4′	G @ 3′	G @ 2$^1/_2$′	F @ 2′
55″ to 60″	I @ 5′	H @ 3′	H @ 3′	H @ 2$^1/_2$′	G @ 2′
61″ to 72″	I @ 3′	I @ 3′	I @ 2$^1/_2$′	H @ 2′	
73″ to 84″	K @ 3′	J @ 2$^1/_2$′	J @ 2′		
85″ to 96″	L @ 2$^1/_2$′	K @ 2′	K @ 2′		
Over 96″		H @ 2$^1/_2$′*			

NOTES:

1. Reinforcement class refers to transverse joint or intermediate members having stiffness and other characteristics indicated in tables.
2. Joint spacing is unrestricted.
3. Reinforcement is evaluated for each duct side separately. When required on four sides, corners shall be tied. When required on two sides, they shall be tied with rods or angles at the ends on 4-inch w.g. (995 Pa), 6-inch w.g. (1493 Pa) and 10-inch w.g. (2488 Pa) pressure classes.
4. The same gage of metal shall be used on all four sides on a cross section.

*Plus tie rods at 48 inches (1219 mm) maximum along joints and intermediates. Tie rod sizes: $^1/_4$-inch (6.4 mm) diameter for 36-inch length (914 mm) or less, $^3/_8$-inch (9.5 mm) diameter over 36 inches (914 mm). Space at even divisions of duct width.

TABLE A6-1-N—RECTANGULAR DUCT REINFORCEMENT

6" w.g. (1494 Pa) STATIC POSITIVE	NO REINFORCEMENT DUCT GAGE	MINIMUM RIGIDITY CLASS ON MINIMUM GAGE DUCT			
		Reinforcement Spacing			
	0.058" (16 gage)	0.047" (18 gage)	0.036" (20 gage)	0.030" (22 gage)	0.024" (24 gage)
× 25.4 for mm	× 304.8 for mm				
Duct Dimension	Minimum Class	Maximum Spacing			
8" down	Not required	Not required	Not required	Not required	Not required
9" to 10"				A @ 5'	A @ 5'
11" to 12"			A @ 10'	A @ 5'	A @ 5'
13" to 14"			A @ 10'	A @ 8'	A @ 5'
15" to 16"		A @ 10'	B @ 10'	A @ 5'	A @ 5'
17" to 18"	C @ 10'	C @ 10'	B @ 5'	B @ 5'	B @ 4'
19" to 20"	C @ 10'	C @ 8'	B @ 5'	B @ 5'	B @ 4'
21" to 22"	D @ 10'	C @ 8'	C @ 5'	C @ 5'	C @ 4'
23" to 24"	D @ 10'	D @ 8'	C @ 5'	C @ 5'	C @ 3'
25" to 26"	D @ 8'	D @ 5'	D @ 5'	C @ 4'	C @ 3'
27" to 28"	E @ 8'	D @ 8'	D @ 5'	D @ 4'	C @ 3'
29" to 30"	D @ 5'	D @ 8'	D @ 4'	D @ 4'	D @ 3'
31" to 36"	F @ 5'	F @ 5'	E @ 4'	E @ 3'	E @ 2½'
37" to 42"	G @ 5'	G @ 4'	F @ 3'	E @ 2½'	
43" to 48"	H @ 4'	H @ 4'	G @ 2½'	G @ 2½'	
49" to 54"	H @ 4'	H @ 3'	H @ 2½'	G @ 2'	
55" to 60"	H @ 3'	H @ 3'	H @ 2½'	H @ 2'	
61" to 72"	J @ 3'	J @ 2½'	I @ 2'		
73" to 84"	L @ 2½'	K @ 2'			
85" to 96"	L @ 2'	L @ 2'			
Over 96"		H @ 2½'*			

NOTES:

1. Reinforcement class refers to transverse joint or intermediate members having stiffness and other characteristics indicated in tables.
2. Joint spacing is unrestricted.
3. Reinforcement is evaluated for each duct side separately. When required on four sides, corners shall be tied. When required on two sides, they shall be tied with rods or angles at the ends on 4-inch w.g. (995 Pa), 6-inch w.g. (1493 Pa) and 10-inch w.g. (2488 Pa) pressure classes.
4. The same gage of metal shall be used on all four sides on a cross section.

*Plus tie rods at 48 inches (1219 mm) maximum along joints and intermediates. Tie rod sizes: $1/4$-inch (6.4 mm) diameter for 36-inch (914 mm) length or less, $3/8$-inch (9.5 mm) diameter over 36 inches (914 mm). Space at even divisions of duct width.

TABLE A6-1-O—RECTANGULAR DUCT REINFORCEMENT

10" w.g. (2490 Pa) STATIC POSITIVE	NO REINFORCEMENT DUCT GAGE	MINIMUM RIGIDITY CLASS ON MINIMUM GAGE DUCT			
		Reinforcement Spacing			
× 25.4 for mm	0.058" (16 gage)	0.047" (18 gage)	0.036" (20 gage)	0.030" (22 gage)	0.024" (24 gage)
		× 304.8 for mm			
Duct Dimension	Minimum Class			Maximum Spacing	
8" down	Not required	Not required	Not required	Not required	Not required
9" to 10"			A @ 5'	A @ 5'	A @ 4'
11" to 12"		A @ 8'	A @ 5'	A @ 5'	A @ 4'
13" to 14"	B @ 8'	B @ 8'	A @ 5'	A @ 4'	A @ 3'
15" to 16"	B @ 8'	B @ 5'	B @ 5'	B @ 4'	A @ 3'
17" to 18"	C @ 8'	C @ 5'	C @ 5'	B @ 4'	B @ 3'
19" to 20"	D @ 8'	C @ 5'	C @ 4'	B @ 3'	B @ 3'
21" to 22"	C @ 5'	C @ 5'	C @ 4'	C @ 3'	C @ 3'
23" to 24"	D @ 5'	D @ 5'	D @ 4'	C @ 3'	C @ 3'
25" to 26"	D @ 5'	D @ 5'	D @ 4'	D @ 3'	C @ 2½'
27" to 28"	E @ 5'	E @ 5'	D @ 4'	D @ 3'	D @ 2½'
29" to 30"	E @ 5'	E @ 4'	D @ 3'	D @ 3'	D @ 2½'
31" to 36"	F @ 5'	F @ 4'	F @ 3'	E @ 2½'	E @ 2'
37" to 42"	H @ 4'	G @ 3'	G @ 2½'	F @ 2'	
43" to 48"	H @ 3'	H @ 2½'	G @ 2'	G @ 2'	
49" to 54"	I @ 3'	H @ 2½'	H @ 2'		
55" to 60"	J @ 3'	I @ 2½'	I @ 2'		
61" to 72"	K @ 2½'	K @ 2'			
73" to 84"	H @ 2'				
85" to 96"	H @ 2'*				
Over 96"	H @ 2'*				

NOTES:

1. Reinforcement class refers to transverse joint or intermediate members having stiffness and other characteristics indicated in tables.
2. Joint spacing is unrestricted.
3. Reinforcement is evaluated for each duct side separately. When required on four sides, corners shall be tied. When required on two sides, they shall be tied with rods or angles at the ends on 4-inch w.g. (995 Pa), 6-inch w.g. (1493 Pa) and 10-inch w.g. (2488 Pa) pressure classes.
4. The same gage of metal shall be used on all four sides on a cross section.

*Plus tie rods at 48 inches (1219 mm) maximum along joints and intermediates. Tie rod sizes: $^1/_4$-inch (9.5 mm) diameter for 36-inch (914 mm) length or less, $^3/_8$-inch (9.5 mm) diameter over 36 inches (914 mm). Space at even divisions of duct width.

TABLE A6-1-P-1—RECTANGULAR ALUMINUM DUCT ADAPTED FROM 3-INCH W.G. (746 Pa) OR LOWER STEEL CONSTRUCTION TABLES

Amend Tables A6-1-F, A6-1-G and A6-1-L by using equivalent thickness from this table.

GALV. STEEL THICKNESS (inches) (gage)	0.016" (28)	0.019" (26)	0.024" (24)	0.030" (22)	0.036" (20)	0.047" (18)	0.058" (16)
			× 25.4 for mm				
Min. alum. equivalent*	0.023	0.027	0.035	0.043	0.052	0.068	0.084
Commercial size	0.025	0.032	0.040	0.050	0.064	0.071	0.090
Aluminum weight 17.1 pounds per cubic foot (2738 kg/m³).							

*The aluminum reference in the table is Alloy 3003-H14. If calculations are performed, the following allowable stresses shall be used: tension or compression, 10,000 psi (68.9 MPa); shear, 6,000 psi (41.4 MPa); bearing, 16,000 psi (110 MPa). Unstiffened flanges have stress reduced for the specified width-to-thickness ratio.

TABLE A6-1-P-2—DIMENSION ADJUSTMENTS

Galvanized rigidity class	A	B	C	D	E	F	G	H	I	J	K	L
Aluminum dimension per galvanized class	C	D	E	F	H	H	I	K	*	*	*	*

*Calculate an I_x equals three times that used for steel.

TABLE A6-1-P-3—REINFORCEMENTS

STEEL ANGLE SIZE (inches)	CODE	EQUIVALENT ALUMINUM* ANGLE SIZE (inches)	STEEL BAR	ALUMINUM BAR*
		× 25.4 for mm		
$1 \times 1 \times 0.058''$ (16 ga.) (1.47 mm) C		$1^{1}/_{4} \times 1^{1}/_{4} \times {}^{1}/_{8}$	$1 \times {}^{1}/_{8}$	$1^{1}/_{2} \times {}^{1}/_{8}$ or $1^{1}/_{4} \times {}^{3}/_{16}$
$1 \times 1 \times {}^{1}/_{8}$ . . . . D		$1^{1}/_{2} \times 1^{1}/_{2} \times {}^{1}/_{8}$	$1^{1}/_{2} \times {}^{1}/_{8}$	$1^{1}/_{2} \times {}^{3}/_{8}$ or $2 \times {}^{3}/_{16}$
$1^{1}/_{4} \times 1^{1}/_{4} \times {}^{1}/_{8}$ . . . . E		$1^{3}/_{4} \times 1^{3}/_{4} \times {}^{1}/_{8}$		
$1^{1}/_{2} \times 1^{1}/_{2} \times {}^{1}/_{8}$ . . . . F		$2 \times 2 \times {}^{3}/_{16}$ or $2^{1}/_{2} \times 2^{1}/_{2} \times {}^{1}/_{8}$		
$1^{1}/_{2} \times 1^{1}/_{2} \times {}^{3}/_{16}$ . . . . G		$2 \times 2 \times {}^{1}/_{4}$ or $2^{1}/_{2} \times 2^{1}/_{2} \times {}^{1}/_{8}$		
$2 \times 2 \times {}^{1}/_{8}$ . . . . H		$2^{1}/_{2} \times 2^{1}/_{2} \times {}^{3}/_{16}$		
$2 \times 2 \times {}^{3}/_{16}$ I		$2^{1}/_{2} \times 2^{1}/_{2} \times {}^{5}/_{16}$ or $3 \times 3 \times {}^{1}/_{4}$		
$2 \times 2 \times {}^{1}/_{4}$ . . . . J		$2^{1}/_{2} \times 2^{1}/_{2} \times {}^{3}/_{8}$ or $3 \times 3 \times {}^{1}/_{4}$		
$2^{1}/_{2} \times 2^{1}/_{2} \times {}^{3}/_{16}$ . . . . K		$3 \times 3 \times {}^{3}/_{8}$ or $3^{1}/_{2} \times 3^{1}/_{2} \times {}^{1}/_{4}$		

*Alloy 6061-T6 strength normally.

NOTES:

1. For Tables A6-1-F, A6-1-G and A6-1-L: Use equivalent thickness from Table A6-1-P-1 for required thickness of aluminum stock.
2. For Tables A6-1-H and A6-1-J:
   a. A connector not using angles or bar stock shall have its thickness increased per Table A6-1-P-1 and its dimensions increased per Table A6-1-P-2.
   b. A connector using angles or bar stock shall have its aluminum thickness increased per Table A6-1-P-1 and shall use either aluminum stock or galvanized stock from Table A6-1-P-3.
3. Table A6-1-I: Galvanized steel members of dimensions given may be used or aluminum members having thickness and dimension conforming to Table A6-1-P-3 may be used. Other suitable aluminum shapes having a moment of inertia three times that of steel may be used.
4. Button-punch snaplock seams shall not be used in fabricating aluminum rectangular duct.

Tie Rod Installations

In Tables A6-1-F, A6-1-G, A6-1-L, A6-1-M, A6-1-N and A6-1-O, duct sizes over 48 inches (1219 mm) have a tie rod optional construction for positive pressures.

TABLE A6-1-Q—INTERMEDIATE TIE RODS AT REINFORCEMENT
(Between Joints)

DUCT WIDTH	TABLE REINFORCEMENT GRADE	REINFORCEMENT GRADE FOR TIE ROD OPTION
× 25.4 for mm		× 25.4 for mm
49" to 96"	G, H, I or J	$1^{1}/_{2}'' \times {}^{1}/_{2}'' \times {}^{1}/_{8}''$ angle with tie rod at center
73" to 96"	K or L	$1^{1}/_{2}'' \times 1^{1}/_{2}'' \times {}^{3}/_{16}''$ angle with tie rod at center
97" up	H with tie rod	$2'' \times 2'' \times {}^{1}/_{8}''$ angle with tie rod at 60" maximum intervals

Tie Rods at Joints

The direct attachment of the tie rod by brazing or welding to a vertical leg of the joint is allowed for joints T-15, T-20, T-22 and T-23.

The attachment of a tie rod to an angle that reinforces a joint is allowed for joints T-4, T-8, T-9, T-15, T-16, T-19 and T-21. The angle shall meet the requirements for tie-rodded intermediate reinforcement.

The attachment of two tie rods or tie straps to the duct wall by welding or bolting within 1 inch (25 mm) of both sides of joints T-15, T-20, T-21 and T-23 is allowed.

Additional General Requirements

Ties shall be attached in such a manner that they will not loosen or detach with normal operating pressure fluctuations in the duct. When ties are to be welded to the duct wall the rod or strap shall have a 90 degree bend with ${}^{5}/_{8}$-inch (16 mm) minimum extension beyond the bend. The extension of the rod shall be welded to the duct. The strap shall be welded to duct at the 90-degree bend.

Holes made in the duct wall for tie rod passage shall be the minimum size.

Tie rods shall be galvanized steel of ${}^{1}/_{4}$-inch (6.4 mm) minimum diameter if 36-inch (914 mm) length or less and ${}^{3}/_{8}$-inch minimum (9.5 mm) diameter for greater length.

Tie straps shall be 1-inch by ${}^{1}/_{8}$-inch (25 mm by 3.2 mm) galvanized steel minimum and a smallest edge shall face the airflow direction.

Ties shall be spaced at even intervals of duct width not exceeding 60 inches (1524 mm).

The use of ties does not void the need to attach reinforcements to the duct wall; however, when ties occur outside of the duct as on two-side reinforcements at 4-inch w.g. (995 Pa) and over, the attachment within 2 inches (51 mm) of the corner is not required.

When ties occur in two directions in the same vicinity, they shall either be prevented from contacting or shall be in permanent contact.

Ties may be used as components of the suspension system for ducts over 96-inch (2438 mm) width, provided that the hanger load is directly transmitted to a trapeze or duct reinforcement member beneath the duct.

The construction of ducts of widths greater than 96 inches (2438 mm) requires use of tie rods on Grade H joints and intermediates (2 inches by 2 inches by ${}^{1}/_{8}$ inch) (51 mm by 51 mm by 3.2 mm) at intervals not exceeding 60 inches (1524 mm) in the transverse direction. For 10 inches w.g. (2488 Pa), 16 gage (1.47 mm) duct with 2 feet (610 mm) reinforcement spacing is required; 18 gage (1.19 mm) duct is required at lower pressures with spacings of 2 feet (610 mm) at 6 inches w.g. (1493 Pa); $2^{1}/_{2}$ feet (762 mm) at 1 inch to 4 inches w.g. (249 Pa to 995 Pa) and 5 feet (1524 mm) at ${}^{1}/_{2}$ inch w.g. (124 Pa).

UNIFORM MECHANICAL CODE STANDARD 6-2
TEST METHOD FOR FIRE AND SMOKE CHARACTERISTICS OF ELECTRICAL CABLE, OPTICAL FIBER RACEWAYS AND PLASTIC SPRINKLER PIPE

Based on Standard 910, 1985 and Standard 1887, 1989, of Underwriters Laboratories Inc.

See Section 601.4, *Uniform Mechanical Code*

SECTION 6.201 — SCOPE

This is a test method for determining values of flame distance and smoke density for exposed electrical cables, optical fiber raceways and plastic sprinkler pipe that are to be installed in concealed spaces above suspended ceilings used as air plenums without the cables being enclosed in raceways in those spaces. The purpose of this test method is to determine whether the flame-propagation and smoke-generating characteristics of these cables without raceways, optical fiber raceways and the plastic sprinkler pipe are in accordance with the provisions of Exception 5 or 6 to Section 601.4 of this code.

SECTION 6.202 — EXCLUSIONS

This test method does not cover the construction or performance requirements for cables or sprinkler pipe, nor does it cover the electrical requirements of the cables.

SECTION 6.203 — FIRE-TEST CHAMBER

The fire-test chamber shall consist of a horizontal duct having the shape and size shown in Figures A6-2-1, A6-2-2 and A6-2-3. The sides and base of the duct shall be lined with insulating masonry as illustrated in Figure A6-2-2 consisting of a row of A.P. Green G-26 refractory firebrick. The operation and calibration of this equipment is based on the use of A.P. Green G-26 refractories. One side shall be provided with a row of double-pane (inside pane mounted flush with inner wall—see Figure A6-2-3) pressure-tight (as described in Section 6.207) observation windows located so that the entire length of the specimens being tested can be observed from outside the fire-test chamber.

The ledges shall be fabricated of structural metal. Water-cooled structural-steel tubing is acceptable for this purpose.

To provide air turbulence for combustion, turbulence-inducing baffling shall be provided by positioning six A.P. Green G-26 refractory firebricks [long dimension vertical and 4.5-inch (114 mm) dimension parallel to wall] along the side walls of the chamber at distances of 7.0, 12.0 and 20.0, ± 0.5 feet (2134 mm, 2438 mm and 6096 mm ± 152 mm) on the window side and 4.5, 9.5 and 16.0, ± 0.5 feet (1372 mm, 2896 mm and 44 877 mm ± 152 mm) on the opposite side.

The top shall consist of a removable metal-and-mineral-insulation composite unit whose insulation consists of nominal 2.0-inch-thick (51 mm) mineral-composition material. The top unit is shown in Figure A6-2-3 and shall completely cover the fire-test chamber. The mineral-composition material shall have physical characteristics comparable to the following:

Maximum effective temperature—1,200°F (649°C)

Bulk density—21.0 lbm/ft^3 (33.6 kg/m^3) ± 1.5 lbm/ft^3 (± 2.4 kg/m^3)

Thermal conductivity—0.50-0.71 Btu · inch per hour · square foot · °F [0.072 to 0.1 W/(M·K)] at 300°F to 700°F (149°C to 371°C)

The entire top-panel unit shall be protected with flat sections of high-density (nominally 110 lbm/ft^3) (176 kg/m^3) 0.25-inch (6.4 mm) mineral-fiber/cement board maintained in unwarped and uncracked condition through continued replacement. While in place, the top panel shall be completely sealed against the leakage of air into the fire-test chamber during the test.

The ladder-type cable tray used to support the open-cable test specimens or the wiring-in-raceway test specimens is shown in Figures A6-2-2 and A6-2-3. The tray shall be fabricated from cold-rolled steel, 50,000 psi (324 MPa) minimum tensile strength. The solid-bar-stock side rails shall be as shown in Section S-S in Figure A6-2-3. The C-shaped-channel rungs shall be as shown in Section Q-Q in Figure A6-2-3. Each rung shall be 11.25 inches (286 mm) long. The rungs shall be welded to the side rails 9.00 inches (229 mm) on centers along the tray length. The tray may consist of several sections having a total assembled length of 23.90 feet (7285 mm) and shall be supported with 16 supports equally spaced along the length of the tray. The supports shall be fabricated from bar steel.

One end of the test chamber, designated as the "fire end," shall be provided with two gas burners delivering flames upward that engulf the cross section of the test specimens midway between two rungs of the cable tray. The burners shall be positioned transversely to each side of the center line of the furnace so that the flame is evenly distributed over the width of the specimens. See Figure A6-2-2.

The controls used to maintain a constant flow of gas to the burners shall consist of a pressure regulator, a gas meter calibrated to read in increments of not more than 0.1 ft^3 (2.8 L), a gauge to indicate gas pressure in inches of water, a quick-acting gas-shutoff valve, a gas-metering valve, and an orifice plate in combination with a manometer to assist in maintaining uniform gas-flow conditions. An air intake fitted with a vertically sliding shutter extending the entire width of the test chamber shall be provided at the fire end. The shutter is to be positioned to provide an air-inlet port as shown in Figure A6-2-1.

The other end of the test chamber, designated as the "vent end," shall be fitted with a rectangular-to-round transition piece, which shall be fitted to a round flue pipe. The movement of air shall be by induced draft. The draft-inducing system shall have a total draft capacity of at least 0.15-inch water column (37 Pa) with the specimens in place, with the shutter at the fire end open to its normal position, and with the damper in the wide-open position. A draft-gauge manometer to indicate static pressure shall be inserted through the top at the midwidth of the tunnel, just downstream of the air-intake shutter.

The damper shall be installed in the vent pipe downstream of the smoke-indicating attachment described in this section.

An automatic draft-regulator controller may be mounted in the vent pipe downstream of the manual damper. Other manual, automatic or special draft-regulation devices may be incorporated to maintain airflow control throughout each test run.

The room in which the test chamber is located shall have provision for a free inflow of air to maintain the room at atmospheric pressure throughout each test run.

A light source shall be mounted on a horizontal section of the vent pipe at a point at which it is preceded by a straight run of round pipe at least 12 diameters or 16 feet (4877 mm) from the vent end of the rectangular-to-round transition section, and it is not affected by flame from the test chamber. The light beam shall be directed upward along the vertical axis of the vent pipe. The vent pipe shall be insulated with high-temperature mineral-composition material from the vent end of the chamber to the photometer location. A photoelectric cell having an output directly proportional to the amount of light received shall be mounted over the light source with an overall light-to-cell path length of 36.00 inches ± 2.00 inches (914 mm ± 51 mm), 16 inches (406 mm) of which are taken up by the smoke in the vent-pipe interior as shown in Section C-C of Figure A6-2-1. The cell shall be connected to recording devices for indicating changes in the attenuation of incident light by passing smoke, by particulate matter and by other effluents.

The output of the photoelectric cell shall be connected to a recording device that processes the signal into a continuous record of smoke obscuration.

$$\text{Optical density } = \log_{10} \frac{T_o}{T}$$

WHERE:

T = the light transmission during the test. T varies with the amount of smoke.

T_o = the initial light transmission (without smoke).

A No. 18 AWG 0.04 inch (1 mm) thermocouple (nominal wire cross section of 1,620 cmil) (8.2×10^{-7} m^2) with 0.375 ± 0.125 inch (9.5 ± 3.2 mm) of the junction exposed in the fire-chamber air shall be inserted through the floor of the test chamber so that the tip is 1.00 ± 0.031 inch (25.4 ± 0.78 mm) below the top surface of the gasketing tape 23 feet ± $1/2$ inch (7010 ± 13 mm) from the center line of the burner ports and at the center of the width of the chamber.

A No. 18 AWG (1 mm) thermocouple (nominal wire cross section of 1,620 cmil) (8.2×10^{-7} m^2) embedded 0.125 inch (3.2 mm) below the floor surface of the test chamber shall be mounted in refractory or portland cement at distances of 13.5 and 23.0 feet (4115 and 7011 mm) from the fire end of the burner ports.

SECTION 6.204 — TEST SPECIMENS—CABLES

Cable specimens in 24.0-foot (7315 mm) lengths shall be installed in a single layer across the bottom of the cable tray. The specimens shall be laid into the tray in parallel, straight rows without any space between adjacent specimens other than that needed for the cable fasteners described in the following paragraph. The number of cable specimens shall equal the measured inside width of the rack divided by the cable diameter as determined using a diameter tape or the equivalent, with the result of the division rounded off to the nearest lower whole number of specimens that fit, considering the presence of cable fasteners.

Bare copper tie wires not larger than No. 18 AWG (1 mm) (nominal wire cross section of 1,620 cmil) (8.2×10^{-7} m^2) may be used to fasten cable specimens to the rungs of the cable tray wherever a tie is necessary to keep a cable in contact with the rung, straight and parallel with all of the other cable specimens and to minimize movement during the test. A tie shall not be used in any manner

that alters the ability of the cable to transmit gases and/or vapors longitudinally through the core of the cable.

Properties applicable to identification of the cable specimens shall be determined and recorded.

SECTION 6.205 — TEST SPECIMENS—PIPE

Plastic sprinkler pipe shall be installed to fill the bottom of the tray.

The pipe specimens shall be placed on a mesh screen in the tray. The mesh screen shall be galvanized wire cloth with 0.047-inch (1.2 mm) wire diameter and having 0.75-inch (19 mm) openings. The length of pipe is to be fastened to the screen with fasteners as described in the next paragraph.

Bare copper tie wires not larger than No. 18 AWG (1 mm) (nominal wire cross section of 1,620 cmil) (8.2×10^{-7} m^2) may be used to fasten the specimen to the mesh screen and rungs of the tray wherever a tie is necessary to keep a specimen in contact with the rung and to minimize movement during the test. A tie is not to be used in any manner that alters the ability of the specimen to transmit gases or vapor longitudinally through the core of the specimen.

SECTION 6.206 — TEST SPECIMENS — OPTICAL FIBER RACEWAY

Optical fiber raceway specimens in 24-foot (7315 mm) lengths shall be installed in a single layer across the bottom of the cable tray. The specimens shall be laid into the tray in parallel, straight rows without any space between adjacent specimens other than that needed for the fasteners described in the following paragraph. The number of specimens shall equal the measured inside width of the rack divided by the raceway diameter as determined using a diameter tape or the equivalent, with the result of the division rounded off to the nearest lower whole number of specimens that fit, considering the presence of fasteners.

The raceway specimens shall be placed on a mesh screen in the tray. The mesh screen shall be galvanized wire cloth with 0.047-inch (1.2 mm) wire diameter and 0.75-inch (19 mm) openings. The lengths of raceway are to be fastened to the screen with fasteners as described in the next paragraph.

Bare copper tie wires not larger than No. 18 AWG (1 mm) (nominal wire cross section of 1,620 cmil) (8.2×10^{-7} m^2) may be used to fasten specimens to the rungs of the cable tray wherever a tie is necessary to keep a raceway in contact with the rung, straight and parallel with all of the other specimens and to minimize movement during the test. A tie shall not be used in any manner that alters the ability of the raceway to transmit gases or vapors longitudinally through the core of the raceway.

Properties applicable to identification of the raceway specimens shall be determined and recorded.

SECTION 6.207 — CALIBRATION OF TEST EQUIPMENT

One 0.250-inch (6 mm) mineral-fiber/cement board shall be placed on the ledge of the furnace chamber. The removable top of the test chamber shall be placed in position.

With the board in position and with the removable top in place, the draft shall be established to produce a 0.15-inch (37 Pa) water-column reading on the draft manometer with the fire-end shutter open 3.000 inches ± 0.062 inch (76 mm ± 1.6 mm) and with the manual damper in the wide-open position. Then, the fire-end shutter shall be closed and sealed. The manometer reading shall increase to at least a 0.375-inch water column (92 Pa), indicating that no excessive air leakage exists.

In addition, a supplemental leakage test shall be conducted periodically by activating a smoke bomb in the fire chamber while the fire shutter and exhaust duct beyond the differential manometer tube are sealed. The bomb shall be ignited and the chamber pressurized to 0.375-inch ± 0.150-inch (92 Pa ± 37 Pa) water column. All points of leakage observed in the form of escaping smoke particles shall be sealed.

A draft reading shall be established within the range of a 0.055- to 0.085-inch (14 Pa to 21 Pa) water column. The required draft-gauge reading shall be maintained by regulating the manual damper. The air velocity at each of seven points, each located 1.0 foot (305 mm) from the vent end shall be recorded. These points shall be determined by dividing the width of the tunnel into seven equal sections and recording the velocity at the geometric center of each section. The average velocity shall be 240 feet ± 5.0 feet per minute (1.22 m/s ± 0.03 m/s).

The air supply shall be maintained at 70.0°F ± 5.0°F (21°C ± 3°C) and the relative humidity shall be kept at 35 to 40 percent.

The test fire which produces approximately 300,000 Btu per hour (87.8 kW) shall be fueled with bottled methane gas of uniform quality and with a heating value of approximately 1,000 Btu per cubic foot (372 340 kJ/m³). The gas supply shall be initially adjusted to approximately 5,000 Btu per minute (8.8 kW). The gas pressure, the pressure differential across the orifice plate, and the volume of gas used shall be recorded in each test. A length of coiled copper tubing shall be inserted into the gas line between the supply and the metering connection to compensate for possible errors in the indicated flow because of reductions in the gas temperature associated with the pressure drop and expansion across the regulator, or other applicable means of correction may be used. With the draft and the gas supplies adjusted, the test flames shall extend downstream to a distance of 4.5 feet (1372 mm) over the specimens, with negligible upstream coverage.

The test chamber shall be preheated with the mineral-fiber/cement board and the removable top in place and with the fuel supply adjusted to the required flow. The preheating shall be continued until the temperature indicated by the floor thermocouple at 24.0 feet (7315 mm) reaches 150°F ± 5°F (65°C ± 3°C). During the preheat test, the temperatures indicated by the thermocouple at the vent end of the test chamber shall be recorded at 15-second intervals and shall be compared to the preheat temperatures taken at the same intervals from the representative curve of temperature as a function of time shown in Figure A6-2-4. The preheating is for the purpose of establishing the conditions that exist following successive tests and to indicate the control of the heat input into the test chamber. If appreciable variation from the temperatures shown in the representative preheat curve occurs because of variations in the characteristics of the gas used, adjustments in the fuel supply shall be made prior to proceeding with the red-oak calibration tests.

The furnace shall cool after each test. As soon as the floor thermocouple at 14 feet (4267 mm) shows a temperature of 105°F ± 5°F (40.5°C ± 3°C), the next set of specimens shall be placed in position for test.

With the test equipment adjusted and conditioned as described in this section, a test or series of tests shall be made using nominally $^{23}/_{32}$-inch (18 mm) select grade red-oak flooring in place of the mineral-fiber/cement board. Prior to the testing, the wood shall be conditioned to a moisture content of 6 to 8 percent as determined by the 221°F (105°C) oven-dry method in accordance with nationally recognized standards. Observations shall be made continually and the time shall be recorded when the flame reaches the end of the specimen—that is, 19.5 feet (5944 mm) from the end of the ignition fire. The end of the ignition fire shall be considered as being

4.5 feet (1372 mm) from the burners. The flame shall reach the end point in 5.5 minutes ± 15 seconds. The flame shall be judged to have reached the end point when the vent-end thermocouple registers a temperature of 980°F (572°C). The temperature measured by the thermocouple near the vent end shall be recorded at least every 30 seconds. The photoelectric-cell output shall be recorded immediately prior to the test and at least every 15 seconds during the test. The test shall be run for 10 minutes.

The temperature and change in photoelectric-cell readings shall be plotted separately on coordinate paper. Figures A6-2-5 to A6-2-7 are representative curves for the flame spread on red oak, fuel contribution of red oak, and the optical density from red oak.

Following the 10-minute calibration tests for red oak, a similar test or tests shall be conducted on specimens of 0.250-inch (6.4 mm) mineral-fiber/cement board. The temperature readings shall be plotted separately on coordinate paper. Figure A6-2-8 is a representative curve for the fuel contribution of mineral-fiber/cement board.

SECTION 6.208 — TEST PROCEDURE

The cable tray and supports shall be placed in the test chamber with the end 1.0 inch (25.4 mm) downstream from the center line of the burners.

The furnace shall be preheated and cooled as described in Section 6.207.

The specimens shall be installed and the removable test-chamber top placed in position on top of the furnace side ledge.

The test equipment shall be adjusted and conditioned as described in Section 6.207 with the test specimens in place.

The test gas flame shall be ignited. The distance and time of maximum flame front shall be observed and recorded. The test shall be continued for 20 minutes.

The photoelectric-cell output shall be recorded immediately prior to the test and continuously during the test.

The gas pressure, the pressure differential across the orifice plate, and the volume of gas used shall be recorded for the duration of the test.

After the gas supply to the ignition flame is shut off, smoldering and other conditions within the furnace shall be observed and recorded, and the specimens removed for examination.

SECTION 6.209 — REPORT

The report shall include all of the following for each test:

1. A detailed description of the open-cable specimens tested.

2. The number of lengths used as specimens for the test.

3. The graph of flame distance versus time for the duration of the test.

4. The values of the peak optical density and average optical density.

5. The graph of the optical density of the smoke generated during the test versus time for the duration of the test. Optical density may be obtained by computer-assisted computation of the logarithm to the base 10 of the light-transmission data.

6. Observations of the condition of the test specimens after completion of the test.

7. For electrical cable, the weight of nonmetallic components normalized to a figure based on 1,000 feet (304.8 m) of tray length. For example, if the weight of a length of 1 foot (305 mm) of the specimen cable minus the metallic-component weight, is 0.016

pound (0.0073 kg) and there are 15 cables in the tray, the normalized value is 0.016 × 15 × 1000 = 240 pounds (0.0073 × 15 × 1000 = 108.8 kg) per 100 feet (30.5 m) of tray.

SECTION 6.210 — ACCEPTANCE CRITERIA

To be acceptable for installation exposed in concealed space above suspended ceilings used as air plenums, electrical cable, optical fiber raceway and plastic sprinkler pipe shall:

1. Exhibit a flame travel not greater than 5 feet (1524 mm), and

2. Produce smoke having an average optical density not greater than 0.15 and a peak optical density not greater than 0.5 when tested as outlined in this standard.

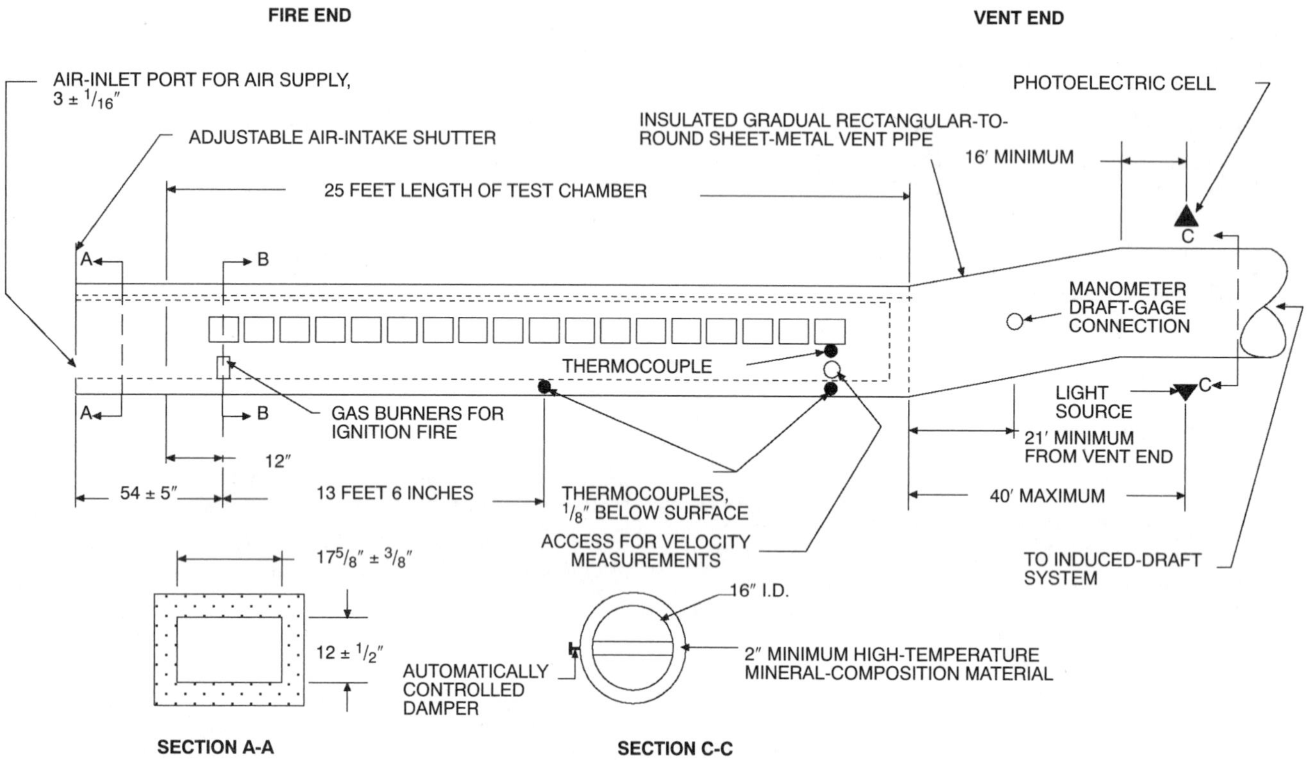

FIRE END

VENT END

AIR-INLET PORT FOR AIR SUPPLY, 3 ± $^1/_{16}$"

PHOTOELECTRIC CELL

ADJUSTABLE AIR-INTAKE SHUTTER

INSULATED GRADUAL RECTANGULAR-TO-ROUND SHEET-METAL VENT PIPE

16' MINIMUM

25 FEET LENGTH OF TEST CHAMBER

A

B

MANOMETER DRAFT-GAGE CONNECTION

THERMOCOUPLE

A

B

GAS BURNERS FOR IGNITION FIRE

LIGHT SOURCE

12"

21' MINIMUM FROM VENT END

54 ± 5"

13 FEET 6 INCHES

THERMOCOUPLES, $^1/_8$" BELOW SURFACE

40' MAXIMUM

ACCESS FOR VELOCITY MEASUREMENTS

TO INDUCED-DRAFT SYSTEM

16" I.D.

$17^5/_8$" ± $^3/_8$"

12 ± $^1/_2$"

AUTOMATICALLY CONTROLLED DAMPER

2" MINIMUM HIGH-TEMPERATURE MINERAL-COMPOSITION MATERIAL

SECTION A-A

SECTION C-C

See Figure A6-2-2 for Section B-B.

(1" = 25.4 mm)
(1' = 305 mm)

FIGURE A6-2-1—DETAILS OF FIRE-TEST CHAMBER

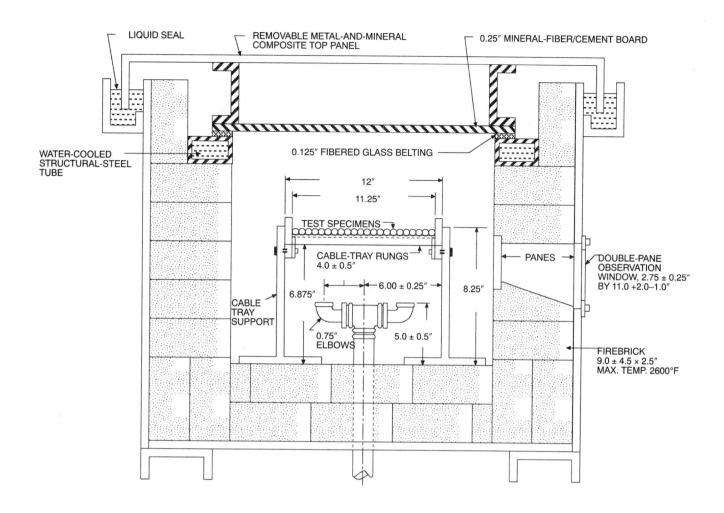

See Figure A6-2-3 for details of the cable tray and supports.
(1″ = 25.4 mm)
(1′ = 305 mm)

FIGURE A6-2-2—SECTION B-B

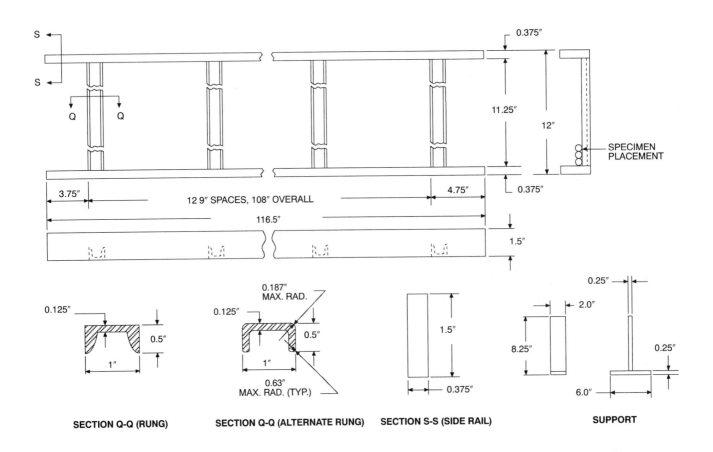

SECTION Q-Q (RUNG)   SECTION Q-Q (ALTERNATE RUNG)   SECTION S-S (SIDE RAIL)   SUPPORT

(1″ = 25.4 mm)
(1′ = 305 mm)

FIGURE A6-2-3—DETAILS OF STEEL CABLE TRAY AND SUPPORTS

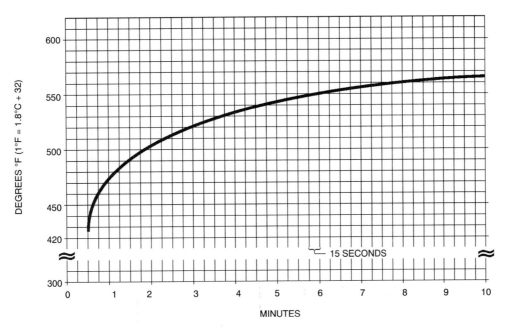

FIGURE A6-2-4—REPRESENTATIVE PREHEAT CURVE

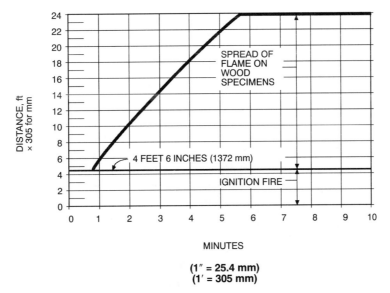

(1″ = 25.4 mm)
(1′ = 305 mm)

FIGURE A6-2-5—REPRESENTATIVE CURVE OF FLAME SPREAD ON RED OAK

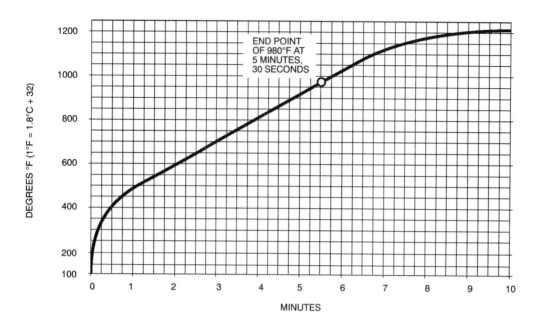

FIGURE A6-2-6—REPRESENTATIVE CURVE OF FUEL CONTRIBUTION OF RED OAK

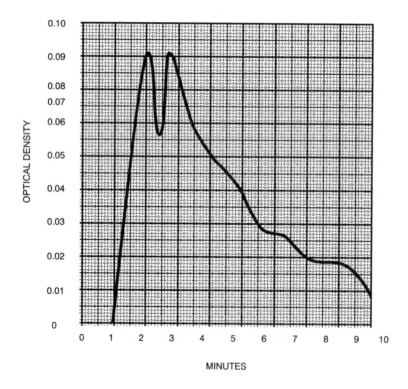

FIGURE A6-2-7—REPRESENTATIVE CURVE OF OPTICAL DENSITY FROM RED OAK

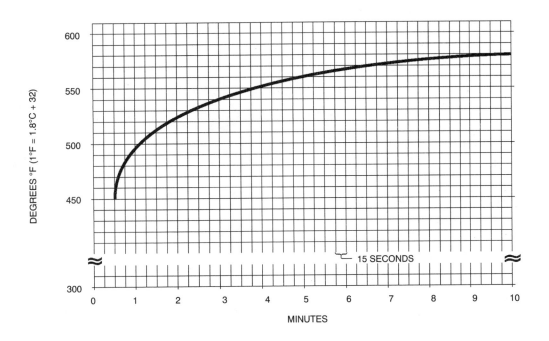

FIGURE A6-2-8—REPRESENTATIVE CURVE OF FUEL CONTRIBUTION OF MINERAL-FIBER/CEMENT BOARD

UNIFORM MECHANICAL CODE STANDARD 6-3
STANDARD FOR INSTALLATION OF
FACTORY-MADE AIR DUCTS

Based on the 1989 Fibrous Glass Duct Construction Standards published
by the Thermal Insulation Manufacturers Association and the Guidelines for Installing Flexible Ducts
published by the Air Diffusion Council

See Section 603.2 of the *Uniform Mechanical Code*

SECTION 6.301 — SCOPE

These requirements are intended to supplement information contained in the manufacturer's installation instruction sheets included in each carton of material, which cover fabrication, closure methods, reinforcement and hanging of factory-made rigid and flexible air ducts complying with UL 181. The standard is divided into two parts: Part A covering rigid ducts and Part B covering flexible ducts.

Part A—Rigid Ducts

SECTION 6.302 — GENERAL

The use of these ducts is governed by Section 601.1, together with the restrictions contained in Section 603.2. For information regarding the fabrication of rectangular ducts from flat sheets of duct board, refer to the document upon which this standard is based, and the manufacturer's instruction sheet.

SECTION 6.303 — CLOSURE SYSTEMS

6.303.1 General. Closure systems are a vital element in the proper assembly of fibrous glass duct systems. They provide both the structural connection and sealing of seams and joints for air tightness. Only listed closure systems identified in the manufacturer's installation instructions are suitable for use with rigid fibrous glass duct systems. Listed closures include:

1. Pressure-sensitive aluminum foil tapes.

2. Heat-activated aluminum foil/scrim tapes.

3. Mastic and glass fabric tape systems.

Listed closure systems may be used on listed duct board materials.

6.303.2 Surface Preparation. In order to obtain satisfactory adhesion and bonding, the surface on which closures will be applied must be free from dust, dirt, oil, grease, moisture and similar substances.

6.303.3 Joint and Seam Preparation. Longitudinal seams are fabricated with a shiplap joint which is closed with the use of outward-clinching staples at 2 inches (51 mm) on center, through the stapling flap of the jacketing material. Transverse joints between two duct sections are prepared by joining two duct sections, pulling the staple flap over the adjoining section and stapling as shown in Figure A6-3-1.

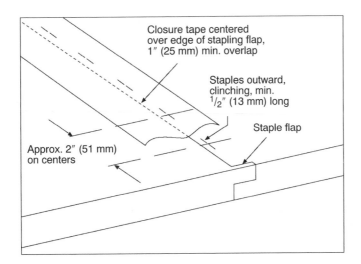

FIGURE A6-3-1—TAPE CLOSURE JOINT WITH STAPLE FLAP

When staple flaps are not present, crosstabs are used to hold seams and joints in position for reinforcing the closure system. Cross tabs, made from 8-inch (203 mm) minimum lengths of closure tape, are to be equally spaced on each side of the joint. Cross tabs are spaced on 12-inch (305 mm) (maximum) centers, with at least one cross tab per duct side (Figure A6-3-2). Cross tabs may be placed either under or over the closure tape.

6.303.4 Application of Pressure-sensitive Aluminum Foil Tapes. Use minimum $2^1/_2$-inch-wide (64 mm) listed pressure-sensitive tape. Position the tape along the edge of the flap in a manner that will allow 1-inch-minimum (25 mm) overlap on adjacent surfaces.

If tape has been stored at temperatures less than 50°F (10°C), it should be conditioned prior to use by placement in a warm environment in order to improve the initial tack.

If the duct board has been located in an atmosphere of less than 50°F (10°C), the surfaces to be taped must be preheated to ensure a satisfactory bond of the tape. Using any suitable heating iron with the plate temperature set at 400°F (± 25°F) (204°C ± 14°C) preheat the area to be taped. Quickly position the tape on the preheated area and press in place. Pass the iron two or three times over the taped area using a rapid "ironing" motion (see Figure A6-3-5).

Rub tape firmly with a plastic squeegee (Figure A6-3-3) until the facing reinforcement shows through the tape.

When operating pressure is less than 1 inch w.g. (249 Pa) (positive pressure), and sheet metal surfaces are cleaned in accordance with tape manufacturer's instructions, pressure-sensitive tape may be used to seal fibrous glass duct to sheet metal.

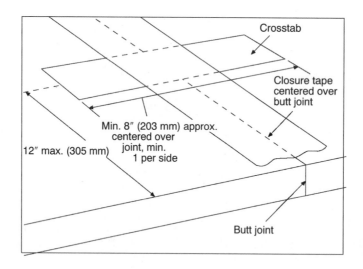

FIGURE A6-3-2—TAPE CLOSURE JOINT WITHOUT STAPLE FLAP

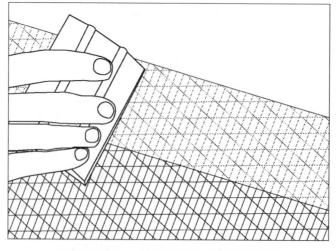

FIGURE A6-3-3—PRESSURE-SENSITIVE TAPE

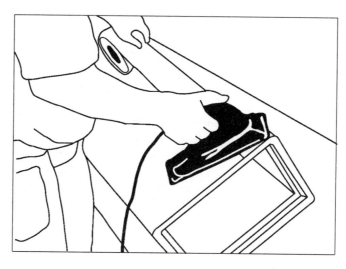

FIGURE A6-3-4—HEAT-ACTIVATED TAPE

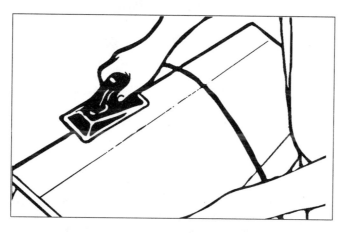

FIGURE A6-3-5—HOT IRON, SECOND PASS

6.303.5 Application of Heat-activated Tapes. Position the $2^1/_2$-inch (64 mm) (minimum) tape along the edge of the flap in a manner that will allow a 1-inch-minimum (25 mm) overlap on adjacent surfaces. Using a suitable heating iron with a plate temperature between 550°F and 600°F (287°C and 315°C), pass the iron along the tape seam with sufficient pressure and dwell time to activate the adhesive (see Figure A6-3-4). A satisfactory bond has been achieved when the heat indicator dots have darkened.

Use a second pass of the iron to complete the bond by applying pressure to the front edge of the iron in a smearing action (see Figure A6-3-5).

Allow all joints and seams to cool below 150°F (65°C) before any stress is applied. Avoid puncturing the tape at staple locations with excessive pressure from the iron.

6.303.6 Application of Glas-fab and Mastic Tape Systems. Apply a thin coat of mastic approximately $3^1/_2$ inches (89 mm) wide over the center of the joint seam. Firmly press the 3-inch-wide (76 mm) glass fabric into the mastic (see Figure A6-3-6).

Apply a second coat of mastic over the glass fabric, filling the scrim pattern as indicated in Figure A6-3-7.

Follow the manufacturer's label instructions on application rate, safety precautions, ventilation requirements, shelf life limitations and minimum setup time required before stress can be applied to the joint or seam.

When connecting fibrous glass duct systems to sheet metal, as in connections to flanges or central air equipment, fasteners such as sheet metal screws and washers must be used to carry the mechanical load. Glass fabric and mastic can then be applied to seal the connections at these points. Usually, two widths of glass fabric will be required.

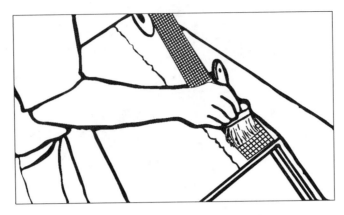

FIGURE A6-3-6—GLASS FABRIC INTO MASTIC

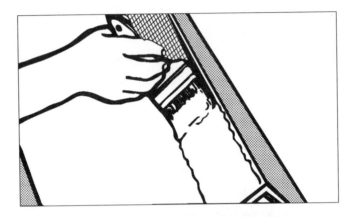

FIGURE A6-3-7—SECOND COAT OF MASTIC

SECTION 6.304 — REINFORCEMENT

6.304.1 General. Reinforcement is used to limit the deflection of the duct surface caused by internal static pressure loading. The maximum dimension of unreinforced ducts, which is a function of the system operating pressure, is shown on the manufacturer's label, affixed to each piece of duct board.

Duct systems made from Types 475 and 800 fibrous glass duct board may use one or more of the following reinforcement methods:

1. Tie rod reinforcement.

2. Channel reinforcement.

The reinforcement schedules contained in Tables A6-3-A, A6-3-B and A6-3-D are suitable for 0 inch to 2 inch w.g. (0 Pa to 498 Pa) duct systems.

While some duct dimensions may not require any reinforcement in straight sections, certain fittings of the same dimension may require reinforcement. This requirement is noted wherever applicable in this standard and in Table A6-3-D. Fitting reinforcement is accomplished by the use of tie rods wherever possible, and with channel reinforcement applied where tie rods cannot be used.

6.304.2 Tie-rod Reinforcement—Positive Pressure.

6.304.2.1 Tie rods. Tie rods consist of straight lengths of 12 gage (2 mm) galvanized steel wire with flat steel volcano-type washers and any of three approved termination devices (see Figure A6-3-8). The $2^1/_2$-inch (64 mm) square shall be installed so turned edges face away from the duct board facing.

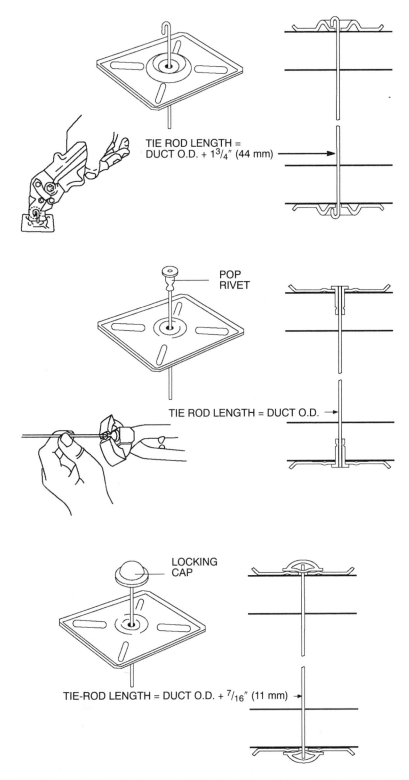

TIE ROD LENGTH =
DUCT O.D. + 1³/₄″ (44 mm)

POP
RIVET

TIE ROD LENGTH = DUCT O.D.

LOCKING
CAP

TIE-ROD LENGTH = DUCT O.D. + ⁷/₁₆″ (11 mm)

FIGURE A6-3-8—TERMINATIONS: FASLOOP; POP RIVET SLEEVE; LOCKING CAP

6.304.2.2 Location. In relation to transverse joints, the tie rods are spaced 4 inches (102 mm) from the end of the female joint, as shown in Figure A6-3-9.

When butt joints are used instead of shiplap joints, tie rods are placed in rows located at 3 inches (76 mm) on either side of the joint.

Alternate: A single tie-rod reinforcement may be used if the butt joint is glued with an adhesive system documented by the duct board manufacturer.

6.304.2.3 Spacing. Tie rods are placed in rows of two to five rods, across the face of the duct, with row spaces varying from 16 inches to 48 inches (406 mm to 1219 mm) depending on duct size and operating pressure.

The spacing of tie rods is shown in Table A6-3-A.

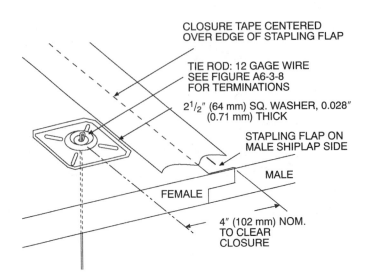

CLOSURE TAPE CENTERED OVER EDGE OF STAPLING FLAP

TIE ROD: 12 GAGE WIRE SEE FIGURE A6-3-8 FOR TERMINATIONS

2-1/2" (64 mm) SQ. WASHER, 0.028" (0.71 mm) THICK

STAPLING FLAP ON MALE SHIPLAP SIDE

MALE

FEMALE

4" (102 mm) NOM. TO CLEAR CLOSURE

FIGURE A6-3-9—TIE-ROD PLACEMENT

TABLE A6-3-A—TIE-ROD SYSTEM REINFORCEMENT SCHEDULE

WASHER, 2-1/2" (64 mm) SQUARE × 0.028" (0.71 mm) THICK WITH TURNED EDGES AWAY FROM FACING, VOLCANO TYPE, HOLE IN CENTER

TIE ROD: 12 GAGE STRAIGHT GALVANIZED STEEL WIRE. SEE FIGURE A6-3-8 FOR APPROVED WIRE TERMINATIONS

Positive Static Pressure (× 249 for Pa)	Maximum inside Duct Dimension, inches (× 25.4 for mm)	Type 475 Board			Type 800 Board		
		No. Rods across Dimension	Maximum Longitudinal Spacing (× 25.4 for mm)	No. Rods Per 4-ft. Section (1219 mm)	No. Rods across Dimension	Maximum Longitudinal Spacing (× 25.4 for mm)	No. Rods Per 4-ft. Section (1219 mm)
0 to 1/2" w.g.	0-36		*			*	
	37-42	2		4	2	48"	2
	43-48						
	49-60	3	24"	6	3		3
	61-64						6
	65-80	4		8	4	24"	8
	81-96	5		10	5		10
Over 1/2" to 1" w.g.	0-24		*			*	
	25-30	1		2	1	48"	1
	31-32						2
	33-36	2		4	2		4
	37-48		24"			24"	
	49-64	3		6	3		6
	65-80	4		8	4		8
	81-96	5		10	5		10
Over 1" to 2" w.g.	0-15		*			*	
	16-18	1	24"	2		*	
	19-24				1		1
	25-32			3		24"	2
	33-48	2		6	2		4
	49-60	3	16"	9	3		6
	61-64						9
	65-80	4		12	4	16"	12
	81-96	5		15	5		15

*Straight ducts of these dimensions do not require reinforcement. However, some fittings of these dimensions may require reinforcement.

NOTES:
1. Tie rods and washers must be no more than 16 inches (406 mm) on centers across duct dimension.
2. Ducts of 48-inch (1219 mm) width and over require use of antisag devices.
3. For duct dimensions over 96 inches (2438 mm), maintain tie rod spacing on 16-inch (406 mm) centers across the duct dimension following longitudinal spacing for the design pressure.

When the sides of the duct exceed the dimensions which require reinforcement (see Table A6-3-A), horizontal tie rods are also installed per the schedule.

6.304.2.4 Typical tie-rod reinforcement examples, positive pressure ducts. See Section 6.304.2.2 for placement of tie rods and sag supports in relation to joints. Sag support is required in ducts 48 inches (1219 mm) and greater in width.

The number of tie rods across the duct width shall be as required in the schedule contained in Table A6-3-A.

The longitudinal spacing of the rows of tie rods is based on the schedule in Table A6-3-A. This spacing will vary from 48 inches (1219 mm) on center to as close as 16 inches (406 mm) on center.

6.304.2.5 Sag control—Tie-rod reinforcement shiplapped joints. Top panels of fibrous glass duct sections or fittings 48 inches (1219 mm) wide or greater may sag due to the weight of the duct board when the system is not pressurized. To control this condition, sag supports must be provided. Figure A6-3-11A shows a typical installation.

Sag supports do not replace tie-rod assemblies as called for in the reinforcement schedule, but must be installed in addition to them. Hangers must be located within 12 inches (305 mm) of the sag supports.

For easier mating of fittings and duct sections during installation, a $1/2$-inch-diameter (13 mm) steel conduit and washers may be added to an existing tie-rod assembly at the female shiplap end.

When ducts are fabricated with butt joints, sag supports must be installed on both sides of the joint. A hanger must be installed within 12 inches (305 mm) of the sag support.

6.304.3 Channel Reinforcement.

6.304.3.1 General. Another reinforcement system, for use in either positive or negative pressure duct systems, consists of formed sheet metal channels wrapped around the perimeter of the duct.

When channels must be attached to the duct, for sag control or negative-pressure reinforcement, No. 10 plated sheet metal screws and $2^1/_2$-inch (64 mm) square, 0.020-inch (0.5 mm) (minimum) thick sheet metal washers are used. These must have turned edges to prevent cutting into the duct board. In positive-pressure applications, wraparound channels need not be attached to the duct board except when required for sag control.

Table A6-3-B gives longitudinal spacing, sheet metal gage and channel height dimensions of reinforcement, depending on the duct board type, maximum inside dimensions and static pressure. This is a minimum reinforcement schedule applying to straight sections. This schedule will also apply to fittings, but a simplified schedule may also be used (see Table A6-3-C).

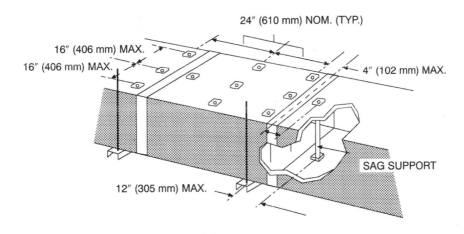

FIGURE A6-3-10—TIE-ROD REINFORCEMENT ROWS ON 24-INCH (610 mm) CENTERS, 48-INCH (1219 mm) DUCT SECTION

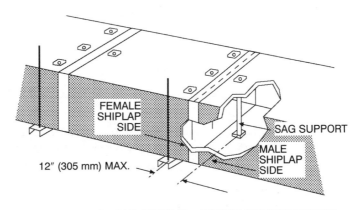

FIGURE A6-3-11A—SAG CONTROL—TIE-ROD REINFORCEMENT

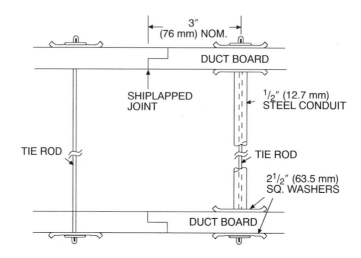

FIGURE A6-3-11B—SAG CONTROL DETAIL

TABLE A6-3-B—CHANNEL SYSTEM REINFORCEMENT SCHEDULE

		CHANNEL SYSTEM REINFORCEMENT SCHEDULE					
		Type 475 Board			**Type 800 Board**		
Static Pressure	**Maximum inside Duct Dimension (I.D.), in.**	**Maximum Longitudinal Spacing**	**Channel Gage (See Appendix D for sheet gage equivalency)**	**H Dimension (See Below)**	**Maximum Longitudinal Spacing**	**Channel Gage (See Appendix D for sheet gage equivalency)**	**H Dimension (See Below)**
× 249 for Pa	× 25.4 for mm		× 25.4 for mm			× 25.4 for mm	
0 to 1/2" w.g. — Negative	0-30	*			*		
0 to 1/2" w.g. — Negative	31-36	24"	22	1"	48"	22	1"
0 to 1/2" w.g. — Positive	0-36	*			*		
0 to 1/2" w.g. positive or negative	37-42	24"	22	1"	48"	22	1"
	43-48	24"	22	1"	48"	22	1"
	49-60	24"	22	1"	48"	22	1 1/2"
	61-72	24"	22	1"	48"	22	1 1/2"
	73-84	24"	22	1"	24"	22	1"
	85-96	24"	22	1 1/4"	24"	22	1"
Over 1/2" to 1" w.g. positive or negative	0-24	*			*		
	25-30	24"	22	1"	48"	22	1"
	31-36	24"	22	1"	48"	22	1"
	37-42	24"	22	1"	24"	22	1"
	43-48	24"	22	1"	24"	22	1"
	49-60	24"	22	1"	24"	22	1"
	61-72	24"	18	1"	24"	18	1"
	73-84	24"	18	1 1/4"	24"	18	1 1/4"
	85-96	24"	18	1 1/4"	24"	18	1 1/4"
Over 1" to 2" w.g. positive or negative	0-15	*			*		
	16-18	24"	22	1"	*		
	19-24	24"	22	1"	24"	22	1"
	25-36	24"	22	1"	24"	22	1"
	37-48	16"	22	1"	24"	22	1 1/4"
	49-60	16"	22	1"	24"	22	1 1/4"
	61-72	16"	18	1"	24"	18	1"
	73-84	16"	18	1 1/4"	16"	18	1 1/4"
	85-96	16"	18	1 1/2"	16"	18	1 1/2"

*Straight ducts of these dimensions do not require reinforcement; however, some fittings of these dimensions may require reinforcement.

NOTE: Ducts of 48-inch (1219 mm) maximum width and over require use of antisag devices.

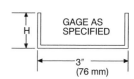

GAGE AS SPECIFIED

6.304.3.2 Channels. Channels must be fabricated from galvanized sheet metal of the gage shown in Table A6-3-B.

Channels are 3 inches (76 mm) wide, with a height (H) as shown in Table A6-3-B.

Each reinforcement may be fabricated from a continuous length of channel having three 90-degree bends and a fourth 90-degree corner which is fastened with bolts, screws, rivets, spot welds or staples. Reinforcements may also be fabricated with two, three or four securely fastened corners.

6.304.3.3 Location of channels. Channels are normally offset 4 inches (102 mm) from the end of the duct section to facilitate installation of sag supports and the closure system.

Where wraparound channels without sag support are used, the channel is slipped over the closure tape after the tape is applied, and centered over the female shiplap end for maximum support.

6.304.3.4 Sag support and typical channel reinforcement. When the duct is 48 inches (1219 mm) wide or greater,

channels are secured to the top for sag support with No. 10 plated sheet metal screws and $2^1/_2$-inch (64 mm) square washers (see Detail A). The number of channels along the duct shall be in accordance with Table A6-3-B.

6.304.4 Negative-pressure Channel Reinforcement.

6.304.4.1 Locating reinforcing channels. In negative-pressure applications such as return-air ducts, the channel reinforcement is applied over the male shiplap. Special clips are installed inside the duct (see Figure A6-3-13), which will support both the male and female sides of the duct joint. The clips are fastened in place with two sheet metal screws.

6.304.4.2 Clips. Clips are formed from 20 gage (0.036 inch) (0.91 mm) galvanized steel, with turned edges as shown in Detail B.

Clips are spaced not more than 16 inches (406 mm) apart and not more than 16 inches (406 mm) from the sides of a duct. The number of clips required is shown in Table A6-3-C.

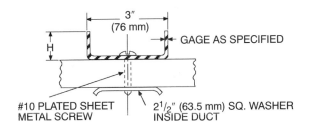

3"
(76 mm)

GAGE AS SPECIFIED

H

#10 PLATED SHEET
METAL SCREW

$2^1/_2$" (63.5 mm) SQ. WASHER
INSIDE DUCT

DETAIL A.
DETAIL A. TYPICAL, CENTER OF EACH CHANNEL

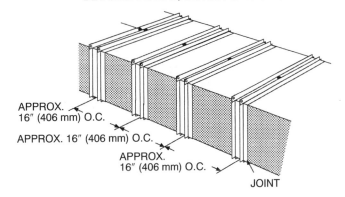

APPROX.
16" (406 mm) O.C.

APPROX. 16" (406 mm) O.C.

APPROX.
16" (406 mm) O.C.

JOINT

FIGURE A6-3-12—16-INCH (406 mm) CENTERS, 48-INCH (1219 mm) DUCT SECTIONS

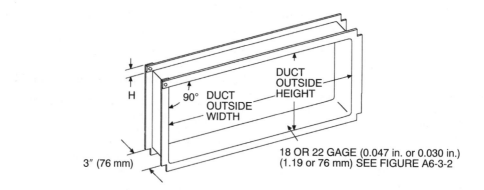

DETAIL B. CHANNEL REINFORCEMENT

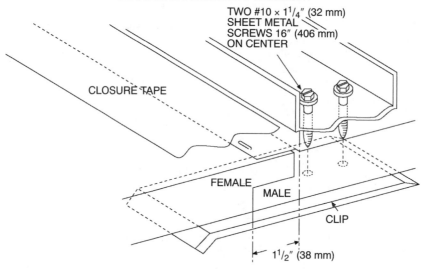

FIGURE A6-3-13—CHANNEL REINFORCEMENT FOR NEGATIVE-PRESSURE SYSTEMS

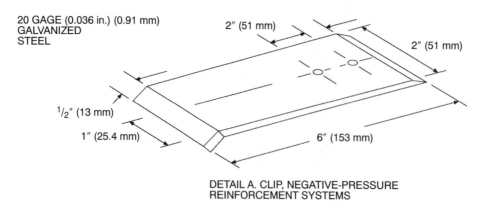

DETAIL A. CLIP, NEGATIVE-PRESSURE
REINFORCEMENT SYSTEMS

FIGURE A6-3-14—DETAIL B—CLIP, NEGATIVE-PRESSURE SYSTEMS

TABLE A6-3-C—NEGATIVE-PRESSURE FASTENERS

FASTENER REQUIREMENTS, NEGATIVE PRESSURE	
Transverse Dimension (inches) × 25.4 mm	Minimum Number of Clips or Washers per Reinforcing Member
16-32	1
33-48	2
49-64	3
65-80	4
81-96	5

NOTE: The foregoing arrangements are important and, if not followed closely, may result in system failure.

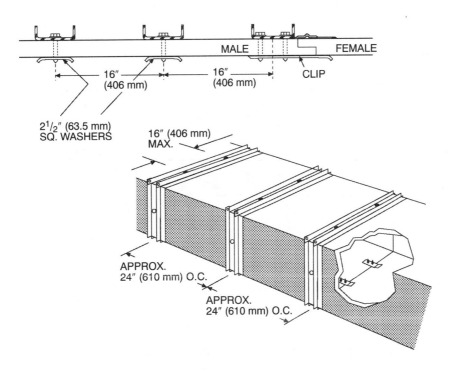

FIGURE A6-3-15—CHANNEL REINFORCEMENT ON 24-INCH (610 mm) CENTERS, 48-INCH (1219 mm) DUCT SECTION

6.304.4.3 Additional fasteners. When additional channels are required [as with 24-inch and 16-inch (610 mm and 406 mm) spacing], they are attached to the duct with No. 10 plated sheet metal screws and $2^1/_2$-inch (64 mm) square washers (see Detail A of Figure A6-3-12).

The spacing of the fasteners through each reinforcement channel is the same as for joint clips (see Table A6-3-C). A typical layout for negative-pressure ductwork is shown in Figure A6-3-15 and Detail C.

6.304.5 Fitting Reinforcement—Positive-pressure Systems.

6.304.5.1 General. Fittings are reinforced with tie rods or channels based on the duct dimensions, using the criteria found in Tables A6-3-A and A6-3-B.

Some fittings, branches, tees or offsets may require reinforcement even though schedules for straight ducts of the same dimension may show reinforcement is not required.

6.304.5.2 Partial wraparound reinforcement. Where reinforcement is required but cannot be fastened to opposite sides of a duct section or fitting, it is necessary to install formed sheet metal channels that partially wrap around a fibrous glass duct system fitting at the required location. (See Table A6-3-B for appropriate gage and profile.) In such cases, No. 10 by $1^1/_4$-inch (31.8 mm) plated sheet metal screws and $2^1/_2$-inch (64 mm) square washers, 0.020 inch (0.51 mm) (minimum) thick, are used to attach the ends of the channels to the duct board. (See Detail D and Table A6-3-D.)

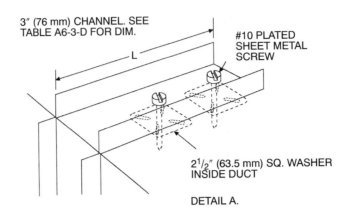

3" (76 mm) CHANNEL. SEE TABLE A6-3-D FOR DIM.

#10 PLATED SHEET METAL SCREW

2¹/₂" (63.5 mm) SQ. WASHER INSIDE DUCT

DETAIL A.

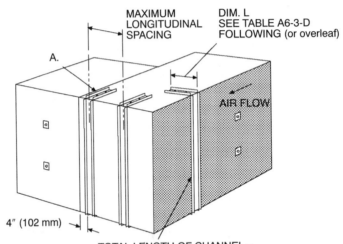

MAXIMUM LONGITUDINAL SPACING

DIM. L SEE TABLE A6-3-D FOLLOWING (or overleaf)

AIR FLOW

4" (102 mm)

TOTAL LENGTH OF CHANNEL = OUTSIDE DUCT DIMENSION + TWICE L DIM., TABLE A6-3-D

FIGURE A6-3-16—PARTIAL WRAP-AROUND REINFORCEMENT

TABLE A6-3-D—PARTIAL WRAP-AROUND REINFORCEMENT

PARTIAL WRAP-AROUND REINFORCEMENT SCHEDULE								
	Type 475 Board				Type 800 Board			
Positive Static Pressure	Maximum inside Duct Dimension (inches)	Longitudinal Spacing	Dimension L	No. of Screws, Each End	Maximum inside Duct Dimension (inches)	Longitudinal Spacing	Dimension L	No. of Screws, Each End
× 249 for Pa		× 25.4 for mm				× 25.4 for mm		
0" to ¹/₂" w.g.	0-36	Not required			0-36	Not required		
	37-96	24"	4"	1	37-60	48"	4"	1
					61-96	24"		
Over ¹/₂" to 1" w.g.	0-24	Not required			0-24	Not required		
	25-48	24"	4"	1	25-30	48"	4"	1
	49-64		7"	2	31-48			
	65-80		10"	3	49-64	24"	7"	2
	81-96		13"	4	65-80		10"	3
					81-96		13"	4
Over 1" to 2" w.g.	0-15	Not required			0-18	Not required		
	16-24	24"	4"	1	19-24	24"	4"	1
	25-32				25-32		7"	2
	33-48	16"	7"	2	33-48		10"	3
	49-64		10"	3	49-60		13"	4
	65-80		13"	4	61-64	16"	10"	3
	81-96		16"	5	65-80		14"	
					81-96		16"	5

6.304.5.3 Fitting reinforcement—90-degree elbows. If neither dimension A nor B (see Figure A6-3-17) is greater than the maximum unreinforced duct dimension (see Table A6-3-A), but diagonal X-Y is greater than the maximum unreinforced duct dimension in accordance with Table A6-3-A, install tie-rod reinforcement at midspan of diagonal at point No. 1 in Figure A6-3-17.

If either A or B is greater than the maximum unreinforced duct dimension:

Reinforce in accordance with Table A6-3-A.

Reinforce 4 inches (102 mm) upstream from female shiplap joints.

Reinforce at point No. 1 (Figure A6-3-17) where center lines intersect.

NOTE: Turning vanes in Figure A6-3-17 are omitted for clarity. Turning vanes do not replace reinforcement.

If duct dimension *H* (see Figure A6-3-18) is less than the maximum unreinforced duct dimension from Table A6-3-A, but more than 24 inches (610 mm), install sheet metal angle in accordance with Detail E. (Angle may also be installed on inside of throat.)

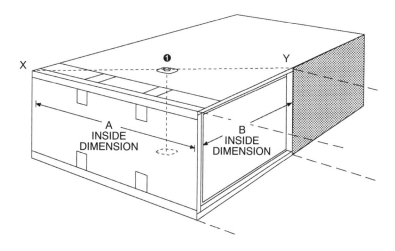

FIGURE A6-3-17—TIE-ROD REINFORCEMENT AT DIAGONAL X-Y—MIDSPAN

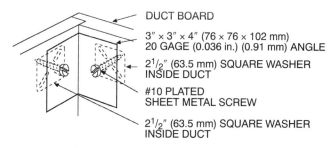

DETAIL E—THROAT REINFORCEMENT

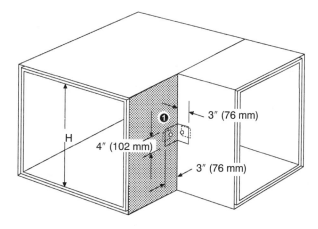

SHEET METAL ANGLE REINFORCEMENT AT THROAT OF 90-DEGREE ELBOW

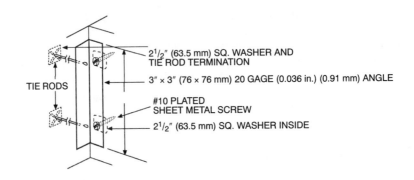

DETAIL F—THROAT REINFORCEMENT

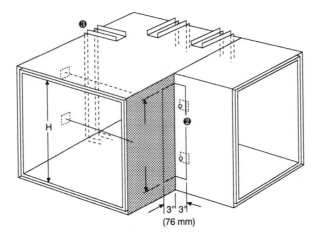

FIGURE A6-3-18—SHEET METAL ANGLE AT THROAT LARGE 90-DEGREE ELBOWS

When duct dimension H normally requires reinforcing, install sheet metal angle as shown at No. 2, Figure A6-3-18 and Detail F. Install tie rods through angle on upstream side, 16 inches (406 mm) on center, in accordance with Table A6-3-A, with angle of length L from table below.

No. Tie Rods	1	2	3	4	5
	× 25.4 for mm				
Angle Length L, in.	4	20	36	52	68

Install 3-inch (76 mm) channel reinforcement on heel panels as shown in Figure A6-3-18, spaced in accordance with Table A6-3-D and fastened in accordance with Figure A6-3-16.

NOTES: 1. Attachment of angles is best done after closure is completed. This requires sections to be short enough to allow the installer to reach inside to install the $2^1/2$-inch (64 mm) square washers.

2. For reinforcement of mitered elbows, refer to reinforcement standards for offsets.

6.304.5.4 Branch connections (tees). Many branches may require reinforcement even though schedules for straight ducts of the same dimensions may show reinforcement is not required.

Angled branches and positive takeoffs may be reinforced using the same methods as for tees. The amount and type of reinforcement depends on the dimensions of the takeoff and the system pressure (see Table A6-3-A).

If H is not greater than 16 inches (406 mm) and W (see Figure A6-3-19) is greater than 12 inches (305 mm), install reinforcement in accordance with Detail E on the top of the branch where it intersects the trunk duct.

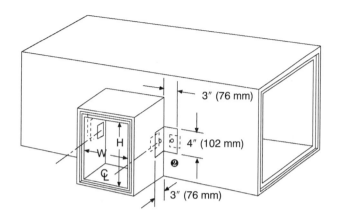

FIGURE A6-3-19—SHEET METAL ANGLE REINFORCEMENT; SIDES OF BRANCH

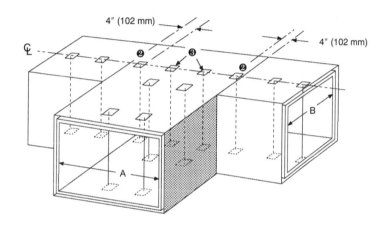

FIGURE A6-3-20—TEE REINFORCEMENT NORMAL TIE-ROD LOCATIONS

If *H* is greater than 16 inches (406 mm) and *W* is less than the maximum unreinforced duct dimension, reinforce side of branch as shown at No. 2, Figure A6-3-19.

NOTE: The maximum unreinforced dimension is 36 inches (914 mm) at $^1/_2$ inch w.g. (124 Pa), 24 inches (610 mm) at 1 inch w.g. (249 Pa), and 16 inches (406 mm) at 2 inches w.g. (498 Pa).

If *H* (Figure A6-3-19) is greater than 16 inches (406 mm) and *W* is greater than the maximum unreinforced duct dimension (see Table A6-3-A), install long angle clips in accordance with Detail C of Figure A6-3-15 with tie-rod reinforcement through the branch and trunk ducts (similar to Figure A6-3-18) as required by Table A6-3-A. A combination of tie rods and partial wraparound reinforcement (see Figure A6-3-16) may be used.

If *A* (see Figure A6-3-20) is less than the maximum unreinforced duct dimension but diagonals X-Y or Y-Z exceed the maximum allowable unreinforced duct dimension, install tie rods as shown at No. 2, 4 inches (101 mm) from female shiplaps.

If *A* is greater than the maximum unreinforced duct dimension and *B* is greater than one half the maximum unreinforced duct di-

mension, install tie rods 4 inches (101 mm) from female shiplap joints as shown at No. 2 and also along branch center lines and, additionally, spaced per Table A6-3-D in the trunk duct.

Where a splitter damper interferes with tie-rod reinforcement, wraparound channels must be used in their place.

NOTE: Turning vanes do not replace reinforcement.

6.304.5.5 Offsets. Offsets require different types of reinforcement for the cheek panels (sides, as shown in Figure A6-3-21) and the heel and throat panels (top and bottom, per Figure A6-3-22).

If *B* is greater than the maximum unreinforced duct dimension and cheek panels have shiplap joints, reinforce in accordance with No. 1, 4 inches (101 mm) from female shiplap (see Figure A6-3-21) with spacing in accordance with Table A6-3-A.

If the fitting uses butt joints, install the required spacing of tie rods 3 inches (76 mm) on each side of the butt joint.

Where Table A6-3-A requires more than one row of reinforcement, the rows shall be parallel to the edges of the duct, and the spacing between sets of tie rods shall be in accordance with Table A6-3-A.

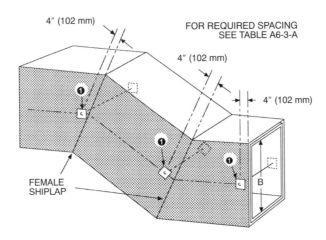

FIGURE A6-3-21—OFFSET REINFORCEMENT CHEEK PANELS WITH SHIPLAP JOINTS

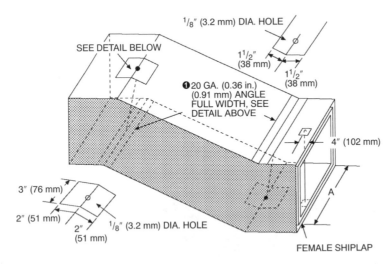

FIGURE A6-3-22—OFFSET REINFORCEMENT WITH SHEET METAL PLATES AND TIE RODS

The reinforcement for heel and toe joints is in accordance with Figure A6-3-22. Additional tie rods may be installed by using a longer plate at the heel, and also in the duct panel spaced in accordance with Table A6-3-A. The penetrations at the toe plate are grouped as close to the break in the metal as possible.

When dimension A requires more than one tie rod (see Table A6-3-A), sets of tie rods with metal angles shall be installed in rows parallel to the side of the duct.

Transitions are reinforced in the same manner with a tie rod ex-tending from the flat side of the duct, through a plate or plates positioned on the heel joint of the fitting.

6.304.5.6 Access doors—Positive pressure. If the access door width is not greater than the maximum longitudinal reinforcement spacing from Table A6-3-A, but interferes with reinforcement locations required by the table, install tie rods 4 inches (101 mm) from both sides of door opening in accordance with No. 1, Figure A6-3-23. Maximum reinforcement spacing must be in accordance with Table A6-3-A.

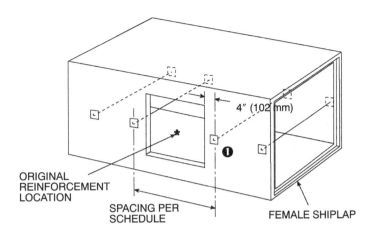

ORIGINAL
REINFORCEMENT
LOCATION

SPACING PER
SCHEDULE

4″ (102 mm)

FEMALE SHIPLAP

FIGURE A6-3-23—ACCESS DOOR LOCATION INTERFERING WITH REINFORCEMENT

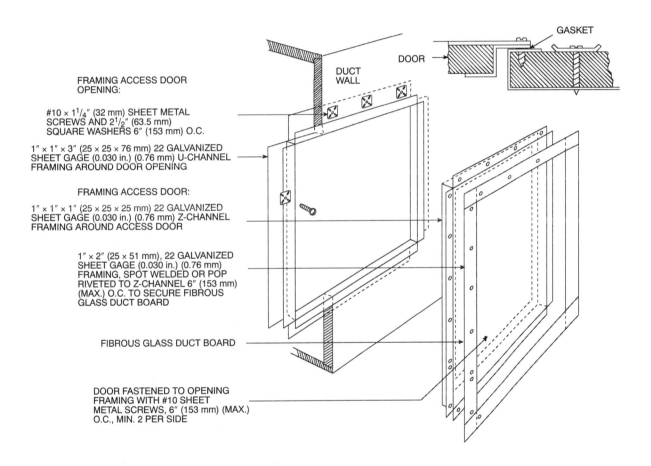

GASKET

DOOR

DUCT
WALL

FRAMING ACCESS DOOR
OPENING:

#10 × 1¹/₄″ (32 mm) SHEET METAL
SCREWS AND 2¹/₂″ (63.5 mm)
SQUARE WASHERS 6″ (153 mm) O.C.

1″ × 1″ × 3″ (25 × 25 × 76 mm) 22 GALVANIZED
SHEET GAGE (0.030 in.) (0.76 mm) U-CHANNEL
FRAMING AROUND DOOR OPENING

FRAMING ACCESS DOOR:

1″ × 1″ × 1″ (25 × 25 × 25 mm) 22 GALVANIZED
SHEET GAGE (0.030 in.) (0.76 mm) Z-CHANNEL
FRAMING AROUND ACCESS DOOR

1″ × 2″ (25 × 51 mm), 22 GALVANIZED
SHEET GAGE (0.030 in.) (0.76 mm)
FRAMING, SPOT WELDED OR POP
RIVETED TO Z-CHANNEL 6″ (153 mm)
(MAX.) O.C. TO SECURE FIBROUS
GLASS DUCT BOARD

FIBROUS GLASS DUCT BOARD

DOOR FASTENED TO OPENING
FRAMING WITH #10 SHEET
METAL SCREWS, 6″ (153 mm) (MAX.)
O.C., MIN. 2 PER SIDE

FIGURE A6-3-24—DUCT OPENING FRAME

If access door height is greater than 16 inches (406 mm) and its width is greater than the maximum longitudinal reinforcement spacing shown in Table A6-3-A, install the frame for the access door inside the duct, securing it to the duct wall with screws and washers (see Figure A6-3-24).

Install tie rods near the vertical sides of the door (Figure A6-3-23) frame and also near the top and bottom sides of the frame, spaced as specified in Table A6-3-A with a minimum of one tie rod on each side of the frame.

NOTE: Use channel reinforcement in place of tie rods between access door and fire damper where tie rods would interfere with damper access or operation.

The duct door is fabricated from 1 inch (25 mm) duct board installed with 1-inch by 1-inch by 1-inch (25 mm by 25 mm by 25 mm), 22 gage (0.76 mm) Z-channel framing around access door. Doors are gasketed and secured in place with sheet metal screws, or they may be hinged with sash lock fasteners as shown in Detail G on the following page.

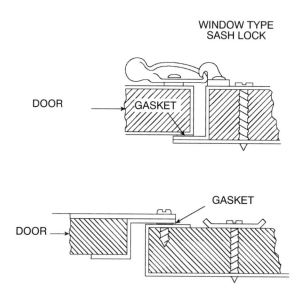

WINDOW TYPE
SASH LOCK

DOOR

GASKET

GASKET

DOOR

DETAIL G—WINDOW TYPE SASH LOCK

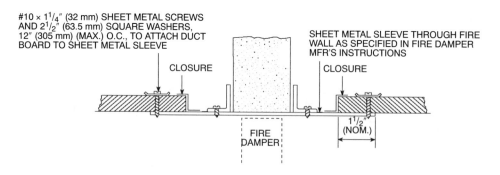

#10 × 1¹/₄″ (32 mm) SHEET METAL SCREWS
AND 2¹/₂″ (63.5 mm) SQUARE WASHERS,
12″ (305 mm) (MAX.) O.C., TO ATTACH DUCT
BOARD TO SHEET METAL SLEEVE

SHEET METAL SLEEVE THROUGH FIRE
WALL AS SPECIFIED IN FIRE DAMPER
MFR'S INSTRUCTIONS

CLOSURE

CLOSURE

FIRE
DAMPER

1¹/₂″
(NOM.)

FIGURE A6-3-25—ATTACHMENT TO FIRE DAMPER SLEEVES

SECTION 6.305 — FIRE DAMPERS

When fire dampers are required at penetrations of fire-rated walls, fibrous glass ducts must terminate at either side of such walls. Fire dampers shall be installed in accordance with the damper manufacturer's instructions and must be installed in a steel sleeve. The opening in the wall shall be large enough to allow for thermal expansion of the sleeve and to permit installation of ⁵/₈-inch (16 mm) gypsum board between the sleeve and framing.

The sleeve must extend not less than 3 inches (76 mm) beyond the face of the wall so that the duct can be slipped onto the sleeve. The duct is secured to the sleeve with screws and washers, as shown in Figure A6-3-25.

Sealing of fibrous glass duct board to the sheet metal sleeve must be made with glass fabric and mastic, except where operating pressure is less than 1-inch w.g. (249 Pa) and the sheet metal surfaces are carefully cleaned, in which case pressure-sensitive aluminum foil tape may be used. See Section 6.303 for methods.

SECTION 6.306 — HANGERS AND SUPPORTS

6.306.1 General. Fibrous glass ducts are light in weight, so that they can be supported with a minimum of hangers if care is taken as to placement of the supports.

The charts and examples illustrated in this section show that the hanger treatment and spacing required is dependent on duct dimensions. Trapeze-style channels suspended by 12 gage (2.1 mm) (minimum) hanger wire (see Figure A6-3-26) are the preferred method of support. Channel gage and profile vary with duct size, but in no case should the supporting channel be less than 2 inches (51 mm) wide. Channels may also be suspended by means of metal rods of 1-inch-wide (25 mm) (minimum) galvanized steel straps.

When channel reinforcement members occur within maximum hanger spacing as shown in Table A6-3-E, sheet metal straps may be bolted to the channel reinforcement as shown in Figure A6-3-27. Support may also be made with 12 gage (2.1 mm) (minimum) wire.

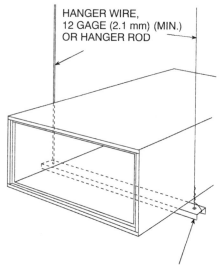

CHANNEL (See Table A6-3-F for sheet metal gage and dimensions)

FIGURE A6-3-26—TYPICAL HANGER

TABLE A6-3-E—HANGER SPACING

DUCT SIZE (× 25.4 for mm)	MAXIMUM HANGER SPACING (feet) (× 304.8 for mm)
48″ wide or greater	4
Less than 48″ wide and less than 12″ deep	6
Width between 24″ and 48″ and greater than 24″ deep	6
Less than 48″ wide and depth between 12″ and 24″	8
Width 24″ or less and depth greater than 12″	8

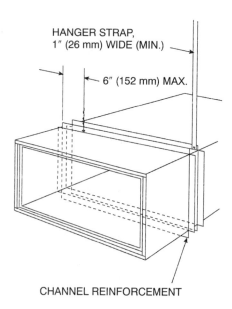

CHANNEL REINFORCEMENT

FIGURE A6-3-27—HANGING FROM CHANNEL REINFORCEMENT

6.306.2 Hanger Design. Occasionally, hanger channels must be extended considerably beyond the duct sides so that the supports will clear other obstructions. The total extension $(E + E')$ of the supports beyond the duct sides (see Figure A6-3-28) governs the minimum dimensions (see Table A6-3-F) of the channel.

6.306.3 Spacing. Hanger spacing per Table A6-3-E or Figure A6-3-29 is based on 3-inch-wide (76 mm) (minimum) channels.

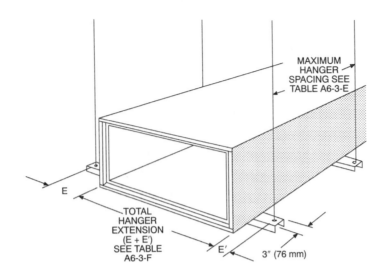

**FIGURE A6-3-28—HANGER SPACING AND EXTENSION USING
3-INCH-WIDE (76 mm) CHANNELS**

TABLE A6-3-F—CHANNEL SELECTION

IF TOTAL EXTENSION IS NOT GREATER THAN: (inches)		MINIMUM CHANNEL PROFILE (inches)
× 25.4 for mm	MINIMUM CHANNEL GAGE	× 25.4 for mm
6	24	3 × 1.5
18	22	3 × 2
30	18	3 × 2

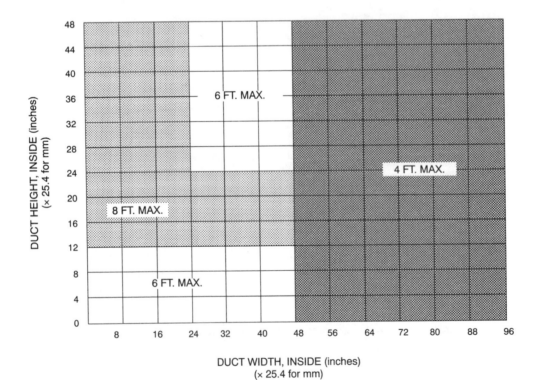

1 ft. = 305 mm

**FIGURE A6-3-29—MINIMUM HANGER SPACING, STRAIGHT DUCT,
3-INCH-WIDE (76 mm) CHANNEL**

For ducts not over 48 inches wide by 24 inches high (1219 mm by 610 mm), 2-inch-wide by $1^1/_2$-inch channels (51 mm by 38 mm), spaced not more than 4 feet (1219 mm) apart may be installed. The total extension of the hanger supports shall not exceed 6 inches (152 mm).

Hanger design and spacing for fibrous glass ducts is based on extensive testing with loads exceeding twice the duct weight located between supports to ensure the integrity of the duct system. Recommended hanger spacing is shown in Figure A6-3-29. Caution should be taken with other types of hanger systems to ensure that excessive stress is not placed on the hanger or the fibrous glass duct system.

6.306.4 Fittings. Proper support of duct fittings may require that additional hangers be installed.

For an elbow, hangers should be on each leg, within 12 inches (305 mm) of the throat. If the width of the duct is greater than 18 inches (457 mm), an additional hanger must be installed (see Figure A6-3-30) so that dimension *D* is approximately two thirds of the diagonal distance from throat to heel.

Tees require support on the trunk as shown in Figure A6-3-31. If a tee run-out hanger falls where the trunk duct is located, add hangers on either side of trunk. Do not exceed maximum hanger spacing.

Branch ducts are treated in a similar manner with hanger spacing on the trunk duct in accordance with Figure A6-3-29.

For diffuser drops, hangers are installed within 3 inches (76 mm) of each side of the drop. The connection of the drop to the duct is reinforced in accordance with Figure A6-3-32.

If the drop assembly, including the diffuser, weighs more than 25 pounds (11.3 kg), the diffuser must be separately supported.

6.306.5 Hanging Rigid Round Duct. Preformed round fibrous glass duct should be hung so the hanger will not damage the duct facing.

Straps or saddles in contact with the duct must not be less than $^5/_8$ inch (16 mm) wide. Avoid sharp edges and burrs.

Space hangers at a maximum of 6 feet (1829 mm) on center. Where practical, hangers should be located at circumferential joints. Provide hanger support at all fittings.

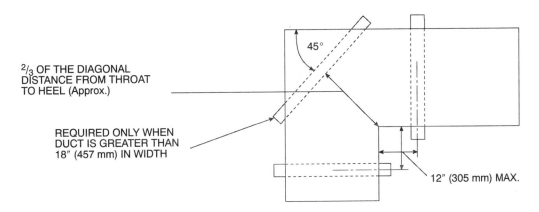

FIGURE A6-3-30—ELBOW SUPPORT

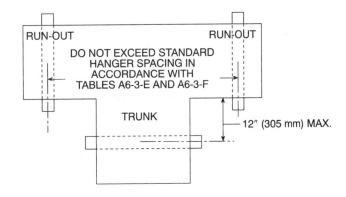

FIGURE A6-3-31—TEE SUPPORT

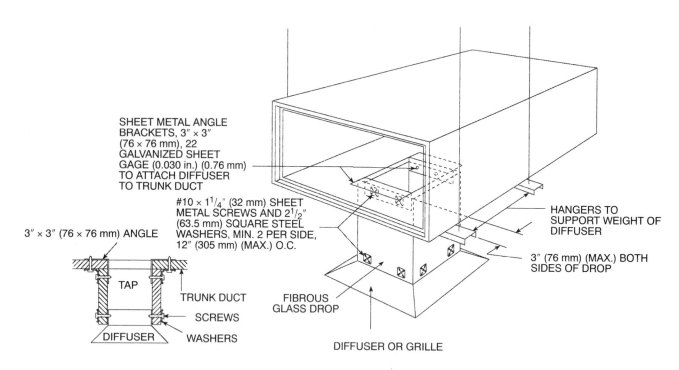

(See Appendix D for sheet gage equivalents.)

FIGURE A6-3-32—DIFFUSER CONNECTION

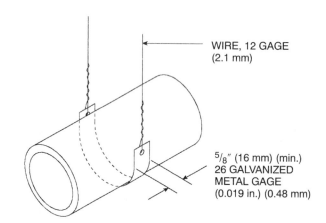

(See Appendix D for sheet gage equivalents.)

FIGURE A6-3-33—HANGING ROUND DUCT WITH SADDLE AND 12 GAGE WIRES

Part B—Flexible Ducts

SECTION 6.307 — SUITABLE INSTALLATIONS

6.307.1 General.

6.307.1.1 The routing and length of flexible duct, the number of bends, the number of degrees of each bend and the amount of sag allowed between support joints will have serious effects on system performance due to the increased resistance each introduces. Use the minimum length of flexible duct to make connections. It is not recommended that excess lengths of ducts be installed to allow for possible future relocations of air terminal devices.

6.307.1.2 Avoid installations where exposure to direct or indirect sunlight can occur, e.g., turbine vents, skylights, canopy windows, etc. Prolonged exposure to sunlight will cause degradation of the vapor barrier.

6.307.1.3 Terminal devices shall be supported independently of the flexible duct.

6.307.1.4 Repair torn or damaged vapor barrier jacket with approved duct tape. If internal core is penetrated, replace flexible duct or treat as a connection.

6.307.2 Installation.

6.307.2.1 Install duct fully extended, do not install in the compressed state or use excess lengths. This will noticeably increase friction losses.

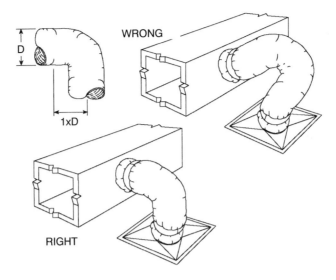

FIGURE A6-3-34—EXTEND DUCT FULLY

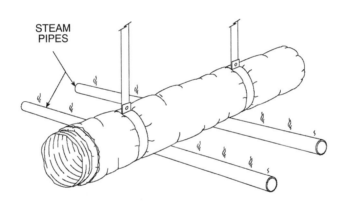

FIGURE A6-3-35—WRONG METHOD OF SUPPORT

6.307.2.2 Avoid bending ducts across sharp corners, or incidental contact with metal fixtures, pipes or conduits. Radius at center line shall not be less than one duct diameter.

6.307.2.3 Do not install near hot equipment (e.g., furnaces, boilers, steam pipes, etc.) that is above the recommended flexible duct use temperature.

SECTION 6.308 — CONNECTING, JOINING AND SPLICING FLEXIBLE DUCT

All connections, joints and splices shall be made in accordance with the manufacturer's installation instructions. Unless specified by the manufacturer, adhesives are not recommended for use with nonmetallic flexible duct as they will chemically react with the duct materials, causing deterioration and degradation. Sheet metal collars to which the flexible ducts are attached shall be a minimum of 2 inches (51 mm) in length. Sheet metal sleeves used for joining two sections of flexible duct shall be a minimum of 4 inches (102 mm) in length.

Installation Instructions
Nonmetallic Air Ducts with Plain Ends
6.308.1 Connections.

6.308.1.1 After desired length is determined, cut completely around and through duct with knife. Cut wire with snips or side cutters.

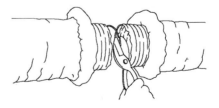

FIGURE A6-3-36A—END CONNECTORS

6.308.1.2 Pull back jacket and insulation from core. Slide at least 1 inch (25 mm) of core over collar, pipe or fitting. Tape with at least two wraps of approved duct tape. Secure with approved clamp.

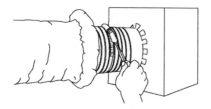

FIGURE A6-3-36B—PULL JACKET AND INSULATION

6.308.1.3 Pull jacket and insulation back over core. Tape jacket with two wraps of approved tape. An approved clamp may be used in place of or in conjunction with duct tape.

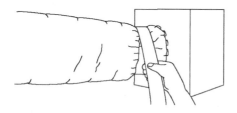

FIGURE A6-3-36C—SPLICES

6.308.2 Splices.

6.308.2.1 Peel back jacket and insulation from core. Butt two cores together on a minimum 4-inch-wide (102 mm) collar.

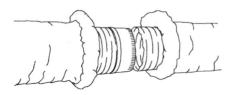

FIGURE A6-3-37A—SPLICING

6.308.2.2 Tape together with at least two wraps of approved duct tape. Secure with two approved clamps.

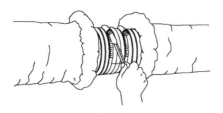

FIGURE A6-3-37B—DUCT CLAMPS

6.308.2.3 Pull jacket and insulation back over cores. Tape jackets together with two wraps of approved duct tape.

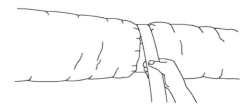

FIGURE A6-3-37C—RETAPE

NOTES: 1. For uninsulated duct/connector, disregard reference to insulation and jacket.

2. See manufacturer's installation instructions for approved tapes and clamps.

3. Use beaded fittings for pressures exceeding 4 inches w.g. (955 Pa) and for diameters 12 inches (305 mm) and larger.

SECTION 6.309 — SUPPORTING FLEXIBLE DUCT

6.309.1 Flexible duct shall be supported at manufacturer's recommended intervals, but at no greater distance than 4 feet. Maximum permissible sag is $^1/_2$ inch per foot (42 mm/m) of spacing between supports.

A connection to rigid ducting or equipment shall be considered a support joint.

Long horizontal duct runs with sharp bends shall have additional supports before and after the bend approximately one duct diameter distance from the center line of the bend.

6.309.2 Hanger or saddle material in contact with the flexible duct shall be of sufficient width to prevent any restriction of the internal diameter of the duct when the weight of the supported section rests on the hanger or saddle material. In no case will the material contacting the flexible duct be less than $1^1/_2$ inches (38 mm) wide.

6.309.3 Factory-installed suspension systems integral to the flexible duct are an acceptable alternative hanging method when manufacturer's recommended procedures are followed.

6.309.4 Flexible ducts may rest on ceiling joists or truss supports. A maximum spacing between supports shall not exceed the maximum spacing per manufacturer's installation instructions.

6.309.5 Support the duct between a metal connection and a bend by allowing the duct to extend straight for a few inches before making the bend. This will avoid possible damage of the flexible duct by the edge of the sheet metal collar.

6.309.6 Vertically installed duct shall be stabilized by support straps at a maximum of 6 feet (1829 mm) on center.

NOTE: Factory-made air ducts may not be used for vertical risers in air duct systems serving more than two stories. See Section 603.2.

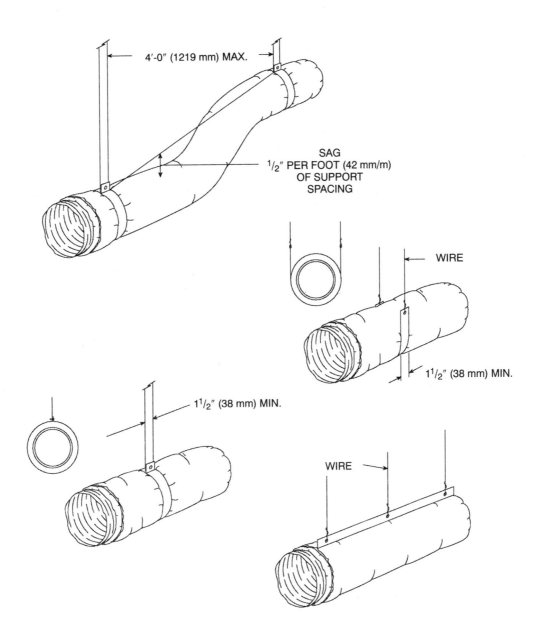

4'-0" (1219 mm) MAX.

SAG
$1/2$" PER FOOT (42 mm/m)
OF SUPPORT
SPACING

WIRE

$1^1/_2$" (38 mm) MIN.

$1^1/_2$" (38 mm) MIN.

WIRE

FIGURE A6-3-38—FLEXIBLE DUCT SUPPORTS

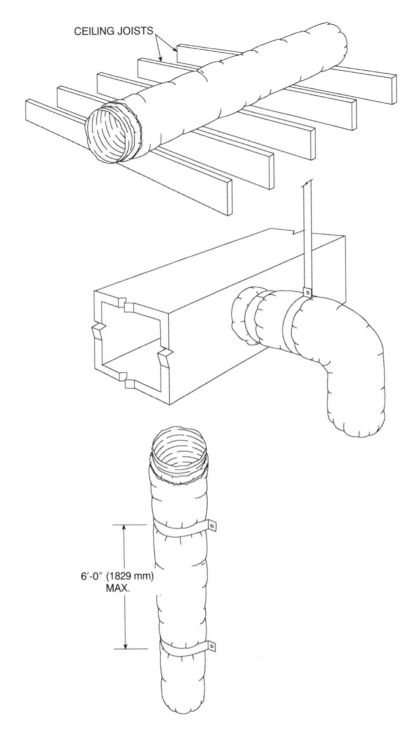

CEILING JOISTS

6'-0" (1829 mm)
MAX.

FIGURE A6-3-39—PROPER SUPPORT

SECTION 6.310 — CHECKLIST

The following checklist is provided for the benefit of the inspector, as well as the installer. It is designed so that the correct answer to all questions is yes.

Product

_____ Is the UL label present? (Although each board is labeled, each section may not be since there is only one label per sheet.) ( ) ( )

General	Yes	No
_____ Have all tears or punctures to facing material been repaired using the proper technique?	( )	( )
_____ Are all sheet metal accessory items galvanized?	( )	( )

Fabrication and Installation

_____ When metal parts are attached, are $2^1/_2$-inch (64 mm) (minimum) square steel washers used on 16-inch (406 mm) (maximum) centers? ( ) ( )

	Yes	No
_____ When staples cannot be used, are 8-inch (203 mm) cross tabs of approved closure being used in place of staples? [Tab spacing requirements are 12 inches (305 mm) on center, minimum one per side.]	( )	( )
_____ Are all system joints tight, free from bulges, with taped joints showing good workmanship?	( )	( )
_____ Have offsets been installed so duct sections are not forced to bend around obstructions?	( )	( )

Fire Dampers

_____ Is sheet metal sleeve present? Is duct properly attached to sleeve with screws and washers 16 inches (406 mm) on center? (Fibrous glass ducts must not penetrate assemblies required to have a fire damper.)   ( ) ( )

Access Doors

_____ Is installation in accordance with Section 6.304.5.6?   ( ) ( )

Grills, Diffusers, Registers

_____ Is the extra weight of the item being separately supported and not dependent on the duct alone for support? [Exception: Registers not greater than 150 square inches (96.7 × 10^3 mm^2) in area may be attached to the duct with metal channel, without other support.]   ( ) ( )

Connection to Units

_____ Are sheet metal screws and washers used to secure duct system to flange extensions? (Securing the duct to the unit flange without mechanical fasteners is sufficient.)   ( ) ( )

Closures

_____ Are all joints in the system properly sealed?   ( ) ( )

_____ Are closure materials of a listed type as evidenced by presence of UL instruction sheet in duct board carton, or imprinted UL 181A on the tape?   ( ) ( )

_____ Are there staples or cross tabs, properly spaced, on circumferential joints?   ( ) ( )

_____ Are all pressure-sensitive tape closures rubbed down adequately, with staples or scrim in facing clearly visible through the tape?   ( ) ( )

_____ If heat-sealable tape closure was used, was it applied correctly, as evidenced by dot color change?   ( ) ( )

_____ If glass fabric and mastic are used, is the mesh of the glass fabric completely filled with mastic?   ( ) ( )

Reinforcement

_____ Is reinforcement system in accordance with Section 6.304?   ( ) ( )

_____ Is tie-rod spacing correct according to duct span, board type and static pressure?   ( ) ( )

_____ Are tie-rod washers $2^1/_2$ inches (64 mm) square?   ( ) ( )

_____ Do tie-rod washers have turned edges facing away from duct board so they will not cut into it?   ( ) ( )

_____ If tie rods reinforce a butt joint, are rods used on *both sides* of butt joint?   ( ) ( )

_____ Is wire termination one of those documented in Section 6.304.2?   ( ) ( )

_____ Are antisag devices used on ducts 48-inch (1219 mm) span or greater, to support top panel of ducts?   ( ) ( )

_____ Are heels of tees, elbows and end caps reinforced (formed sheet metal channel, tie rod, combination)?   ( ) ( )

_____ When formed sheet metal channel reinforcement is used, are sheet metal gauges, dimensions and spacing correct?   ( ) ( )

_____ On return ducts, are sheet metal channel reinforcements attached to ducts with screws and $2^1/_2$-inch (64 mm) square washers or 2-inch by 6-inch (51 mm by 152 mm) clips?   ( ) ( )

Hangers and Supports

_____ Are hangers installed in accordance with Section 6.306?   ( ) ( )

_____ Are hanger designs in accordance with Table A6-3-F?   ( ) ( )

_____ Are accessories that add weight to the duct system separately supported so as not to stress the system?   ( ) ( )

_____ If formed sheet metal reinforcements are used as hangers, are attachments within 6 inches (152 mm) of duct sides?   ( ) ( )

_____ Are all fittings supported by hangers?   ( ) ( )

UNIFORM MECHANICAL CODE STANDARD 11-1
Standard Test Method of Concentration Limits of Flammability of Chemicals

Based on Standard Test Method E 681-85 of the American Society for Testing and Materials

See Section 1102.4, *Uniform Mechanical Code*

SECTION 11.101 — SCOPE

11.101.1 Concentration Limits of Flammability. This test method covers the determination of the lower and upper concentration limits of flammability of chemicals having sufficient vapor pressure to form flammable mixtures in air at one atmosphere pressure at the test temperature. This method may be used to determine these limits in the presence of inert dilution gases. No oxidant stronger than air should be used.

NOTE: The lower flammability limit and upper flammability limit are also referred to as the lower explosive limit (LEL) and upper explosive limit (UEL), respectively.

11.101.2 Limitations of Method. This test method is limited to an initial pressure of 101 kPa (1 atm) or less, with a practical lower pressure limit of approximately 13.3 kPa (0.13 atm). The maximum practical operating temperature of this equipment is approximately 150°C (302°F).

11.101.3 Other Test Methods. This test method is one of several being developed by ASTM Committee E 27 for determining the flammability of chemicals.

11.101.4 Applicability. This standard may be used to measure and describe the properties of materials, products or assemblies in response to heat and flame under controlled laboratory conditions and should not be used to describe or appraise the fire hazard or fire risk of materials, products or assemblies under actual fire conditions. However, results of this test may be used as elements of a fire risk assessment which takes into account all of the factors which are pertinent to an assessment of the fire hazard of a particular end use.

11.101.5 Precaution. This standard may involve hazardous materials, operations and equipment. This standard does not purport to address all of the safety problems associated with its use. It is the responsibility of whoever uses this standard to consult and establish appropriate safety and health practices and determine the applicability of regulatory limitations prior to use. Specific precaution statements are given in Section 11.107.

SECTION 11.102 — SUMMARY OF METHOD

A uniform mixture of a gas or vapor with air is ignited in a closed vessel and the upward and outward propagation of the flame away from the ignition source is noted by visual observation. The concentration of the flammable component is varied between trials until the composition which will just sustain propagation of the flame is determined.

SECTION 11.103 — DEFINITIONS

LOWER LIMIT OF FLAMMABILITY or **LOWER FLAMMABLE LIMIT (LFL)** is the minimum concentration of a combustible substance that is capable of propagating a flame through a homogeneous mixture of the combustible and a gaseous oxidizer under the specified conditions of test.

UPPER LIMIT OF FLAMMABILITY or **UPPER FLAMMABLE LIMIT (UFL)** is the maximum concentration of a combustible substance that is capable of propagating a flame through a homogeneous mixture of the combustible and a gaseous oxidizer under the specified conditions of test.

PROPAGATION OF FLAME, as used in this method, is the upward and outward movement of the flame front from the ignition source to the vessel walls, which is determined by visual observation.

SECTION 11.104 — SIGNIFICANCE AND USE

11.104.1 LFL and UFL. The lower and upper limits of flammability of gases and vapors define the range of flammable concentrations in air.

11.104.2 Use. Limits of flammability may be used to determine guidelines for the safe handling of volatile chemicals. They are used particularly in assessing ventilation requirements for the handling of gases and vapors.

NOTE: The break point between nonflammability and flammability occurs over a narrow concentration range at the lower flammable limit but is less distinct at the upper limit.

SECTION 11.105 — INTERFERENCES

11.105.1 Inapplicability. This method is not applicable to certain readily oxidized chemicals. If significant oxidation takes place when the vapors are mixed with air, unreliable results are obtained. Flow systems designed to minimize hold-up time may be required for such materials.

11.105.2 Flame-quenching Effects. Measured flammable limits are influenced by flame-quenching effects of the test vessel walls. The test vessel employed in this method is of sufficient size to eliminate the effects of flame quenching for most materials. However, there may be quenching effects, particularly on tests run at subambient pressures. For certain amines, halogenated materials, etc., which have large ignition-quenching distances, tests should be conducted in larger-diameter vessels.

SECTION 11.106 — APPARATUS

Figure A11-1-1 is a schematic diagram of the apparatus. The apparatus consists of a glass test vessel (1), an insulated chamber (2) equipped with a source of controlled-temperature air (3), an ignition device with an appropriate power supply (4), a magnetic stirrer (5), and a cover (6) equipped with the necessary operating connections and components.

SECTION 11.107 — SAFETY PRECAUTIONS

11.107.1 Limitations. Tests should not be conducted in this apparatus with oxidizers stronger than air since explosive violence increases as oxidizer strength increases. Do not use oxygen, nitrous oxide, nitrogen dioxide, chlorine, etc., in this glass apparatus.

11.107.2 Shielding. Adequate shielding must be provided to prevent injury in the event of equipment rupture, due to both implosions and explosions. A metal enclosure is one method suitable for this purpose.

11.107.2.1 Implosion hazard. Implosion of the test vessel at high vacuum levels is possible and, therefore, all evacuations must be made with the required shielding to protect against flying fragments.

11.107.2.2 Precautions to avoid rupture. Energetic explosions may be produced if tests are made at concentrations within the flammable range, between the LFL and UFL. The glass test vessel, equipped with a lightly held or loose cover, vents most explosions adequately; nevertheless, shielding is required to protect against any probability of test vessel rupture.

11.107.2.3 Self-ignition. In rare instances, particularly with upper-limit tests, self-ignition may be encountered when air is rapidly introduced into the partially evacuated test vessel containing vaporized sample. Valves permitting remote operation, changes in sample and air introduction sequences, simple shields and other techniques may be employed to ensure safe operations.

11.107.2.4 Safety interlocks. The test area should be equipped with electrical interlocks to prevent activation of the ignition source unless adequate shielding is in place.

11.107.3 Avoid Explosive Decomposition. Tests should not be conducted on thermally unstable materials which might undergo explosive decomposition reactions.

11.107.4 Fume Hood Required. Tests should be conducted in a fume hood or other ventilated area to prevent personnel exposure to toxic chemicals or combustion products.

11.107.5 Integrity of Electrical Insulation. Precautions must be taken to ensure that the high-voltage spark ignition source does not contact temperature- or pressure-measuring devices or other conductive paths which could create an electrical hazard to personnel or instrumentation outside the shielded area. Careful attention to electrical insulation integrity can reduce the possibility of hazard. Disconnects for all instrumentation lines will provide positive protection.

SECTION 11.108 — EQUIPMENT CALIBRATION

11.108.1 Importance of Flask Volume. Accurate determination of the flask volume is necessary for the calculation of flammable limits when sample measurement is on a weight or volume basis.

11.108.1.1 Method. Determine the total volume of the flask as follows: Weigh a clean, dry flask with all components installed. Fill the flask with distilled water. Reinsert the cover, allowing the excess water to overflow, dry the outside of the flask, and reweigh. Record the difference in grams as the net volume of the flask in cubic centimeters. (Slight errors associated with water density differences are beyond the accuracy of this method.)

11.108.2 Maintenance. Calibrate pressure-, temperature-, and liquid-measuring devices against adequate standards.

SECTION 11.109 — PROCEDURE

11.109.1 Preliminaries. Assemble the equipment, as in Figure A11-1-1, within an appropriate fume hood or other ventilated area and secure the door of the metal enclosure. The test vessel and all components should be clean and dry. Evacuate the system and flush with air to ensure removal of residual volatile materials that

may be present as a result of cleaning or prior tests. As many as three evacuation/flush cycles may be required to ensure complete removal of combustion products between tests.

11.109.2 Test Temperature. Adjust the flask to the desired test temperature. This temperature must be above the vapor condensation temperature of the mixture being tested.

It may be necessary to heat or insulate cover components and feed lines separately to prevent vapor condensation.

11.109.3 Read Barometer. Record the actual barometric pressure at the test location.

11.109.4 Safety Reminder. Double check to make certain all safety precautions have been taken.

11.109.5 Procedure for Sample Introduction as a Liquid.

1. Evacuate the flask to a pressure of 1.33 to 6.65 kPa.

2. Place the desired liquid volume in a hypodermic syringe of appropriate size. Transfer the liquid to the inlet separatory funnel (see Section 11.109.5, Item 4).

3. Turn on the stirrer at a minimum speed of 400 revolutions per minute.

4. Open the inlet stopcock. Allow the sample to be drawn into the flask. Close the stopcock when all the liquid has entered. Place a cover on the inlet separatory funnel. A serum-bottle septum may be used in place of the separatory funnel.

In this case, inject the sample directly into the flask by piercing the septum with the hypodermic needle. It will be necessary to make a volume correction if a significant volume of liquid is drawn from the needle or uncalibrated portion of the syringe.

5. When sample vaporization is complete, remove the separatory funnel cover and open the stopcock, permitting air to enter the test vessel slowly through the separatory funnel. Entering air sweeps traces of residual sample into the flask.

6. Release the cover hold-down devices and close the hood door.

7. Continue stirring for at least five minutes to obtain complete mixing and attainment of thermal equilibrium. Final trials should be made at longer mixing times to ensure optimal mixing conditions are achieved.

8. Turn off the stirrer.

9. Record the test temperature, T.

10. Disconnect instrumentation lines as required.

11. Darken the viewing area. Activate the ignition source. Observe for ignition and flame propagation away from the ignition source. Record as flammable any mixture producing a flame front that spreads from the ignition source and reaches the vessel walls.

NOTE: Mixtures having a composition just outside the flammable range exhibit a small cap of flame above the arc position; in some cases a vertical streak of flame may propagate to the vessel cover. (Absence of a cap flame may be an indication of insufficient ignition energy.) The onset of spherical, upward and partial outward flame propagation signifies a limit or near-limit mixture. It is suggested that detailed observations of flame behavior be recorded on all trials. Include such notes as flame cap, no flame cap, upward and outward propagation, downward propagation, etc. These observations can serve as a guide to narrowing the region of uncertainty between go and no-go trials.

12. Vary sample size as required to find the minimum sample size, L_1, that gives flame propagation and the maximum sample size, L_2 below L_1, that does not give flame propagation. (The dif-

ference between L_1 and L_2 is a measure of the variability of the procedure for the material being studied.)

13. If numerous trials are required for a given series of tests, it may be necessary to remove the vessel for cleaning periodically, particularly for upper-limit studies.

14. Final trials shall be made in a clean vessel.

NOTE: Ignition failures and inconsistent performances are occasionally encountered when highly conductive or very high ignition energy materials are tested using a spark ignition source. Limits for these materials should be determined using a fuse wire ignition source. Fuse wire ignition should also be used to confirm reduced pressure limit values arrived at on the basis of spark ignition source trials.

15. Record the values of the sample volumes L_1 and L_2. If partial propagation occurs over a range of sample sizes greater than 10 percent of the sample size, the range should be specified in the report, for example, LFL is 5.4 ± 0.6 percent.

16. Commence upper-limit tests at a concentration greater than U_2, as defined in Section 11.109.5, Item 17.

17. Record the values for the greatest sample quantity, U_1, that will propagate a flame and the least quantity, U_2 above U_1 that will not propagate a flame.

11.109.6 Procedure for Sample Introduction as a Vapor.

1. Sample concentration can be measured for gases and readily vaporized liquids on the basis of vapor pressure. In this instance, equip the vessel and a pressure transducer capable of reading to the nearest 0.0667 kPa. The system must also be capable of maintaining a vacuum of 0.0667 kPa or less.

2. Evacuate vessel and sample lines to a pressure of 0.0667 kPa.

3. Introduce the sample as a vapor through an appropriate inlet valve until the desired pressure is achieved. Introduce air as in Section 11.109.5, Item 5, raising the pressure to atmospheric.

4. Carry out steps outlined in Section 11.109.5, Items 6 through 17, as needed.

11.109.7 Procedure for Sample Introduction as a Solid.

1. Chemicals having melting points above room temperature but which totally melt and vaporize or totally sublime at the test conditions may be added to the test vessel as solids.

2. Bring the test vessel to atmospheric pressure (prior evacuation must be employed, as in Section 11.109.1, to ensure cleanliness).

3. Place the desired sample weight in the flask by raising the cover and inserting the sample.

4. Carry out Items 6 through 17 of Section 11.109.5, as needed.

NOTE: A small portion of the sample may be lost from the test vessel as the sample vaporizes and warms up to the test temperature. Losses are minimized by delaying the start of stirring until vaporization is complete. Maximum theoretical sample loss, which is small, may be readily calculated.

SECTION 11.110 — CALCULATIONS

11.110.1 Procedures. Calculate the sample quantity, L or U, as follows:

$$L = \tfrac{1}{2}(L_1 + L_2) \qquad (1)$$
$$U = \tfrac{1}{2}(U_1 + U_2) \qquad (2)$$

WHERE:

L = sample quantity used to calculate the lower flammable limit by Formula (3).

U = sample quantity used to calculate the upper flammable limit by Formula (3).

For L_1 and L_2, see Section 11.109.5, Item 12. For U_1 and U_2, see Section 11.109.5, Item 17.

11.110.2 LFL and UFL. Calculate the LFL and UFL from the sample quantities. Ideal vapor phase behavior is assumed.

11.110.2.1 Liquid samples. Ideal vapor phase behavior is assumed:

$$\text{LFL} = \frac{(L_v)(d)(T)}{(MW)(P)} \times \frac{(22.4)(P_o)(100)}{(V)(T_o)} \qquad (3)$$

WHERE:

d = sample density, g/cm^3.

LFL = lower flammable limit in mole or volume %.

L_v = L = sample volume from Formula (1), cm^3.

MW = sample molecular weight, g.

P = test pressure, absolute, kPa.

T = test temperature, K.

The second term is a constant for a given test apparatus where: P_o = standard pressure (760 mm Hg), V = vessel volume (litres), and T_o = standard temperature (273 K). (Any set of consistent units may be used for these calculations.)

Calculate upper flammable limits by replacing LFL with UFL and L_v with U_v in Formula (3).

11.110.2.2 Vapor samples. Ideal vapor phase behavior is assumed:

$$\text{LFL} = (L_p/P) \times 100 \qquad (4)$$

WHERE:

L_p = L = sample partial pressure (mm Hg) from Formula (1).

Calculate upper limits by replacing LFL with UFL and L_v with U_v.

11.110.2.3 Solid samples. Ideal vapor phase behavior is assumed:

Calculate LFL by using Formula (3) with the terms (L_v) (d) replaced by L_w where: L_w = L = sample weight (g) from Formula (1).

Calculate upper flammable limits by replacing LFL with UFL and L_w with U_w.

11.110.3 Complex Liquids, Solids and Mixtures. Flammability limits of some materials cannot be calculated in terms of mole or volume percent [Formula (3)] since the molecular weight of the vapors is not known. This occurs in the case of unknown materials, multicomponent mixtures and materials exhibiting nonideal vapor phase behavior. It is more meaningful to express these limits in terms of weight of combustible per unit volume of mixture (mg/L).

NOTE: Such limits are often given in the literature as weight of combustible per litre of air at standard conditions (0°C and 760 mm Hg). These limits may be calculated from the following expression or by a similar expression for UFL:

$$\text{LFL, mg/liter} = \frac{\text{LFL (volume \%)}}{[100 - \text{LFL(volume \%)}]\left[\frac{22.414(\text{litre})}{MW(\text{mg})}\right]}$$

Calculate lower flammable limits of mixed vapors and materials exhibiting nonideal vapor phase behavior as follows:

$$LFL_w = \frac{L_w}{V} \text{ or } \frac{L_v(d)}{V} \times 100 \qquad (5)$$

WHERE:

LFL_w = lower flammable limit, in milligrams per litre.

Calculate upper flammable limits using Formula (5) replacing LFL_w with UFL_w, L_w with U_w, and L_v with U_v.

SECTION 11.111 — REPORT

Report flammability limits, LFL and UFL, calculated in accordance with Formula (3), (4) or (5), along with the test temperature, test pressure and ignition source (spark or fuse wire) used.

Report the limits initially in accordance with the units of measurement used in the determinations, that is, on a volumetric basis (mole or volume percent) for gases or vapor samples and on a gravimetric basis (mg/L) for liquid or solid samples.

By substitution in Formula (3), calculated limits may then also be given for the gases or vapors on a gravimetric basis and for the liquids or solids on a volumetric basis, provided molecular weights of the combustibles are known. The report shall note if nonideal vapor phase behavior is suspected or known to occur.

Report the test variability if it exceeds 10 percent of the sample size (see Section 11.109.5, Item 15).

SECTION 11.112 — PRECISION AND BIAS

The precision and bias of this method have not yet been established.

The minimum precision of the method shall be ± 0.5 percent for limits of 10 volume %. Test data available at present are inadequate to establish any measure of repeatability or reproducibility.

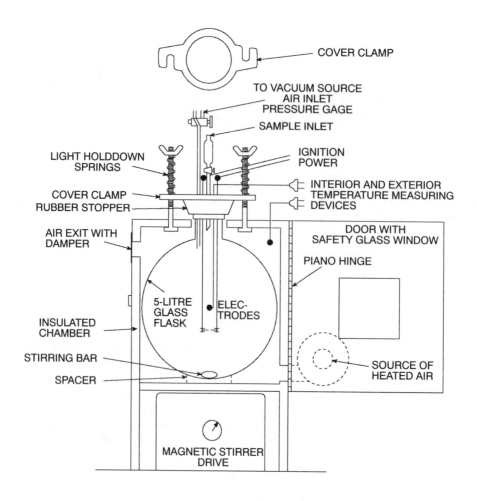

FIGURE A11-1-1—SCHEMATIC DIAGRAM OF TEST APPARATUS

UNIFORM MECHANICAL CODE STANDARD 11-2
METHODS FOR SYSTEM IDENTIFICATION

Based in Part on ASME/ANSI Standard A13.1-1981

SECTION 11.201 — SCOPE

This standard covers the identification requirements for systems and components thereof to facilitate immediate recognition of contents or function.

SECTION 11.202 — CONTENTS

11.202.1 Materials of Inherently High Hazard. Materials contained within systems shall be classified as of inherently high hazard if they are defined by any of the following groupings.

11.202.1.1 Flammable or explosive. This grouping includes materials ignitable or capable of forming explosive atmospheres.

11.202.1.2 Chemically active or toxic. This grouping includes materials which are reactive, unstable, corrosive, toxic or produce toxic byproducts.

11.202.1.3 At temperatures or pressures. This grouping includes materials which are contained at elevated or depressed temperatures or pressures which if released have the potential of injury or damage whether by burns, freezing, impingement or flashing to vapor.

11.202.1.4 Radioactive. This group includes materials which emit ionizing radiation.

11.202.2 Materials of Inherently Moderate Hazard. Materials contained within systems shall be classified as of inherently moderate hazard if they are defined by any of the following groupings.

11.202.2.1 Septic. This grouping includes materials which are potentially harmful if ingested or in contact with openings in the skin but not otherwise classified. This grouping includes materials such as sanitary waste or nonpotable water.

11.202.2.2 Industrial. This grouping includes materials which are potentially harmful under conditions of prolonged contact or high concentrations which are not otherwise classified and which may not be suitable for discharge without analysis or treatment to the sanitary sewer.

11.202.3 Materials of Inherently Low Hazard. Materials contained within systems shall be classified as of inherently low hazard if they are at temperatures and pressures sufficiently close to ambient such that little risk to persons in contact with releases can occur and the materials are not normally hazardous in themselves. These materials shall be grouped according to whether they are gas or liquid.

11.202.4 Fire-extinguishing Materials. Materials contained within fixed fire-extinguishing systems shall be classified as fire-extinguishing materials.

SECTION 11.203 — FUNCTIONS

When required by the Mechanical Code to be identified, equipment, valves and similar devices and the like shall have legends fixed to the device identifying the device by name, function, flow diagram number and as otherwise required by the code. Legends shall be sized as for 6-inch (152 mm) pipe in Table A11-2-B.

EXCEPTION: Valves and similar devices may be identified with tags as required in Section 11.205.

SECTION 11.204 — METHODS OF IDENTIFICATION

11.204.1 Legend. Positive identification of materials and function shall be primarily by lettered legend. The legend shall be terse and simple. Letters and numerals shall be bold and sans serif. Size of characters shall be in accordance with Table A11-2-B. Color of legends, fields and tags shall be in accordance with Table A11-2-A.

11.204.2 Additional Information. Arrows indicating direction of flow shall be located adjacent to the legend. Where temperature or pressure information is needed to more fully identify the nature of the hazard, it shall be included in the legend.

11.204.3 Background. Legends shall appear on a background consisting of a colored field. The length of the field shall be in accordance with Table A11-2-B. The color of the field shall be in accordance with Table A11-2-A.

EXCEPTION: When the entire piping system is painted the required field color, no separate field area is required.

SECTION 11.205 — TAGGING

Valves, similar devices and small-diameter piping, which cannot readily accept legends, shall be positively identified by approved tags. Tags and their attachments shall be durable and corrosion resistant for the environment to which they are exposed. Tags shall be secured to the device in an approved manner which does not interfere with the device, function or use. Tags shall tersely state the function of the device and shall be numbered to match valve charts and flow diagrams when required. The minimum dimension of a tag shall not be less than 2 inches (51 mm).

SECTION 11.206 — LOCATION

Methods of identification shall be located as required by the Mechanical Code and the following:

    1. At valves and devices.

    2. At changes in direction or branches of piping.

    3. At each side of penetrations of walls, floors, roofs or similar barriers.

    4. At sufficient intervals on piping to provide ready visibility from any point on the floor of the space. Ready visibility does not require simultaneous legibility.

SECTION 11.207 — VISIBILITY

Legends shall be arranged to provide visibility from normal working levels.

SECTION 11.208 — METHODS OF APPLICATION

Identification may be applied by paint and stencils, manufactured markers, engraving or stamping.

TABLE A11-2-A—COLORS FOR FIELDS AND LEGENDS

CLASSIFICATION	GROUP	FIELD OR TAG	LEGEND
Inherently high hazard	Flammable or explosive	Yellow	Black
	Chemically active or toxic	Yellow	Black
	At temperatures or pressures	Yellow	Black
	Radioactive	Yellow	Black
Inherently moderate hazard	Septic	Orange	Black
	Industrial	Orange	Black
Inherently low hazard	Gas	Blue	White
	Liquid	Green	White
Fire extinguishing		Red	White

TABLE A11-2-B—MINIMUM SIZE OF FIELDS AND LEGEND CHARACTERS

OUTSIDE DIAMETER OF PIPE OR COVERING (inches)	LENGTH OF FIELD (inches)	HEIGHT OF CHARACTERS (inches)	WIDTH OF PRINCIPAL STROKE (inches)
	$\times$ 25.4 mm		
Less than $3/4$	Use tags	—	—
$3/4$ to $1^1/4$	8	$1/2$	$1/8$
$1^1/2$ to 2	8	$3/4$	$3/16$
$2^1/2$ to 6	12	$1^1/4$	$5/16$
8 to 10	24	$2^1/2$	$5/8$
over 10	32	$3^1/2$	$7/8$

APPENDIX B

Chapter 15

SOLAR SYSTEMS

SECTION 1501 — HEAT SOURCE

Hydronic panel heating systems are permitted to utilize solar heat collection systems as a source of energy. Solar arrays are permitted to include booster or backup heating units.

APPENDIX C

Chapter 8

SIZING OF VENTING SYSTEMS SERVING APPLIANCES EQUIPPED WITH DRAFT HOODS AND APPLIANCES LISTED FOR USE WITH TYPE B VENTS

See Sections 103 and 801, *Uniform Mechanical Code*

SECTION 819 — USE OF TABLES

819.1 General. Gas-venting systems serving appliances equipped with draft hoods and appliances listed for use with Type B vents may be sized in accordance with tables in this chapter, when such design method has been approved by the building official.

819.2 Symbols. Symbols used in Tables C8-A, C8-B and C8-C are as indicated in Figures C8-1 and C8-3. Symbols used in Tables C8-D, C8-E and C8-F are as indicated in Figures C8-2 and C8-4.

819.3 Notes for Tables C8-A, C8-B and C8-C. Notes for appliance vents covered in Tables C8-A, C8-B and C8-C are as indicated below:

1. When the specified diameter of the draft hood supplied by the manufacturer or the diameter of the appliance vent collar is larger than the vent size determined from Table C8-A, C8-B or C8-C, a one-size-smaller vent may be used, provided the height, *H,* is at least 10 feet (3048 mm) [10 inches to 8 inches (254 mm to 203 mm) is a one-size reduction].

> **EXCEPTION:** Irrespective of the required vent size obtained from the tables, 4-inch (102 mm) draft hoods shall not be connected to 3-inch (76 mm) vents.

2. Only vertical vent connectors rising from top-outlet draft hoods may employ zero lateral capacities.

3. High-altitude installations shall be sized based on sea-level input ratings.

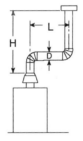

FIGURE C8-1

Double-wall or asbestos cement Type B vent serving a single appliance. (See Tables C8-A and C8-B.)

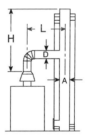

FIGURE C8-3

Masonry chimney serving a single appliance. (See Table C8-C.)

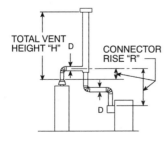

FIGURE C8-2

Double-wall or asbestos cement Type B vents serving two or more appliances. (See Tables C8-D and C8-E.)

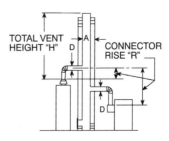

FIGURE C8-4

Masonry chimney serving two or more appliances. (See Table C8-F.)

819.4 Notes for Tables C8-D, C8-E and C8-F. Notes for multiple appliance vents covered in Tables C8-D, C8-E and C8-F are as indicated below:

1. The connector length shall not exceed $1^1/_2$ feet (457 mm) for every inch (25 mm) of connector diameter.

2. The connector capacity shall be reduced 10 percent for each 90-degree turn in excess of two.

3. The common vent capacity shall be reduced by 10 percent for each 90-degree turn in excess of two.

4. Connectors shall be equal to or larger than draft hood outlets.

5. If both connectors are the same size, the common vent shall be at least one size larger, regardless of tabulated capacity.

6. The common vent shall be equal to or larger than the largest connector.

7. Interconnection fittings shall be the same size as the common vent.

8. High-altitude installations shall be sized based on sea-level input rating.

TABLE C8-A—CAPACTIY OF DOUBLE-WALL OR ASBESTOS CEMENT TYPE B VENTS WITH SINGLE-WALL CONNECTORS SERVING A SINGLE APPLIANCE

TOTAL VENT HEIGHT H (feet)	LATERAL L (feet)	VENT DIAMETER—D (inches)							
		× 25.4 for mm							
		3	4	5	6	7	8	10	12
		Maximum Appliance Input Rating in Thousands of Btu/h							
× 304.8 for mm		× 293.071 for W							
6	0	39	70	116	170	232	312	500	750
	2	31	55	94	141	194	260	415	620
	5	28	51	88	128	177	242	390	600
8	0	42	76	126	185	252	340	542	815
	2	32	61	102	154	210	284	451	680
	5	29	56	95	141	194	264	430	648
	10		49	86	131	180	250	406	625
10	0	45	84	138	202	279	372	606	912
	2	35	67	111	168	233	311	505	760
	5	32	61	104	153	215	289	480	724
	10		54	94	143	200	274	455	700
	15			84	130	186	258	432	666
15	0	49	91	151	223	312	420	684	1,040
	2	39	72	122	186	260	350	570	865
	5		67	110	170	240	325	540	825
	10			103	158	223	308	514	795
	15				144	207	291	488	760
	20					195	273	466	726
20	0		101	163	252	342	470	770	1,190
	2		80	136	210	286	392	641	990
	5			123	192	264	364	610	945
	10				178	246	345	571	910
	15				163	228	326	550	870
	20					306	525	832
30	0			183	276	384	529	878	1,370
	2				230	320	441	730	1,140
	5				210	296	410	694	1,080
	10					274	388	656	1,050
	15						366	625	1,000
	20						344	596	960
	30							540	890
50	0						590	980	1,550
	2						492	820	1,290
	5						474	780	1,230
	10							730	1,190
	15							705	1,130
	20								1,080
	30								1,010

See Figure C8-1 for single-appliance vents.

TABLE C8-B—CAPACITY OF TYPE B DOUBLE-WALL VENTS WITH TYPE B DOUBLE-WALL CONNECTORS SERVING A SINGLE APPLIANCE

TOTAL VENT		VENT DIAMETER—D (inches) ×25.4 for mm													
Height H (feet) ×304.8 for mm	Lateral L (feet)	3	4	5	6	7	8	10	12	14	16	18	20	22	24
		Maximum Appliance Input Rating in Thousands of Btu/h ×293.071 for W													
6	0	46	86	141	205	285	370	570	850	1,170	1,530	1,960	2,430	2,950	3,520
	2	36	67	105	157	217	285	455	650	890	1,170	1,480	1,850	2,220	2,670
	6	32	61	100	149	205	273	435	630	870	1,150	1,470	1,820	2,210	2,650
	12	28	55	91	137	190	255	406	610	840	1,110	1,430	1,795	2,180	2,600
8	0	50	94	155	235	320	415	660	970	1,320	1,740	2,220	2,750	3,360	4,010
	2	40	75	120	180	247	322	515	745	1,020	1,340	1,700	2,110	2,560	3,050
	8	35	66	109	165	227	303	490	720	1,000	1,320	1,670	2,070	2,530	3,030
	16	28	58	96	148	206	281	458	685	950	1,260	1,600	2,035	2,470	2,960
10	0	53	100	166	255	345	450	720	1,060	1,450	1,925	2,450	3,050	3,710	4,450
	2	42	81	129	195	273	355	560	850	1,130	1,480	1,890	2,340	2,840	3,390
	10	36	70	115	175	245	330	525	795	1,080	1,430	1,840	2,280	2,780	3,340
	20		60	100	154	217	300	486	735	1,030	1,360	1,780	2,230	2,720	3,250
15	0	58	112	187	285	390	525	840	1,240	1,720	2,270	2,900	3,620	4,410	5,300
	2	48	93	150	225	316	414	675	985	1,350	1,770	2,260	2,800	3,410	4,080
	15	37	76	128	198	275	373	610	905	1,250	1,675	2,150	2,700	3,300	3,980
	30		60	107	169	243	328	553	845	1,180	1,550	2,050	2,620	3,210	3,840
20	0	61	119	202	307	430	575	930	1,350	1,900	2,520	3,250	4,060	4,980	6,000
	2	51	100	166	249	346	470	755	1,100	1,520	2,000	2,570	3,200	3,910	4,700
	10	44	89	150	228	321	443	710	1,045	1,460	1,940	2,500	3,130	3,830	4,600
	20	35	78	134	206	295	410	665	990	1,390	1,880	2,430	3,050	3,760	4,550
	30		68	120	186	273	380	626	945	1,270	1,700	2,330	2,980	3,650	4,390
30	0	64	128	220	336	475	650	1,060	1,550	2,170	2,920	3,770	4,750	5,850	7,060
	2	56	112	185	280	394	535	865	1,310	1,800	2,380	3,050	3,810	4,650	5,600
	20		90	154	237	343	473	784	1,185	1,650	2,200	2,870	3,650	4,480	5,310
	40				200	298	415	705	1,075	1,520	2,060	2,700	3,480	4,270	5,140
40	0	66	132	228	353	500	685	1,140	1,730	2,400	3,230	4,180	5,270	6,500	7,860
	2	59	118	198	298	420	579	960	1,420	2,000	2,660	3,420	4,300	5,260	6,320
	20		96	167	261	377	516	860	1,310	1,830	2,460	3,200	4,050	5,000	6,070
	40				223	333	460	785	1,205	1,710	2,310	3,020	3,840	4,780	5,820
60	0		136	236	373	535	730	1,250	1,920	2,700	3,650	4,470	6,000	7,380	9,000
	2		125	213	330	470	650	1,060	1,605	2,250	3,020	3,920	4,960	6,130	7,400
	40			170	275	397	555	930	1,440	2,050	2,780	3,640	4,700	5,730	7,400
	80					334	475	830	1,285	1,870	2,560	3,380	4,330	5,420	6,600
80	0			239	384	550	755	1,290	2,020	2,880	3,900	5,100	6,450	8,000	9,750
	2			217	350	495	683	1,145	1,740	2,460	3,320	4,310	5,450	6,740	8,200
	40				275	404	570	980	1,515	2,180	2,980	3,920	5,000	6,270	7,650
	80						850	1,420	2,000	2,750	3,640	4,680	5,850	7,200	
100	0				400	560	770	1,310	2,050	2,950	4,050	5,300	6,700	8,600	10,300
	2				375	510	700	1,170	1,820	2,550	3,500	4,600	5,800	7,200	8,800
	50					405	575	1,000	1,550	2,250	3,100	4,050	5,300	6,600	8,100
	100						870	1,430	2,050	2,850	3,750	4,900	6,100	7,500	

TABLE C8-C—CAPACITY OF MASONRY CHIMNEYS AND SINGLE-WALL VENT CONNECTORS SERVING A SINGLE APPLIANCE

TOTAL VENT HEIGHT H (feet) ×304.8 for mm	LATERAL L (feet)	SINGLE-WALL VENT CONNECTOR DIAMETER—D (inches) ×25.4 for mm / To be used with chimney areas not less than those at bottom / Maximum Appliance Input Rating in Thousands of Btu/h ×293.071 for W							
		3	4	5	6	7	8	10	12
6	2	28	52	86	130	180	247	400	580
	5		48	81	118	164	230	375	560
8	2	29	55	93	145	197	265	445	650
	5		51	87	133	182	246	422	638
	10			79	123	169	233	400	598
10	2	31	61	102	161	220	297	490	722
	5		56	95	147	203	276	465	710
	10			86	137	189	261	441	665
	15				125	175	246	421	634
15	2		67	113	178	249	335	560	840
	5		61	106	163	230	312	531	825
	10			96	151	214	294	504	774
	15				138	198	278	481	738
	20					184	261	459	706
20	2		73	123	200	273	374	628	950
	5			115	183	252	348	594	930
	10				170	235	330	562	875
	15				156	217	311	536	835
	20					202	292	510	800
30	2			136	215	302	420	715	1,110
	5				196	279	391	680	1,090
	10					260	370	644	1,020
	15						349	615	975
	20						327	585	932
	30							544	865
50	2							810	1,240
	5							770	1,220
	10							728	1,140
	15							695	1,090
	20								1,040
	30								970
Minimum internal area of chimney in square inches		19		28	38	50	63	95	132

See Table C8-G for masonry chimney liner sizes.

See Figure C8-3 for single-appliance vents.

TABLE C8-D—CAPACITY OF TYPE B DOUBLE-WALL VENTS WITH TYPE B DOUBLE-WALL CONNECTORS SERVING TWO OR MORE APPLIANCES

VENT CONNECTOR CAPACITY

Vent Connector Diameter—D (inches) × 25.4 for mm

Maximum Appliance Input Rating in Thousands of Btu/h × 293.071 for W

Total Vent Height H (feet) × 304.8 for mm	Connector Rise R (feet)	3	4	5	6	7	8	10	12	14	16	18	20	22	24
6	1	26	46	72	104	142	185	289	416	577	755	955	1,180	1,425	1,700
	2	31	55	86	124	168	220	345	496	653	853	1,080	1,335	1,610	1,920
	3	35	62	96	139	189	248	386	556	740	967	1,225	1,510	1,830	2,180
8	1	27	48	76	109	148	194	303	439	601	805	1,015	1,255	1,520	1,810
	2	32	57	90	129	175	230	358	516	696	910	1,150	1,420	1,720	2,050
	3	36	64	101	145	198	258	402	580	790	1,030	1,305	1,610	1,950	2,320
10	1	28	50	78	113	154	200	314	452	642	840	1,060	1,310	1,585	1,890
	2	33	59	93	134	182	238	372	536	730	955	1,205	1,490	1,800	2,150
	3	37	67	104	150	205	268	417	600	827	1,080	1,370	1,690	2,040	2,430
15	1	30	53	83	120	163	214	333	480	697	910	1,150	1,420	1,720	2,050
	2	35	63	99	142	193	253	394	568	790	1,030	1,305	1,610	1,950	2,320
	3	40	71	111	160	218	286	444	640	898	1,175	1,485	1,835	2,220	2,640
20	1	31	56	87	125	171	224	347	500	740	965	1,225	1,510	1,830	2,190
	2	37	66	104	149	202	265	414	596	840	1,095	1,385	1,710	2,070	2,470
	3	42	74	116	168	228	300	466	672	952	1,245	1,575	1,945	2,350	2,800
30	1	33	59	93	134	182	238	372	536	805	1,050	1,330	1,645	1,990	2,370
	2	39	70	110	158	215	282	439	632	910	1,190	1,500	1,855	2,240	2,670
	3	44	79	124	178	242	317	494	712	1,035	1,350	1,710	2,110	2,550	3,040
40	1	35	62	97	140	190	248	389	560	850	1,110	1,405	1,735	2,100	2,500
	2	41	73	115	166	225	295	461	665	964	1,260	1,590	1,965	2,380	2,830
	3	46	83	129	187	253	331	520	748	1,100	1,435	1,820	2,240	2,710	3,230
60 to 100	1	37	66	104	150	204	266	417	600	926	1,210	1,530	1,890	2,280	2,720
	2	44	79	123	178	242	316	494	712	1,050	1,370	1,740	2,150	2,590	3,090
	3	50	89	138	200	272	355	555	800	1,198	1,565	1,980	2,450	2,960	3,520

COMMON VENT CAPACITY

Common Vent Diameter—D (inches) × 25.4 for mm

Combined Appliance Input Rating in Thousands of Btu/h × 293.071 for W

Total Vent Height H (feet) × 304.8 for mm	3	4	5	6	7	8	10	12	14	16	18	20	22	24
6	—	65	103	147	200	260	410	588	815	1,065	1,345	1,660	1,970	2,390
8	—	73	114	163	223	290	465	652	912	1,190	1,510	1,860	2,200	2,680
10	—	79	124	178	242	315	495	712	995	1,300	1,645	2,030	2,400	2,920
15	—	91	144	206	280	365	565	825	1,158	1,510	1,910	2,360	2,790	3,400
20	—	102	160	229	310	405	640	916	1,290	1,690	2,140	2,640	3,120	3,800
30	—	118	185	266	360	470	740	1,025	1,525	1,990	2,520	3,110	3,680	4,480
40	—	131	203	295	405	525	820	1,180	1,715	2,240	2,830	3,500	4,150	5,050
60	—		224	324	440	575	900	1,380	2,010	2,620	3,320	4,100	4,850	5,900
80	—			344	468	610	955	1,540	2,250	2,930	3,710	4,590	5,420	6,600
100	—				479	625	975	1,670	2,450	3,200	4,050	5,000	5,920	7,200

See Figure C8-2 and notes for multiple-appliance vents.

TABLE C8-E—CAPACITY OF DOUBLE-WALL AND ASBESTOS-CEMENT TYPE B VENTS WITH SINGLE-WALL CONNECTORS SERVING TWO OR MORE APPLIANCES

		SINGLE-WALL VENT CONNECTOR CAPACITY					
		Vent Connector Diameter—D (inches)					
		× 25.4 for mm					
Total Vent Height H (feet)	**Connector Rise R (feet)**	3	4	5	6	7	8
		Maximum Appliance Input Rating in Thousands of Btu/h					
× 304.8 for mm		× 293.071 for W					
6 to 8	1	21	40	68	102	146	205
	2	28	53	86	124	178	235
	3	34	61	98	147	204	275
15	1	23	44	77	117	179	240
	2	30	56	92	134	194	265
	3	35	64	102	155	216	298
30 and up	1	25	49	84	129	190	270
	2	31	58	97	145	211	295
	3	36	68	107	164	232	321

	COMMON VENT CAPACITY					
	Common Vent Diameter—D (inches)					
	× 25.4 for mm					
Total Vent Height H (feet)	4	5	6	7	8	10	12
	Combined Appliance Input Rating in Thousands of Btu/h					
× 304.8 for mm	× 293.071 for W					
6	48	78	111	155	205	320	NR
8	55	89	128	175	234	365	505
10	59	95	136	190	250	395	560
15	71	115	168	228	305	480	690
20	80	129	186	260	340	550	790
30		147	215	300	400	650	940
50				360	490	810	1,190

See Figure C8-2 and notes for multiple-appliance vents.

TABLE C8-F—CAPACITY OF A MASONRY CHIMNEY AND SINGLE-WALL VENT CONNECTORS SERVING TWO OR MORE APPLIANCES

		SINGLE-WALL VENT CONNECTOR CAPACITY					
		Vent Connector Diameter—D (inches)					
		× 25.4 for mm					
Total Vent Height H (feet)	**Connector Rise R (feet)**	3	4	5	6	7	8
		Maximum Appliance Input Rating in Thousands of Btu/h					
× 304.8 for mm		× 293.071 for W					
6 to 8	1	21	39	66	100	140	200
	2	28	52	84	123	172	231
	3	34	61	97	142	202	269
15	1	23	43	73	112	171	225
	2	30	54	88	132	189	256
	3	34	63	101	151	213	289
30 and up	1	24	47	80	124	183	250
	2	31	57	93	142	205	282
	3	35	65	105	160	229	312

	COMMON CHIMNEY CAPACITY					
	Minimum Internal Area of Chimney-A (square inches)					
	× 645.16 for mm²					
Total Vent Height H (feet)	19	28	38	50	78	113
	Combined Appliance Input Rating in Thousands of Btu/h					
× 304.8 for mm	× 293.071 for W					
6	45	71	102	142	245	
8	52	81	118	162	277	405
10	56	89	129	175	300	450
15	66	105	150	210	360	540
20	74	120	170	240	415	640
30		135	195	275	490	740
50				325	600	910

See Table C8-G for masonry chimney liner sizes.

See Figure C8-4 and notes for multiple-appliance vents.

TABLE C8-G—MASONRY CHIMNEY LINER DIMENSIONS WITH CIRCULAR EQUIVALENTS[1]

NOMINAL LINER SIZE (inches)	INSIDE DIMENSIONS OF LINER (inches)	INSIDE DIAMETER OR EQUIVALENT DIAMETER (inches)	EQUIVALENT AREA (square inches)
	× 25.4 for mm		× 645.16 for mm²
4 × 8	$2^1/_2 \times 6^1/_2$	4	12.2
		5	19.6
		6	28.3
		7	38.3
8 × 8	$6^3/_4 \times 6^3/_4$	7.4	42.7
		8	50.3
8 × 12	$6^1/_2 \times 10^1/_2$	9	63.6
		10	78.5
12 × 12	$9^3/_4 \times 9^3/_4$	10.4	83.3
		11	95.0
12 × 16	$9^1/_2 \times 13^1/_2$	11.8	107.5
		12	113.0
		14	153.9
16 × 16	$13^1/_4 \times 13^1/_4$	14.5	162.9
		15	176.7
16 × 20	13 × 17	16.2	206.1
		18	254.4
20 × 20	$16^3/_4 \times 16^3/_4$	18.2	260.2
		20	314.1
20 × 24	$16^1/_2 \times 20^1/_2$	20.1	314.2
		22	380.1
24 × 24	$20^1/_4 \times 20^1/_4$	22.1	380.1
		24	452.3
24 × 28	$20^1/_4 \times 24^1/_4$	24.1	456.2
28 × 28	$24^1/_4 \times 24^1/_4$	26.4	543.3
		27	572.5
30 × 30	$25^1/_2 \times 25^1/_2$	27.9	607.0
		30	706.8
30 × 36	$25^1/_2 \times 31^1/_2$	30.9	749.9
		33	855.3
36 × 36	$31^1/_2 \times 31^1/_2$	34.4	929.4
		36	1,017.9

[1]When liner sizes differ dimensionally from those shown, equivalent diameters may be used.

APPENDIX D

UNIT CONVERSION TABLES

SI SYMBOLS AND PREFIXES

BASE UNITS		
Quantity	Unit	Symbol
Length	Meter	m
Mass	Kilogram	kg
Time	Second	s
Electric current	Ampere	A
Thermodynamic temperature	Kelvin	K
Amount of substance	Mole	mol
Luminous intensity	Candela	cd

SI SUPPLEMENTARY UNITS		
Quantity	Unit	Symbol
Plane angle	Radian	rad
Solid angle	Steradian	sr

SI PREFIXES		
Multiplication Factor	Prefix	Symbol
$1\ 000\ 000\ 000\ 000\ 000\ 000 = 10^{18}$	exa	E
$1\ 000\ 000\ 000\ 000\ 000 = 10^{15}$	peta	P
$1\ 000\ 000\ 000\ 000 = 10^{12}$	tera	T
$1\ 000\ 000\ 000 = 10^{9}$	giga	G
$1\ 000\ 000 = 10^{6}$	mega	M
$1\ 000 = 10^{3}$	kilo	k
$100 = 10^{2}$	hecto	h
$10 = 10^{1}$	deka	da
$0.1 = 10^{-1}$	deci	d
$0.01 = 10^{-2}$	centi	c
$0.001 = 10^{-3}$	milli	m
$0.000\ 001 = 10^{-6}$	micro	μ
$0.000\ 000\ 001 = 10^{-9}$	nano	n
$0.000\ 000\ 000\ 001 = 10^{-12}$	pico	p
$0.000\ 000\ 000\ 000\ 001 = 10^{-15}$	femto	f
$0.000\ 000\ 000\ 000\ 000\ 001 = 10^{-18}$	atto	a

SI DERIVED UNIT WITH SPECIAL NAMES			
Quantity	Unit	Symbol	Formula
Frequency (of a periodic phenomenon)	hertz	Hz	$1/s$
Force	newton	N	$kg \cdot m/s^2$
Pressure, stress	pascal	Pa	N/m^2
Energy, work, quantity of heat	joule	J	$N \cdot m$
Power, radiant flux	watt	W	J/s
Quantity of electricity, electric charge	coulomb	C	$A \cdot s$
Electric potential, potential difference, electromotive force	volt	V	W/A
Capacitance	farad	F	C/V
Electric resistance	ohm	Ω	V/A
Conductance	siemens	S	A/V
Magnetic flux	weber	Wb	$V \cdot s$
Magnetic flux density	tesla	T	Wb/m^2
Inductance	henry	H	Wb/A
Luminous flux	lumen	lm	$cd \cdot sr$
Illuminance	lux	lx	lm/m^2
Activity (of radionuclides)	becquerel	Bq	$1/s$
Absorbed dose	gray	Gy	J/kg

CONVERSION FACTORS

To convert	to	multiply by
LENGTH		
1 mile (U.S. statute)	km	1.609 344
1 yd	m	0.9144
1 ft	m	0.3048
	mm	304.8
1 in	mm	25.4
AREA		
1 mile^2 (U.S. statute)	km^2	2.589 998
1 acre (U.S. survey)	ha	0.404 6873
	m^2	4046.873
1 yd^2	m^2	0.836 1274
1 ft^2	m^2	0.092 903 04
1 in^2	mm^2	645.16
VOLUME, MODULUS OF SECTION		
l acre ft	m^3	1233.489
1 yd^3	m^3	0.764 5549
100 board ft	m^3	0.235 9737
1 ft^3	m^3	0.028 316 85
	L(dm^3)	28.3168
1 in^3	mm^3	16 387.06
	mL (cm^3)	16.3871
1 barrel (42 U.S. gallons)	m^3	0.158 9873
(FLUID) CAPACITY		
1 gal (U.S. liquid)*	L**	3.785 412
1 qt (U.S. liquid)	mL	946.3529
1 pt (U.S. liquid)	mL	473.1765
1 fl oz (U.S.)	mL	29.5735
1 gal (U.S. liquid)	m^3	0.003 785 412
*1 gallon (UK) approx. 1.2 gal (U.S.)		
**1 liter approx. 0.001 cubic meters		
SECOND MOMENT OF AREA		
1 in^4	mm^4	416 231 4
	m^4	416 231 4 $\times$ 10^{-7}
PLANE ANGLE		
1° (degree)	rad	0.017 453 29
	mrad	17.453 29
1′ (minute)	urad	290.8882
1″ (second)	urad	4.848 137
VELOCITY, SPEED		
1 ft/s	m/s	0.3048
1 mile/h	km/h	1.609 344
	m/s	0.447 04
VOLUME RATE OF FLOW		
1 ft^3/s	m^3/s	0.028 316 85
1 ft^3/min	L/s	0.471 9474
1 gal/min	L/s	0.063 0902
1 gal/min	m^3/min	0.0038
1 gal/h	mL/s	1.051 50
1 million gal/d	L/s	43.8126
1 acre ft/s	m^3/s	1233.49
TEMPERATURE INTERVAL		
1°F	°C or K	0.555 556 $^5/_9$°C = $^5/_9$K
EQUIVALENT TEMPERATURE (t$_{°C.}$ = T$_K$ − 273.15)		
t$_{°F}$	t$_{°C}$	t$_{°F}$ = $^9/_5$t$_{°C}$ + 32

(Continued)

CONVERSION FACTORS—(Continued)

To convert	to	multiply by
MASS		
1 ton (short ***)	metric ton	0.907 185
	kg	907.1847
1 lb	kg	0.453 5924
1 oz	g	28.349 52
***1 long ton (2,240 lb)	kg	1016.047
MASS PER UNIT AREA		
1 lb/ft^2	kg/m^2	4.882 428
1 oz/yd^2	g/m^2	33.905 75
1 oz/ft^2	g/m^2	305.1517
DENSITY (MASS PER UNIT VOLUME)		
1 lb/ft^3	kg/m^3	16.01846
1 lb/yd^3	kg/m^3	0.593 2764
1 ton/yd^3	t/m^3	1.186 553
FORCE		
1 tonf (ton-force)	kN	8.896 44
1 kip (1,000 lbf)	kN	4.448 22
1 lbf (pound-force)	N	4.448 22
MOMENT OF FORCE, TORQUE		
1 lbf·ft	N·m	1.355 818
1 lbf·in	N·m	0.112 9848
1 tonf·ft	kN·m	2.711 64
1 kip·ft	kN·m	1.355 82
FORCE PER UNIT LENGTH		
1 lbf/ft	N/m	14.5939
1 lbf/in	N/m	175.1268
1 tonf/ft	kN/m	29.1878
PRESSURE, STRESS, MODULUS OF ELASTICITY (FORCE PER UNIT AREA) (1 Pa = 1 N/m^2)		
1 tonf/in^2	MPa	13.7895
1 tonf/ft^2	kPa	95.7605
1 kip/in^2	MPa	6.894 757
1 lbf/in^2	kPa	6.894 757
1 lbf/ft^2	Pa	47.8803
Atmosphere	kPa	101.3250
1 inch mercury	kPa	3.376 85
1 foot (water column at 32°F)	kPa	2.988 98
WORK, ENERGY, HEAT(1J = 1N·m = 1W·s)		
1 kWh (550 ft·lbf/s)	MJ	3.6
1 Btu (Int. Table)	kJ	1.055 056
	J	1055.056
1 ft·lbf	J	1.355 818
COEFFICIENT OF HEAT TRANSFER		
1 Btu/(ft^2·h·°F)	W/(m^2·K)	5.678 263
THERMAL CONDUCTIVITY		
1 Btu/(ft·h·°F)	W/(m·K)	1.730 735
ILLUMINANCE		
1 lm/ft^2 (footcandle)	lx (lux)	10.763 91
LUMINANCE		
1 cd/ft^2	cd/m^2	10.7639
1 foot lambert	cd/m^2	3.426 259
1 lambert	kcd/m^2	3.183 099

GAGE CONVERSION TABLE

APPROXIMATE MINIMUM THICKNESS (inch/mm) FOR CARBON SHEET STEEL CORRESPONDING TO MANUFACTURER'S STANDARD GAGE AND GALVANIZED SHEET GAGE NUMBERS

| Manufacturer's Standard Gage No. | CARBON SHEET STEEL | | | | GALVANIZED SHEET | | | | | |
| | Decimal and Nominal Thickness Equivalent | | Recommended Minimum Thickness Equivalent[1] | | Galvanized Sheet Gage No. | Decimal and Nominal Thickness Equivalent | | Recommended Minimum Thickness Equivalent[1] | |
	(inch)	(mm)[2]	(inch)	(mm)[2]		(inch)	(mm)[2]	(inch)	(mm)[2]
8	0.1644	4.17	0.156	3.46	8	0.1681	4.27	0.159	4.04
9	0.1495	3.80	0.142	3.61	9	0.1532	3.89	0.144	3.66
10	0.1345	3.42	0.127	3.23	10	0.1382	3.51	0.129	3.23
11	0.1196	3.04	0.112	2.84	11	0.1233	3.13	0.114	2.90
12	0.1046	2.66	0.097	2.46	12	0.1084	2.75	0.099	2.51
13	0.0897	2.28	0.083	2.11	13	0.0934	2.37	0.084	2.13
14	0.0747	1.90	0.068	1.73	14	0.0785	1.97	0.070	1.78
15	0.0673	1.71	0.062	1.57	15	0.0710	1.80	0.065	1.65
16	0.0598	1.52	0.055	1.40	16	0.0635	1.61	0.058	1.47
17	0.0538	1.37	0.050	1.27	17	0.0575	1.46	0.053	1.35
18	0.0478	1.21	0.044	1.12	18	0.0516	1.31	0.047	1.19
19	0.0418	1.06	0.038	0.97	19	0.0456	1.16	0.041	1.04
20	0.0359	0.91	0.033	0.84	20	0.0396	1.01	0.036	0.91
21	0.0329	0.84	0.030	0.76	21	0.0366	0.93	0.033	0.84
22	0.0299	0.76	0.027	0.69	22	0.0336	0.85	0.030	0.76
23	0.0269	0.68	0.024	0.61	23	0.0306	0.78	0.027	0.69
24	0.0239	0.61	0.021	0.53	24	0.0276	0.70	0.024	0.61
25	0.0209	0.53	0.018	0.46	25	0.0247	0.63	0.021	0.53
26	0.0179	0.45	0.016	0.41	26	0.0217	0.55	0.019	0.48
27	0.0164	0.42	0.014	0.36	27	0.0202	0.51	0.017	0.43
28	0.0149	0.38	0.013	0.33	28	0.0187	0.47	0.016	0.41
					29	0.0172	0.44	0.014	0.36
					30	0.0157	0.40	0.013	0.33

[1]The thickness of the sheets set forth in the code correspond to the thickness shown under these columns. They are the approximate minimum thicknesses and are based on the following references:

Carbon sheet steel—Thickness 0.071 inch and over:
    ASTM A 568-74, Table 3, Thickness Tolerances of Hot-Rolled Sheet
    (Carbon Steel).

Carbon sheet steel—Thickness less than 0.071 inch:
    ASTM A 568-74, Table 23, Thickness Tolerances of Cold-Rolled Sheet
    (Carbon and High Strength Low Alloy).

Galvanized sheet steel—All thicknesses:
    ASTM A 525-79, Table 4, Thickness Tolerances of Hot-Dip Galvanized Sheet.

Minimum thickness is the difference between the thickness equivalent of each gage and the maximum negative tolerance for the widest rolled width.

[2]The SI equivalents are calculated and rounded to two significant figures following the decimal point.

INDEX

For Table of Contents by chapters and sections, see pages vii to xiii.